Introductory Statistics

A NEW APPROACH FOR
THE BEHAVIORAL SCIENCES

LOUIS S. BERGER, PH.D.

Introductory Statistics

A NEW APPROACH FOR
THE BEHAVIORAL SCIENCES

INTERNATIONAL UNIVERSITIES PRESS, INC.
NEW YORK

Library of Congress Cataloging in Publication Data

Berger, Louis S

Introductory Statistics: A New Approach for the Behavioral Sciences.

Bibliography: p.
Includes index.
1. Psychometrics. I. Title.
BF39.B449 301'.01'5195 79-2484
ISBN 0-8236-2775-6

Manufactured in the United States of America

Table of Contents

Preface

This volume presents a nonstandard approach to the material covered in the usual first statistics course for students in the behavioral or social disciplines. Any significant departure from an established norm—in the present case, the typical textbooks and approaches used in this kind of a course—invites an explanation. I will therefore briefly discuss the rationale on which this particular nonstandard approach is based, why the alternative approach is badly needed, and how it differs from the standard treatments. I would like to introduce that discussion by reporting a bit of personal history.

I had been using statistics for some time in various engineering research applications when a project pertaining to test construction methodology and evaluation, an area that was new and unfamiliar to me, was initiated. I therefore had to learn how statistics is used in psychology, education, and similiar behavioral disciplines. I set out confidently as I had acquired considerable competence in mathematical statistics by then, and expected to have little trouble applying the familiar mathematical methods to the new subject area. The mastery of this application would require, I thought, only a quick survey of the field.

I was disappointed with the many recommended introductory textbooks that I had gathered. Most of the material looked strange, although here and there I would encounter a familiar landmark. It was frustrating. Here was material that from a mathematical standpoint was quite elementary, and still it posed considerable conceptual difficulties for me: I saw few if any connections between that material and the statistics I knew. Furthermore, all the books appeared to be substantially alike. It therefore seemed unlikely that my difficulties could be resolved just by acquiring still another introductory textbook.

How could these difficulties be explained? What was the difference between the two versions of statistics? The principal (and for me essential) ingredient that unifies statistics was scarcely, if at all, visible in the traditional introductions for students in the behavioral or social disciplines. The ingredient that was missing is a mathematical framework called the *random variable*. It is a powerful conceptual tool that provides a clear, comprehensive, and unifying rationale for all of statistics. Its ability to unify that subject matter, and hence its critical role in pedagogy, has been firmly established in the more mathematical disciplines such as physics or engineering, and is widely recognized. Virtually every introductory statistics textbook in those disciplines bases its exposition on the standard random-variable approach. It is *the* logical framework, *the* rationale, that underlies statistics.

Without this framework, statistics must necessarily become an almost meaningless collection of procedures, an assemblage of apparently unrelated, randomly assembled topics. Correspondingly, one finds that the usual first course in the behavioral disciplines presents a disjointed parade of subject matter, techniques, and computational procedures. The exposition lacks a conceptual focus. Columns of data (real or hypothetical), frequency counts, histograms, algebraic formulae and "proofs," notation conventions, S. S. Stevens's four classes of measures, descriptive statistics, parameters, set-theoretical explanations of probability, significance tests, sample values, estimation methods, and many more, all are presented on more or less the same level, the same footing. There is no logical unfolding, no unifying thread, just a succession of apparently ad hoc topics.

As a result, the typical student is at best left bewildered and gun-shy. Faced with an avalanche of apparently unrelated and meaningless material, the student tends to feel overwhelmed, helpless, and to become anxious. All too often the bewildered student simply gives up: since statistics doesn't make any sense, apparently all that one can do is to try to memorize by rote each formula, each proof, each computational technique, just long enough to pass the examination in that subject area. The material is then promptly forgotten. Thus one finds that as a rule students who have completed the usual first course cannot read the experimental literature with even the beginning of a critical understanding; they certainly cannot design experiments; and, very soon after the final examination, nothing is remembered that could serve as a foundation for a subsequent more advanced course. Too often all that remains is a residue of utter distaste for statistics (or anything else mathematical) and a potential for mobilizing anxiety should a subsequent course be required.

I have asserted that if one conceptualizes statistics within a random-variable framework, then the subject matter does not look meaningless or fragmented. Rather, it becomes integrated and makes sense; the topics unfold meaningfully in a logical sequence. Why, then, is this framework not used routinely in introductory courses for students in the behavioral disciplines? Surely it is not because the authors writing for these students fail to realize the central importance of the random-variable concept; the evidence in the literature argues against such a conclusion.

There undoubtedly are a number of reasons that explain the failure to use this approach, and some may be historical. It simply has not been traditional to use the random-variable approach in these kinds of introductory courses. Consequently, any attempt to change that tradition must expect to run into the characteristic resistances that usually arise in the course of any attempt to change the status quo. This leads to a paradoxical state of affairs that is not without its humorous aspects. On the one hand, the unsatisfactory status of the usual first course is widely recognized and admitted; there even are explicit calls in the literature for a "new" approach. On the other hand, a truly nontraditional approach tends to be rejected out of hand, without further ado, just because it *is* new. Rationalizations for this rejection are readily available: the approach is too abstruse and theoretical; too dry; too easy; too demanding; students want, and should have, rote "how-to" methods, and so on. I myself have encountered all of these objections, as well as a few others, at one time or another.

Be that as it may, another reason for not using the random-variable approach is that superficially at least, it seems to be too difficult for those students who have had only high school mathematics. Since the usual random-variable exposition in, for example, engineering, physics, or mathematics does require the use of calculus or even more advanced mathematical tools, it would indeed seem at first glance that the framework is unsuitable for the audience we are considering here.

It obviously is true that a full, rigorous exposition is not suitable for students who lack the appropriate requisite mathematical preparation. However, the random-variable concept *can* be taught effectively at an elementary level provided that the exposition is presented in a sophisticated, judicious simplification that is clear and uncluttered. If one uses simple formal models and an intuitive but mathematically sound approach, then, contrary to the usual assumptions, the random-variable framework can be understood and used with profit even by students who have relatively modest mathematical backgrounds or abilities.

That, at least, has been my experience. I have found in over 15 years of teaching introductory courses, seminars, individual reading courses, but especially in the course of doing a great deal of intensive remedial work with "problem" students (including quite a few at a graduate level), that the approach works well. When a student discovers that there is an underlying rationale, that statistics can be understood in a logical fashion, often the reaction is an amazed "is that all there is to it?" Students begin to see that the confusion previously and incorrectly attributed to their own shortcomings or even stupidity has really been engendered by the fragmented, meaningless method of presentation that forces one to work mechanically. Thus, if one finds a suitable level of presentation and suitable means for introducing the basic concepts, the random-variable framework becomes accessible. Students may even find themselves becoming interested in the previously odious subject matter in spite of themselves.

I believe that all too often we underestimate students. Given the opportunity, many do tend to respond positively to the intellectual interest inherent in fundamentals. Basic concepts are compelling in their own right and do not need to be trivialized or sugarcoated to make them palatable.

This book, then, is based on a random-variable approach. While it of course leans heavily on the previously mentioned approach that is standard in the more mathematical disciplines, it also reflects the outcome of my own struggle to translate between the two conceptions of statistics and thus to relate them to each other. Inevitably it is in some ways a "different" book. While it covers much the same material as traditional texts for students in the behavioral disciplines, there are a number of differences. I would like to comment briefly on some of the more important of these.

First, it will be apparent immediately that there are considerably fewer calculations, formulae, algebraic proofs, and other mathematical manipulations than one finds in traditional expositions. This tends to give the book an air of simplicity, but that is deceptive. The book *is* simple in that it relies relatively little on the usual mathematical manipulations, as I have mentioned. However, under the apparent simplicity lies a conceptual sophistication. In that sense, this book is not at all simple. (These considerations may explain why some have thought that this approach is too easy, whereas others have thought that it is too difficult.) The approach does mean that the student will need to do a considerable amount of hard thinking about concepts and their applications. In the usual approach, one can escape genuine intellectual effort by engaging in essentially meaningless busywork that gives the satisfying illusion of doing "hard work." One cannot escape in this fashion with the present approach.

Second, since the random-variable approach does have an inner logic that dictates a certain order of presentation of some material, one finds that on occasion one must depart from the traditional order. A case in point is descriptive statistics. Usually it is one of the first topics presented in an introductory course, but within a random-variable exposition one must first present and master certain concepts basic to that framework before the topic of description can be properly addressed.

A by-product of this approach is that the process of description comes to be understood in a deep and rich way. For example, the mean, a concept first introduced briefly and somewhat ambiguously, continues to take on added meaning and precision throughout the book. At first it is presented as a simple arithmetical average of data. Subsequently, it is viewed in increasingly complex ways—as one of the members in a family of descriptors, the moments; as a statistic, and so on, until in the final section of the book it becomes an important ingredient in the discussion of various complex multivariate issues such as dependence, correlation, prediction, and the like.

Incidentally, the fact that the random-variable approach permits one to obtain a deeper or even atypical view of standard subject matter is demonstrated repeatedly. Another important example of this feature concerns interval estimation. The framework allows one to conceptualize that important method in a way that is quite different from the usual conceptualization; while the different perspective does ultimately lead to substantially the same technical procedures as those resulting from the usual expositions, the random-variable approach leads to an exposition and explanation that is lucid and mathematically sound.

A third difference between this book and others is that some of the material included in the typical first course has been omitted. There are several reasons for these omissions. For example, consider the usual set-theoretical approach to probability. In my opinion, there is little justification for that kind of an introduction in a first course. The usual exposition condenses a great deal of complex material into a few summary formulae, a procedure that tends to mystify many students; they never quite see the relevance of set theory to probability or to statistics in general, although they may dutifully try to master the information. Furthermore, if one examines these typical expositions, one finds that once presented, set-theoretical concepts are never again mentioned or used. These considerations illustrate one reason for omitting some of the standard material, namely, when it is an unnecessary, although traditional, complication that serves no particular purpose. (I do not believe that the set-theoretical conception of probability will be usefully remembered should the student take a more advanced course later on.) I find that a frequency approach to probability provides a more than adequate introduction.

Similar reasoning applies to the matter of elaborate or complicated mathematical notations. By and large, these can and should be avoided. One instance where a more complicated notation seemed unavoidable concerns Bayes's theorem and related subjects. In that one case, the notational material is presented separately in an appendix.

In other instances material has been omitted because it is readily available elsewhere; there seemed to be little point in duplication. A typical example would be the usual set of statistical tables. Particularly in a primarily conceptual exposition, these seemed unessential. (The one complete table that has been included in this book is presented in a more comprehensive format than usual, and with a full explanation of its method of construction.)

I have furnished references for much of the material that either has been omitted or has been discussed only partially. Three references have been used a great deal: Freeman (1963), Hays (1973), and Kirk (1972). (The complete references are given in the list of references.) These three have been used particularly in conjunction with issues (such as those pertaining to the design of experiments) which are beyond the scope of this book. They also are cited in conjunction with proofs and discussions of some of the more complicated mathematical relationships; for explanations of mathematical techniques such as the algebra of expectations; and, occasionally, for statistical tables. It would be desirable to have these three references available on reserve in the library.

Another, fourth, difference is that there are some terms which appear almost constantly in this book but which are seldom found in the traditional expositions; a prime example is the term "probability density function." Otherwise, the terminology by and large is standard. One exception, however, is the term "outcome" and its qualifiers "actual" and "potential." I needed neutral labels for one of the two principal ingredients of the random-variable framework, and this terminology seemed appropriate and suggestive. As far as I know, it is not used in this fashion elsewhere. This nonstandard terminology, however, is eventually linked to the corresponding standard nomenclature.

Fifth, certain readers may on occasion find the pace of the book somewhat slower than usual, and the material more repetitious. This style of presentation reflects my concern with the previously mentioned problem of student anxiety and is designed to circumvent it as much as possible. If an occasional redundancy or overexplanation will help to allay the massive and debilitating anxiety concerning mathematics that so frequently lies just below the surface, then it will justified; at any rate, it will do little harm.

A sixth and relatively minor difference is the absence of answers to the chapter problems. While the problems are a very important part of the exposition—they are designed to solidify, integrate, and test the mastery of the fundamentals—they are primarily problems in mathematical thinking rather than exercises in computation or algebra. In most instances, the discussion relevant to a given problem already is in the chapter material; it therefore seemed superfluous to repeat it or very similar discussions in the form of an answer to a problem.

It should be apparent from this introductory discussion that a student will complete this course without developing any significant computational skills, and without developing competence as a designer of experiments. That loss, however, is more illusory than real. As I have said, I find that students who have completed traditional first courses also have not developed competence in these areas. What will a student gain from the random-variable approach?

First, as a result of obtaining a rudimentary but sound conceptual understanding of the actual foundations of statistics, a student should be able to comprehend reports in the experimental literature—if not in specific detail, then in principle, at least. In other words, if all goes well, there will be evidence of a budding critical faculty.

Second, the groundwork for a next course in statistics should have been laid; concepts once properly mastered tend to "stick." A second course will be more profitable to the well-prepared student, since he or she will not need to change the conceptual framework acquired in the introductory course. As a matter of fact, because this book does address the fundamentals, it could even be useful to the beginning graduate student as a collateral source. It may help the less-than-optimally prepared student fill any conceptual gaps and weaknesses that remain from earlier undergraduate courses.

Third, the fear (or even dread) of statistics in particular and mathematics in general may have been avoided or reduced. As I have said, I believe that one of the contributing factors to these anxieties is the bewildered helplessness that accompanies a lack of understanding that stems from fragmented expositions, introductions that force the student to memorize procedures mechanically and to guess at answers magically. An understandable, unifying rationale leads to a clear conceptualization, which in turn ought to lead to an emotionally comfortable command of the subject matter.

A break with tradition almost always does introduce some stresses. In the present case, the random-variable approach may require a period of readjustment, particularly on the part of instructors who have been using the standard approach for some time. That may be uncomfortable, but should be a passing hazard. It also should be well worth the effort and temporary discomfort; I am convinced that the benefits derived from shifting to a random-variable approach will far outweigh any costs of making such a change.

PART I

Introduction to the Random Variable Concept

CHAPTER 1

Elementary Considerations

Experimental studies and other investigations in the behavioral disciplines can at first glance exhibit a bewildering variety. Not only is there a great diversity of subject matter, but there also seem to be many different types of data and associated methodological procedures. Yet, as we shall see, it is possible to extract from this large body of apparently unrelated experimental material an underlying common conceptual structure. The logical coherence of this structure provides a unifying framework that allows one to organize and understand most if not all experimental diversities in terms of one comprehensive conceptual system. The resulting integration greatly clarifies statistical issues and permits a considerable economy of thought.

It is a major goal of this text to develop this underlying conceptual basis in a clear and meaningful manner. It will be necessary to study a number of subsidiary topics before the unifying framework can be grasped adequately, but at this point we can at least take a quick, preliminary glance at the key ideas. Let us consider experimental results in general. The yield of most experiments has two readily apparent properties. First, an experimental yield typically comprises numbers; frequently, these are generated directly by experimental observations and various measurements, but they also may stem from mathematical computations based on raw data. In this text we will call such numerical results of experiments, regardless of their origin, *outcomes*. We will learn that there is much that can be said about this very general and deceptively simple concept.

A second characteristic of experimental yields is that in most instances they are not precisely specifiable before the experiment is performed. Particularly in the behavioral disciplines, an investigator usually cannot know the exact value of his outcome in advance. In other words, it is an obvious feature of most studies that prior *uncertainty* characterizes outcomes; one says there is "uncertainty associated with outcomes." Uncertainty is a qualitative notion and correspondingly vague, but mathematicians have developed a discipline that quantifies it and thus makes it mathematically tractable: the concept of *probability* provides a numerical measure of uncertainty.

These two aspects of experiments—numerical outcome and the associated uncertainty or probability—are key ingredients of the mathematical system that will provide our principal conceptual framework. This mathematical system is called a RANDOM VARIABLE. It is useful not only in the behavioral disciplines but also has important applications in many other fields. For example, in engineering, physics, operations research, and economics, the random variable concept has been widely applied in the study of a variety of subjects such as signal analysis, statistical mechanics, systems design, and economic forecasting.

The concept of a random variable (we shall frequently abbreviate that term as RV) greatly facilitates the study of statistics in the behavioral disciplines. As the subsequent material will show, the content of the major branches of our subject—descriptive, inferential, and correlational statistics—can be developed in a logical manner in the random variable context. That system provides a conceptual focus that by its own inner logic dictates a rational sequence of presentation, thus unfolding the subject matter in a natural and meaningful order. As a result, a unified framework is gradually constructed.

One implication for the student of such a logically sequential approach is that earlier material must be thoroughly mastered and firmly retained if later material is to be grasped fully. This brings me to a word of caution. The introductory concepts may on first acquaintance seem almost painfully simple or self-evident. Do not belittle them on that account, nor treat them casually. You may find that as conceptual complexities are introduced, an "obvious" concept has slipped from your grasp, and the new material thus becomes opaque. To some extent, this seems to be unavoidable in a conceptual development of a new subject. It does mean that you probably will have to return to the introductory sections several times for review. If you are alert to the process of temporary forgetting of the simple basics, you yourself will usually be able to recognize your need for review as it arises.

We will begin the study of the random variable concept by separately examining outcomes (chap. 2) and probability (chap. 3). Subsequently we will explore how these two notions are combined in the construction of the random variable framework (chaps. 4 and 5). This will complete the introduction (part I). Next we will study how random variables are described (part II), and how they arise in the experimental situation (part III). The remainder of the text will treat statistical inference in general as well as in a number of important specific applications (part IV), and issues in correlation and related topics (part V).

CHAPTER 2

Outcomes

The concept of "outcome" as the numerical yield of a study or experiment has already been briefly introduced. We will now consider that concept in greater detail. We of course know that experimental measurements and similar procedures produce numbers: an experimenter counts (number of persons in a queue, crossings of a rat in an obstruction box, syllables recalled in verbal learning studies), measures (a height or weight, auditory or visual threshold, galvanic skin response, transit time in a maze, or error rate in a rotor pursuit task), or administers tests (of intelligence, academic achievement, vocational interest, or personality), for example.

These measures illustrate some of the more obvious ways in which numbers are obtained from experiments. There are, however, less direct procedures as well. These typically arise from more complicated experimental studies. For example, consider the following illustrative experiments.

An investigation was conducted to explore the connections between four characteristics: cerebral organization, handedness, hand posture used in writing, and sex. These characteristics were studied in 77 subjects. Various techniques were used. For example, a 5-point scale was used to measure the degree of hand preference shown in several common manual activities (such as combing one's hair); visual tests, including tachistoscopic procedures, were administered; and syllable retention was measured.

In a study of speech patterns exhibited by witnesses during court hearings the experimenters sought to differentiate between a "powerful" and a "powerless" style of giving evidence. They provided 152 subjects with stimulus tapes and written material ostensibly exemplifying witnesses' use of the two speech styles during testimony. The subjects were asked to rate a "witness" on a group of 11-point scales to measure relevant personality traits such as trustworthiness. The subjects were also asked to indicate the amount of money that they thought would be fair compensation for damages assessed by the court. The experimenters were interested in establishing whether speech styles affected a subject's evaluation of the trial situation.

An investigation of techniques for reducing avoidance behavior (phobias) studied four treatment methods based on modeling. The fearfulness of 32 volunteer subjects was measured before and after treatment by a number of methods (a behavior test, Fear Survey Schedule rating, and fear report). The experimenters sought to evaluate the effectiveness of the four different methods of therapy.

The effects of crowding on behavior and mood were studied in an experiment involving 80 college students in two dormitories. Architectural characteristics such as size of rooms and number of rooms on a floor were determined. Various psychological characteristics of the two groups of subjects were assessed by means of a 14-item questionnaire in which each item was rated on a 10-point scale.

An experiment investigated the relationships between social intrusiveness and helping responses; 81 students who were seated by themselves in the campus cafeteria were studied. Different methods were used to approach the subjects. The experimenters used several degrees of intrusiveness (for example, sitting closer or farther from the subject) and of urgency expressed in a request for help. A subject's willingness to respond to the request for help was evaluated by the investigators. In addition, the subjects themselves rated the perceived behavior of the experimenter and their own subjective responses to the intrusion on a set of 7-point items. The experimenters sought to establish relationships between the invasion of personal space, the apparent legitimacy of the invader's request for help, and the "helper's" response patterns.

We have not mentioned so far that these experiments shared one important feature, even though they differed so significantly in diverse ways—subject matter, methodology, logical plan, measurement procedures, and the like. The common feature was that in each case, the experimenters ultimately reduced their considerable mass of data to one single number and, in a sense, viewed that one number as "the" outcome of the experiment. We would be getting far ahead of ourselves if we pursued this aspect of experimentation further at this point. We will consider these matters in detail in parts III through V. For the moment, we shall merely note that this kind of a "single outcome number" typically plays a central role in the elaborate chain of reasoning used by an experimenter to support the final conclusions of a study.

Thus, it seems that the yield from either of two types of experimental procedures—a direct operation such as an ordinary measurement, or a mathematical manipulation of complex masses of data—is a single number. Let us for the time being set aside other experimental considerations and explore the subject of the numerical outcome in its bare essentials; that is, we shall consider certain logical properties of such outcome numbers. For that purpose, we shall use simple "experiments" to illustrate the concepts that are being introduced. The quotation marks are intended to emphasize that these illustrations will be simplified and schematic; they will outwardly bear little resemblance to actual experimental studies such as those reported in the professional literature. These simple examples will highlight, however, the particular formal characteristics that are being examined.

A Single Number and a Set of Numbers: Actual and Potential Outcomes

The taxonomy we are about to construct will be used to categorize or classify whole collections or sets of numbers rather than a single number. We have indicated that one typically obtains a single number, an outcome, *after* an experimental operation has been performed. What can be said about experimental outcomes *before* such an operation has been performed? In general, one is able to specify in conjunction with any one experimental manipulation a corresponding set of numbers, namely, the set comprising all those numbers (and only those) that could conceivably result from that particular experimental procedure. That set will of course include *the* one particular number that would ultimately be obtained *after* actually performing the experimental procedure.

These considerations lead us to make the important distinction between an *actual* and a *potential* outcome. We shall use the former term to refer to a number actually obtained from some experimental manipulation. We shall use the latter term to refer to the set of numbers that we can specify in advance; in a given study, the potential outcome is the *set* of all numbers that could be obtained as actual outcomes. The taxonomy we are about to construct will classify potential outcomes, that is, sets of numbers rather than single numbers.

Classification: Range and Continuity

The method one uses to classify scientific concepts usually will depend on a variety of theoretical as well as pragmatic considerations. For example, in the theory of measurement, certain arithmetical properties of measures are important, and applicable taxonomies reflect that focus. Thus, one well-known scheme (Stevens, 1946, 1951; Gaito, 1960) divides measurements into the following four types of scales: nominal, ordinal, interval, and ratio. These scales reflect an interest in the types of mathematical operations that may be legitimately performed with different "types" of numbers. Other ways of categorizing quantities have been developed to reflect different perspectives (Coombs et al., 1970; Suppes and Zinnes, 1963).

Similarly, various approaches could be used for our purposes. We shall develop a simple scheme for classifying potential outcomes that is particularly useful for discussing the formal characteristics of an RV framework. Two separate classification features or characteristics (sometimes such classification categories are also referred to as "dimensions") will be introduced and discussed: *range* and *continuity*.

An actual outcome is an ordinary number, and it therefore can be geometrically represented as a point located along a numbered coordinate axis. Consider, for example, the actual score one obtains from administering a particular test of intellectual abilities, the Wechsler Adult Intelligence Scale (WAIS). We can represent an obtained score such as 112 (our "experimental" actual outcome) as one point on the numbered axis shown in figure 2.1. When that kind of an axis is used to represent outcome values, we will quite naturally call it an *outcome axis*. What about the potential outcome in the WAIS administration? By looking at the WAIS manual, we learn that a test score must be an integer lying in the numerical range from 41 to 179 inclusive. We can represent that range geometrically; in figure 2.1 the potential outcome range is shown as the interval defined by the specified limiting numerical values of the WAIS test scores. In the present example, the potential outcome (and we remember that a potential outcome is a *set* of numbers) is confined within a portion of the outcome axis. It lies between a least (minimum) and greatest (maximum) numerical value on that axis. A potential outcome that is confined in this way at *both ends* of its numerical extent will be called a potential outcome that is *limited in range*.

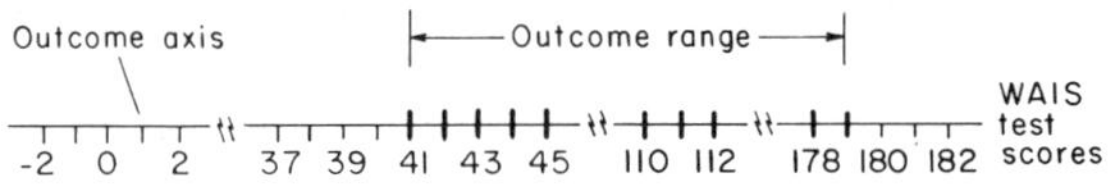

FIGURE 2.1 A limited-in-range discrete potential outcome

As a contrasting illustration, let us consider an "experiment" consisting of counting the number of vehicles that arrive at some specified location, such as a tollgate, within a given 24-hour period. Is the potential outcome limited in this case? We see that there is a lower boundary value. It is zero—one cannot have less than zero vehicles arriving anywhere. There is, however, no patently obvious upper limit that can be placed on the vehicle count, although practical limitations would impose some upper limit (unknown to us, and, in any case, very large).[1] The potential outcome set for the vehicle count experiment is indicated in figure 2.2.

In this or similar situations, where a potential outcome set is

[1]The existing number of registered vehicles, or particular road characteristics that confine traffic flow, are examples of factors that would in practice place some upper limit on the vehicle count.

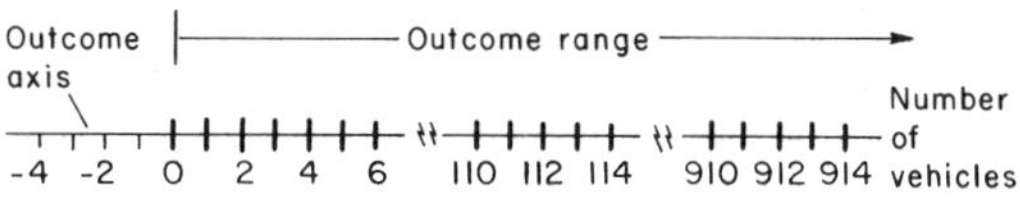

FIGURE 2.2 A not-limited-in-range discrete potential outcome

essentially unlimited at *one or both* of the upper and lower ranges, we say that we have a potential outcome that is *not limited in range*. As a practical matter, we shall classify a potential outcome as "limited in range" *only* when one can readily see that it has specific, obvious upper and lower numerical limits (i.e., all the possible outcomes are constrained to lie within a self-evident, firmly specified range). Otherwise, we shall consider a potential outcome to belong to the category, "not limited in range."

The first classification dimension of potential outcomes, then, is range. The second classification dimension of potential outcomes to be considered is *continuity*. That term refers to the presence or absence of a definite, specifiable arithmetical difference (a numerical increment or interval) between neighboring outcomes in the potential outcome set. Continuity is a concept that will become very important in the RV framework, as we shall see in the material that begins in chapter 4.

Consider once more the two previous "experimental" examples, the WAIS test and the vehicle count. In the corresponding potential outcome sets, does some specifiable, minimum numerical spacing exist between any two actually possible neighboring outcome values? It does. We know that WAIS scores as well as vehicle counts are integers (whole numbers). Therefore, there must always be a numerical "space," an interval of 1, between any two consecutive obtainable outcome values.

We can represent this and similar situations geometrically. In figures 2.1 and 2.2, the possible outcomes in the potential outcome set are indicated by short vertical bars at the appropriate locations along the outcome axis. In these geometrical representations we can plainly see the incremental nature of the potential outcome set. The spaces that exist between any two adjacent possible outcome values are readily apparent.

We will call a potential outcome that displays this incremental character a *discrete* outcome. We infer from the discussion of the two previous "experiments" that a potential outcome is always discrete when it reflects an experimental procedure that consists of counting something (correct test responses, vehicles, etc.). There are, however, other procedures that can lead to a discrete potential outcome set as well. For example, a particular measurement may be made with an instrument that can discriminate only to a limited degree of precision.[2] A simple but representative example would be the digital scale used in many stores to weigh goods. Typically, such scales measure to the nearest 1/100 lb., and thus there exists a minimum numerical interval or space between any two neighboring outcomes in the potential outcome set. The scale has a "resolving power" of 1/100 lb. For this kind of a scale the geometrical representation of its potential outcome would show the "experimentally" attainable outcome values incrementally spaced at intervals (representing 1/100 lb.) along the outcome axis.

If a potential outcome is not discrete, it is called a *continuous outcome*. One example would be the time taken by a rat to run a maze. In principle, this kind of an experimental measurement of time could yield any numerical value. The "in principle" refers to the difference between a mathematical conception and an actual physical measurement. We have already encountered similar issues during the discussion of the existence of an upper limit for counting the number of vehicles. We will reconsider these issues briefly at the end of this chapter.

At any rate, if in our example we ignore certain practical (or even theoretical) general limitations on the measurement of time, then the potential outcome fails to display any self-evident, obvious numerical increments; now there are no readily specifiable minimum spaces (such as the obvious numerical increments between any two WAIS scores) that *must* exist between any two possible neighboring values in a potential outcome set. That is, we cannot say that *in principle* there must be some definite, particular time interval, for example, 1/1000th of a second, that separates any

[2]One sometimes describes such instruments as those having "limited resolving power" or "limited resolution capability."

two possible outcome values. We shall call any potential outcome that is not innately and obviously incremental in character a continuous outcome. We shall see that the distinction with respect to continuity (our second "dimension" of the classification scheme, range being the first) has major implications in the RV theoretical framework.

Continuous potential outcomes can be represented on the outcome axis by a continuous line in the outcome range. We show the "rat time" potential outcome set in figure 2.3 by a heavy line. Incidentally, we recognize that with respect to the first dimension, the range, we should categorize this particular potential outcome set as "not limited in range"; we cannot readily place an upper limit on the outcome values that are possible. For example, our rat could fall asleep in the middle of its maze run, and the measured time thus could be quite long. Or, the animal might be removed from the maze prematurely, or even die in the maze; the actual outcome could then be considered to be an infinitely long time, an infinitely large number.

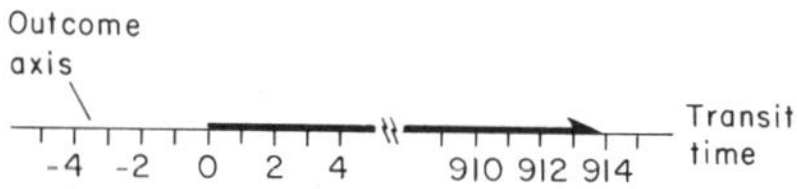

FIGURE 2.3 A not-limited-in-range continuous potential outcome

The two characteristics of range and continuity describe two separate aspects of a potential outcome. Each of these two classification dimensions classifies any given potential outcome into one of two subcategories. That is, the range dimension classifies a given potential outcome as either limited or not limited in range; the continuity dimension classifies that outcome as either discrete or continuous. This gives rise to four logically possible combinations, each one a possible potential outcome subtype: (1) limited and discrete, (2) limited and continuous, (3) not limited and discrete, and (4) not limited and continuous. Any potential outcome set must always be classifiable as belonging to one, and only one, of these four subgroups.

Of these four subtypes, one has a further distinguishing characteristic. The first one of the four subgroups mentioned, a potential outcome that is limited and discrete, has a special characteristic: for a potential outcome belonging to this subtype, and for it alone, we can always prepare a *complete list of all the possible outcomes* that are contained in that given potential outcome set. This is true because among the four subtypes, it is the only one that has a *finite*, and thus completely specifiable, number of possible outcomes. This characteristic can easily be seen from a geometrical argument. First, if a potential outcome is limited in range, it means that the set is confined within an upper and a lower value on the outcome axis (the WAIS scores, for instance). Second, if it also is discrete, then there is, by definition, a particular, firmly specified interval or distance between any and all neighboring outcomes. We have a limited segment on the outcome axis, and a minimum incremental distance that separates neighboring outcome values. Intuitively, we see that one can therefore "squeeze in" only a certain finite number of intervals within a limited segment. For instance, in the WAIS example, only so many unit intervals, 138, fit into the outcome value range between 41 and 179. Since there is a finite number of possible outcomes, we can list them. For the WAIS score, that list would contain the 139 numbers that can be actual outcomes: 41, 42, 43,. . ., 179. That list exhausts all the possibilities; it contains *all* the outcomes that our "experiment" could yield. Since, as we have just seen, we can always make a complete list of outcomes for a potential outcome set that is discrete and also limited in range, we may also call this type of outcome *listable*.

Among the four subtypes previously cited, the remaining three are *not listable*. Basically, this is so because any one of these three types must contain an *infinite number of possible outcome values*; one therefore cannot list them all, obviously. This situation can arise, however, for either or both of two different reasons. On the one hand, a given potential outcome set may contain an infinite number of possible outcome values because it is not limited in range. In that case, the number of possible outcomes is infinite because the outcome values continue indefinitely in one or both directions along the outcome axis. On the other hand, a potential outcome set may contain an infinite number of outcomes because the set is continuous. In this second case, there always are an infinite number of possible outcome values because, roughly speaking, the neighboring values are infinitely close to one another; they are "densely packed." Thus, even a potential outcome that is *limited* in range will contain an infinite number of possible outcome values if it is a *continuous* potential outcome. In fact, that kind of an outcome set will contain an infinite number of possible outcome values, no matter how narrow its numerical range would be—whether it extended from 0 to 1,000, or from 5 to 6, or from 5.499999 . . . to 5.50000 . . ., for example. Each of these outcome ranges will contain an infinite number of possible outcome values if the potential outcome in that range is continuous.

One more remark before we turn to the other basic component in the RV structure, probability. In the preceding discussion we encountered several times the question of distinguishing between "practical" and "theoretical" properties of potential outcomes. While these kinds of considerations can lead to entertaining abstract discussions or even to interesting theoretical paradoxes, they are not relevant for an introduction to the RV framework. We will take a commonsense approach to these matters. Consider first the question of range. If we weigh a human subject, is there an actual upper limit to the potential outcome? There undoubtedly is—1,000 lbs., 2,000 lbs., or more. Can we readily identify a specific, obvious number as the upper limit? We cannot, and in such instances it will be convenient, as well as accurate enough for most practical purposes, to treat the potential outcome as not limited in range. (Our example has, of course, a lower limit of zero.)

Similar considerations would hold for the question of continuity. In the example of a rat running a maze, we concluded that the potential outcome should be classified as continuous. Actually, from an experimental, physical point of view, we know that any real timing procedure must have some physical limit to its resolution capability. That is, real stopwatches measure only to some specified degree of accuracy—to a fifth of a second, a millisecond, etc. In these kinds of situations, however, there is no self-evident, obvious, specifiable minimum spacing. Thus, they differ from such cases as WAIS test scores, vehicle counts, or digitally measured weights; these latter "experiments" all have potential outcomes that in principle are obviously incremental in character. We will take a mathematically practical and convenient approach, and treat a potential outcome as continuous if it is *not* obviously discrete.

Thus, with respect to both the range and the continuity dimension we shall classify outcomes commonsensically on the basis of their obvious properties. We shall not quibble about subtleties such as, is time (or, for that matter, distance) continuous, or is it discrete? In any case, a mathematical or quantitative treatment of a physical situation is always to some extent an idealization, and we will take that for granted.

PROBLEMS

2.1 Discuss the differences and similarities between actual and potential outcomes.

2.2 An investigator performs a complex experimental study and obtains the numerical result 4.1732. Can you classify that outcome in terms of the taxonomy developed in this chapter (range and continuity)? Justify your answer.

2.3 For each of the following "experiments," classify and discuss the potential outcome; sketch it on an outcome axis; and, if possible, make a list of all the possible outcomes:

(a) An experimenter rolls a pair of standard dice. The actual outcome is the number of dots showing.

(b) Cards are drawn from a standard deck one at a time. A card is not replaced after it has been drawn. The experimenter counts the number of cards that have been drawn before one red card is obtained. That count is the actual outcome.

(c) The experiment is identical to the preceding example, except that now the experimenter replaces each card after it has been drawn.

(d) Two teams, A and B, are playing baseball. The actual outcome is obtained by subtracting the total number of runs scored by team B from the total scored by team A.

(e) Two horses, X and Y, are running in a race. The actual outcome is computed by subtracting the track time of horse X from that of horse Y.

(f) A spinner is a device consisting of a freely turning pointer placed on a dial. (It is like a clock with a single hand that can spin.) The actual outcome may be defined as the angle, in degrees, between the position assumed by the pointer after it has been spun and the "12 o'clock" position on the dial face.

(g) [For those who remember high school trigonometry.] The experiment is the same as the preceding example, with the exception that the actual outcome is now defined as the tangent of the angle, rather than the angle itself.

2.4 Among the preceding collection of potential outcomes, there are some for which one can list all the possible outcome values. What, if anything, do these potential outcomes have in common?

CHAPTER 3

Introduction to Probability

Words such as "probably," "likely," or "uncertain" are frequently used informally or colloquially in everyday situations. One might use them in speaking about anything from tomorrow's weather to a poker hand. Used in this fashion, they lack precision; nevertheless, they do seem to convey some useful meaning. They qualitatively describe an incomplete state of knowledge.

In order to quantify these kinds of relatively vague, intuitive perceptions, the mathematical concept of probability has been developed. It is the product of a search for a more precise, numerical counterpart to the qualitative concepts expressed by the informal terminology. In general, there are two principal approaches to probability. On the one hand, one may associate the concept of probability with some physical measurement or other procedure that can generate experimental information. We will call that kind of an approach an empirical approach. On the other hand, one can develop the concept of probability by abstract mathematical reasoning rather than by way of experimentally grounded concepts. One then relies on formal axiomatic methods, logical principles, and the like. Let us call these kinds of approaches theoretical. For most practical purposes, the two approaches are in agreement; they are compatible and lead to comparable results.[1]

[1]There is a third approach, the "subjective" or "personal" view of probability (Savage, 1962) that will be introduced in chapter 22. For mathematicians and philosophers of science, the theoretical foundations of probability remain complex, paradoxical, and even controversial. See, for example, Carnap (1953), Kaplan (1964), and Wright (1973).

Most of the time, our approach will be a straightforward empirical one. Occasionally, we will call on simple versions of theoretical methods. We will begin our introduction to probabilistic concepts with empirical considerations.

Terminology

We shall need a few terms to facilitate our discussion. Consider the familiar example of tossing a coin. Suppose we toss a coin a total of 1,000 times, and decide to pay attention to the number of times that we had obtained heads. We will assume that by actual count, heads occurred 490 times in the 1,000 tosses. We can define several basic terms in the context of this or similar illustrative examples.

1. We can consider the tossing of a coin to be a miniature experiment and call each "performance" (toss) an experimental TRIAL or OBSERVATION.

2. The performance of a trial produces an EVENT. In our example, two types of events could occur: heads or tails. One, and only one, of these must result from any given trial or observation.

3. We may be interested in one particular type among these events. In our example, we decided to attend to the number of heads that occurred in our series of trials. That kind of an event is called the FAVORABLE event. It is subjectively selected and therefore, for any one particular type of an experiment, reflects our point of view and interest. Different experimenters observing the same experimental trials could select different types of events as "the" favorable event.

4. The number of times a particular event occurs in a sequence or series of repeated trials is called the FREQUENCY (or, equivalently, the OBSERVED FREQUENCY) of that event. A frequency is obtained by a straightforward count.

5. We can define the concept of the RELATIVE FREQUENCY of an event in terms of its frequency in a series of experimental trials. It is just the proportion or ratio of the observed frequency to the total number of trials in a given series of observations. (It is calculated by dividing the observed frequency by the total number of trials.) The relative frequency can be expressed either as a proportion or as a decimal.

We can now restate our hypothetical example in the new terminology: we performed 1,000 trials in which the two possible events were heads and tails; we selected heads as our favorable event; its frequency was 490; therefore, the relative frequency of that favorable event was 490/1,000 or 0.490.

As a second illustration, let us assume that we are going to roll a standard die. The six possible results are an ace, deuce, trey, four, five, or six—the number of dots that can show on the "up" face on a given roll of the die. One, and only one, of these events must occur on any one trial. Let us arbitrarily select "ace" as our favorable event. Suppose we had rolled the die a total of 2,000 times and obtained an ace on 320 of these 2,000 rolls. In our new terminology, we would say that an experimental trial consists of one roll of the die. There are six possible events; we chose the event "ace" to be our favorable event. We performed 2,000 repeated trials; the frequency of the favorable event was 320; its relative frequency was 320/2,000 or 0.160.

As another example, let us assume that our experimental trial now consisted of drawing one card from a standard deck and subsequently returning it to that deck. We could specify the set of possible events in a number of different ways, but let us say that in this instance we had decided that we would specify four types of events: the four suits. That specification implies that on any one trial, one, and only one, of these four events can and must occur: clubs, diamonds, hearts, or spades. We will arbitrarily select spades as our favorable event. If we now draw a card 400 times, i.e., perform 400 trials of the "experiment," and count the event "spades" 110 times among these 400 draws, we see that the frequency (or "observed frequency") of our favorable event is 110. Its relative frequency is 110/400 or 0.275.

An Empirical Approach: The Principle of Equivalence

Most of us are already familiar with the idea that "the probability" of an event implies a number. In order to quantify the concept of probability through an empirical approach, we somehow must connect that concept to experimental results such as measurements. For many of the applications in this book, the following straightforward approach will be entirely adequate: we shall just assume that

> THE PROBABILITY OF AN EVENT IS GIVEN BY ITS RELATIVE FREQUENCY, AND VICE VERSA.

This basic assumption, that one may use relative frequencies and probability values interchangeably, we will call THE PRINCIPLE OF EQUIVALENCE. Although it seems to be simple, it will prove to be surprisingly useful and important in a variety of contexts.[2]

It is a principle that by definition has a double implication: if we know the *relative frequency* of an event, we will assume that this numerical value is also the value of the *probability* of that event occurring; conversely, if we know the *probability* of an event occurring, the principle of equivalence states that the *relative frequency* of that event is equal to the value of that probability (regardless of the total number of trials in some repeated experimental sequence).

To illustrate the principle very simply, let us return to our "experiment" of rolling a die. We will assume that we performed a total of 2,000 repeated trials and obtained the results shown in table 3.1. We could use any of the six types of events to illustrate the principle, and we will arbitrarily focus on the event "four." Given the hypothetical data in table 3.1, we see that the frequency of "four" is 330, and its relative frequency is 330/2,000 or 0.165. By the principle of equivalence, therefore, the *probability* of obtaining a four is also 0.165.

We can similarly illustrate the converse use of the principle. Suppose that we somehow (for the moment, it does not matter how) already had known that the probability of obtaining a four was 0.165. Then, by the inverse application of the principle, we

[2]The principle of equivalence is a simplified version of the actual state of affairs. Nevertheless, it is a valuable didactic device that allows one to develop even quite complex concepts in an easily understandable manner. We shall see this particularly in part V, where the principle provides a relatively simple introduction to an intricate RV situation—the so-called bivariate case. Basically, the principle substitutes a single empirically obtained number for a mathematically more complex process.

Table 3.1

Hypothetical results from 2,000 rolls of a die

Event	Frequency	Relative frequency, or probability
ace	320	0.160
deuce	300	.150
trey	270	.135
four	330	.165
five	240	.120
six	540	.270

would know the relative frequency of that event; it would also be equal to 0.165.

Incidentally, we can extend that result further. If we now know the *relative frequency* of an event, we also know (or can very easily calculate) the corresponding *frequency* of that event in *any given total number of experimental trials*. For example, let us see if we can recover the correct frequency from the relative frequency of the event "four." We have just used the principle of equivalence to conclude that if the probability of the event "four" is 0.165, then its relative frequency is also 0.165. What must its *frequency* be in a total of 2,000 trials to yield the stipulated relative frequency of 0.165? Obviously, the corresponding frequency must be 330, the value of the numerator that will yield the specified ratio for the relative frequency.[3] We see that if we know the probability, and thus the *relative* frequency, of an event, we can then easily obtain its *frequency* among any specified, given total number of trials.

After this brief aside, let us return to the principle of equivalence. We demonstrated that one may apply that principle in either of two directions. If one knows the relative frequency of some event, the principle allows one to equate that value to the probability for that event; if one knows the probability of an event, one can

[3]This value can also be obtained more formally by using simple algebra. If we let f = frequency, r = relative frequency, and t = total number of trials, then, by definition, $r = f/t$. Equivalently, $f = r \times t$. In our example, $r = 0.165$ and $t = 2{,}000$; therefore, $f = 330$.

say that this value is equivalent to the relative frequency. (In that case, as we saw in our brief detour, it is also a simple matter to obtain the frequency of that event in any specified number of trials.) In either direction, the principle sanctions the assertion that the numerical value of one of the two entities, relative frequency and probability, is equal to the value of the other.

The Numerical Range of Probability Values

We will now consider the numerical values that a probability can assume. Can it have any value—positive, negative, or zero—or is it limited to some particular values? To answer that question, we will invoke the principle of equivalence to shift the question about probability to a parallel question about relative frequency. We ask, what range of values can a relative frequency assume? Then, if we can answer that question, we shall also have answered (again, by the principle of equivalence) the original question about probability values.

We can easily discover the highest and the lowest possible value that a relative frequency (and thus a probability) can assume if we remember how a relative frequency of an event is defined and calculated. It is the ratio between the frequency of that event in a given total number of repeated trials and that total number of trials. Let us consider some of the possible results that might occur in a given set of trials. We will continue to use our previous example of 2,000 rolls of a die and focus on the event "four." In such a series of repeated trials, what is the *lowest* frequency that we could conceivably observe for our favorable event "four"? It obviously is zero—in 2,000 trials, a four could not occur *less* than zero times. Equally obviously, the *greatest* observed frequency of our favorable event in 2,000 trials would be 2,000—we could not observe a four more often than we had rolled the die, after all. Correspondingly, the lowest and highest value for the *relative frequency* would be 0 and 1 (0/2,000 and 2,000/2,000), and, by the principle of equivalence, these would also be the minimum and maximum possible values that a *probability* could assume.

We now know that the value of a probability cannot be less than 0 or greater than 1. What about other values in that range? Can a probability assume *any* numerical value in the range between 0 and 1, or only certain values? Although we will not demonstrate it, it is not only plausible but also true that any reasonable definition of probability leads to the conclusion that a probability of an event can assume *any* numerical value from 0 to 1, inclusive.

We relied largely on a specific example, the die-rolling experiment, and the event "four" to guide our investigation of the range of probability values; the conclusions hold in general, however, and can be proven by rigorous methods as well. We have not proved our conclusions, but merely made them plausible on the basis of simple, empirical arguments. This is a pattern of intuitive demonstration that we shall resort to frequently.

The preceding conclusions are basic: the value of the probability of an event *must* lie between the extremes of 0 and 1; the probability can assume *any* value in that range, including the extremes (the minimum and maximum values, 0 and 1).

Composite Events

So far we have considered for each of our examples of a probabilistic situation (tossing a coin, drawing a card, or rolling a die) logically simple kinds of events that could occur on a given trial. We will now introduce a logically more complex kind of an event, still using our familiar examples. The more complex kind of event will be constructed from two or more of the simpler events, and in that sense can be considered as an artificially constructed entity.

Let us return to the example of the die. Previously we had considered simple, basic events, such as ace, deuce, etc. We could, however, equally well consider an event, such as "on a trial, an odd-numbered face came up" (or, equivalently, "on a trial, we obtained *either* an ace *or* a trey *or* a five"). We could select that particular event as a favorable event. We would say that it occurred on a given trial if, and only if, any one of the odd-numbered faces had turned up. For example, if we obtained a five on a trial, we would say that the favorable event had occurred; if we had obtained a deuce, we would say that the favorable event had failed to occur on that trial.

The particular choice of the three odd-numbered faces was quite arbitrary. We could just as well have selected any other set of two or more faces and constructed an event from those (for example, "on a trial, either a deuce or a six occurred").[4]

In the same way, we could artificially construct other events from the four simple events specified in the "trial" of drawing a card. For example, instead of asking as before, which of the four suits had been drawn on a trial, we could now ask, did we draw a red suit or a black suit? Each of these two constructed events would be formed by assembling some (in this example, two) of the simple events. Thus, the new event "red suit" implies, equivalently, "on a given trial, we obtained a diamond *or* a heart," and the other new event, "black suit," implies "on a trial, we obtained a club *or* a spade." Other ways of defining events could be invented in this situation.

The distinguishing feature of these new kinds of events is, obviously, that they have been constructed from and defined in terms of more basic, simple events. These kinds of artificially defined events are called COMPOSITE events, to indicate that they have been assembled or composed from simpler, elementary, "building block" kinds of events. To distinguish these latter, elementary kinds of events from the former (composite), we shall call them SIMPLE or ELEMENTARY events.

We shall consider what it means to speak about the frequency, relative frequency, and probability of a composite event.[5] The conceptualization and definition of these quantities follows naturally from the corresponding definitions and concepts for simple events. We will continue to use the illustrative example of rolling a die, and discuss composite events with reference to the hypothetical results shown in table 3.1.

Let us arbitrarily focus on the event, "on a trial of the experi-

[4]To find how many events can be constructed from two or more simple events, one applies the elementary combinatorial methods ("combinations and permutations") usually learned in high school intermediate algebra courses.

[5]We shall construct composite events only from simple events—sometimes called "atomic" events (see Freeman, 1963, pp. 4-8)—and therefore do not need to consider certain complexities such as whether or not events are "mutually exclusive." The introduction of these and similar issues would only needlessly complicate our introductory discussion.

ment, either a deuce or a four or a five occurred." What is the frequency of that event? It continues to be defined simply as the number of times that we observed or counted that event in a series of trials. Thus, our composite event occurred each time that on a trial *one* of the three specified faces came up. Naturally, the observed frequency of our composite event is therefore obtained by adding the three frequencies of the three specified simple events (deuce, four, and five). From the data of table 3.1, the observed frequency of the composite event is just

$$300 + 330 + 240, \text{ or } 870. \tag{3.1}$$

The *relative frequency of a composite event* is now defined in the obvious way. As before, it is the ratio of the observed frequency of an event to the total number of trials. In the present example, the frequency is given by (3.1), and the total number of trials remains equal to 2,000. Thus, the relative frequency of the composite event is

$$870/2{,}000 \text{ or } 0.435. \tag{3.2}$$

The principle of equivalence retains its previous implications and is applied without modification. Thus, the probability of our composite event equals 0.435, the relative frequency of that event.

We have presented basic definitions of *observed* and *relative frequencies* of *composite events*, and adopted the *principle of equivalence* without change. These definitions and the calculations they imply are obvious, simple extensions of the corresponding ideas and procedures that were originally developed for simple events. We have used these basic definitions in the preceding illustrative calculations; their rationale followed from the fundamental definitions. In accordance with these, to obtain the *probability of a composite event* we first obtained the *frequency* of that event from the appropriate sum of the frequencies of the pertinent simple events (in 3.1); we then used the frequency as numerator and calculated the ratio that specifies the *relative frequency* (3.2); and, finally, we invoked the principle of equivalence to assert that the *probability* value was given by the relative frequency of the composite event.

As I have said, this procedure follows in a straightforward way from the basic definitions of frequency and relative frequency of a composite event. There is, however, an alternative method of obtaining that probability. I will now demonstrate it. We shall see that it involves an apparently insignificant arithmetical manipulation; the implied conclusion, however, will be of considerable conceptual significance and practical utility in subsequent chapters. To begin with, by using (3.1) we can rewrite the relative frequency expressed in (3.2)—and therefore its equivalent, the probability—as

$$\frac{300 + 330 + 240}{2{,}000}\,. \tag{3.3}$$

Thus, we can express the probability of the composite event also as

$$\frac{300}{2{,}000} + \frac{330}{2{,}000} + \frac{240}{2{,}000}\,. \tag{3.4}$$

We now take a small but conceptually critical step. We recognize the three terms in (3.4) as the relative frequencies (and thus the probabilities) of the three *simple* events that were used to construct the composite event. The steps of (3.3) and (3.4) thus demonstrate, or at least make plausible, the following important general conclusion:

> To obtain the *probability of a given composite event, we may add together all the probabilities of the simple events that constitute that composite event*.

In other words, if we know (or can calculate) the probabilities of the relevant simple events that enter into the construction of a composite event, we can use these probabilities in the manner of (3.4) and obtain the probability of the composite event *directly*. We do not need to use frequencies, etc., in our calculation, as in (3.1) and (3.2). In the above example, this alternative method did not seem to offer any significant computational advantages.[6]

[6]We see on closer scrutiny that the alternative calculations only invert the order of the original arithmetical operations. Originally, we first *added frequencies* (3.1) and then *divided* the sum to obtain a relative frequency and/or probability (3.2). In the alternative method, we first *divide each of the frequencies* of a set

The above considerations are important enough to justify working out a second illustrative example to ensure that these matters are quite clear. Let us continue to use the die-rolling experiment and the hypothetical data in table 3.1 to illustrate the ideas. Suppose we define the composite event: "an odd-numbered face appeared on a trial." We know this implies the event that is constructed from the three simple events ace, trey, and five. Let us first calculate the probability of this composite event by our "new" *direct* procedure. We simply obtain the *probabilities* of the three elementary events from the table, and add them. In this way we immediately obtain the desired probability of the composite event—following the rationale reflected in (3.4):

$$0.160 + 0.135 + 0.120 = 0.415. \tag{3.5}$$

We will now calculate the probability of this composite event again, using the original procedure that follows from the basic definitions. First, we need to obtain its *frequency* by adding the relevant frequencies of the constituent simple events:

$$320 + 270 + 240 = 830. \tag{3.6}$$

Having obtained its frequency, we next calculate its *relative frequency* as we had done in (3.2). According to the basic definition, the relative frequency is

$$\frac{830}{2{,}000}, \text{ or } 0.415. \tag{3.7}$$

Finally, we invoke the principle of equivalence and assert that the probability of our composite event is numerically equal to its relative frequency, 0.415.

We have developed an alternative "direct" method of calculating the probabilities of composite events from those of constituent simple events by using particular examples as demonstrations. These demonstrations do not constitute a formal proof of the

of simple events to obtain corresponding relative frequencies and/or probabilities (that step is not shown explicitly)—and then *add* the resulting set of relative frequencies or probabilities (3.4).

general case. The conclusions are true in general, however, and can be reached by more formal and rigorous methods as well.

The Sum of the Probabilities

In a given situation, do the probabilities of all the simple events that can possibly occur add to some specific numerical value? For our familiar example, rolling a die, we see from the data of table 3.1 that the six probability values corresponding to the six simple events add to 1. Is this a coincidence?

We are examining the following sum: "the probability of ace plus the probability of deuce plus the probability of trey plus the probability of four plus the probability of five plus the probability of six." Let us consider the implied arithmetical calculation more closely. From table 3.1, we find that the sum of all the probabilities is

$$0.160 + 0.150 + 0.135 + 0.165 + 0.120 + 0.270. \tag{3.8}$$

By the principle of equivalence, we can replace each term, each probability, by its equivalent, a relative frequency. By rewriting each term in (3.8) as a ratio, we obtain

$$\frac{320}{2{,}000} + \frac{300}{2{,}000} + \frac{270}{2{,}000} + \frac{330}{2{,}000} + \frac{240}{2{,}000} + \frac{540}{2{,}000}. \tag{3.9}$$

The common denominator of all the terms allows us to express (3.9) as

$$\frac{320 + 300 + 270 + 330 + 240 + 540}{2{,}000}. \tag{3.10}$$

Let us examine the numerator of (3.10). We recognize it as the sum of the six frequencies of the six simple events. Thus, this sum represents the number of times in 2,000 rolls that we obtained an ace plus the number we obtained a deuce plus the number of times we obtained a trey, and so on for the remaining three faces. What is the sum of these six frequencies? The numerator of (3.10) *must* stand for the total number of times we rolled the die, 2,000.[7] Since the numerator of (3.10) equals 2,000, and the denominator equals 2,000 as well (or, more generally, since both the denominator and numerator each are equal to the total number of trials), the value of the ratio, and thus the *value* of the *sum of all the probabilities of the six simple events, must be equal to 1*, exactly.

We have once more obtained an important general result, although the demonstration was based on a specific, numerical example. Our conclusion holds in *any* situation where we can meaningfully speak about probabilities of elementary, simple events.

There is another, slightly different, approach that also demonstrates that the sum of simple probabilities such as those in (3.8) must be 1. It will be instructive to explore that alternative. The sum of (3.8) is the sum of six probabilities, but we can say something further about that kind of a sum. We remember that the probability of a *composite* event can be obtained by adding the appropriate probabilities of the constituent or component simple events—our "direct" method; see (3.4) and (3.5) and the relevant discussion. This fact raises the possibility that the sum of the probabilities of several simple events, such as the sum in (3.8), *might* represent the probability of a composite event. That is, we may be able to identify some composite event whose probability would be correctly expressed by the sum in (3.8). In our example, can we identify a composite event whose probability is correctly given by the sum in (3.8)? We can. In that sum, we are adding the probabilities of all six faces, and that is just what we should do had we wanted to "directly" calculate the probability of the composite event: "ace or deuce or trey or four or five or six."[8] What kind of event is this composite event, "ace or deuce or . . ."? It is the event that *must* occur on each and every roll of the die, on every dial. This should be obvious. On every trial, one, and only one, of the

[7]If this is not obvious, consider the following. After each single roll or trial, the value 1 is added to one and only one of the six frequency counts. It is added to that frequency that corresponds to the result obtained on that trial, of course; if the outcome is a trey, 1 is added to the frequency of that event, etc. The other five frequency counts remain unchanged by that trial. Thus, each trial is counted exactly once, in the appropriate "frequency bin"; keeping track of the six frequencies of the six simple events constitutes a simple bookkeeping procedure that counts the total number of rolls of the die.

six faces must come up; this, by the specification of our particular composite event, means that the composite event had occurred on that trial. Since this particular composite event is that event that must occur on each trial, we can call it the *certain* or *inevitable* event. What is its probability? Intuitively, we may know that it is 1, and we can demonstrate this logically. What is the frequency of the certain event? Since by definition it occurs on every trial of a series of repeated trials, its *frequency* must be the same as the total number of trials. Therefore, its *relative* frequency must be 1, and, by the principle of equivalence, so must its probability.

This second demonstration has been somewhat intricate, and it might be well to review the steps. We were still evaluating the sum of all the probabilities of the simple events that constitute a given probabilistic situation such as rolling a die, or drawing a card, or tossing a coin. We formed a sum of all the simple probabilities in one situation, the die-rolling trial, in (3.8). We then noticed that since it was a sum of the probabilities of simple events, it *might* turn out to express the probability of some (as yet unknown to us) composite event; we had previously learned that the probability of a composite event could be calculated by this procedure—see (3.4) and (3.5). We next asked ourselves, what composite event would give rise to, "go with," the particular sum shown in (3.8)? We discovered that it was the certain or inevitable event, the event that *must* occur once on each trial. We saw that the frequency of that kind of an event must be equal to the total number of trials, and that therefore its relative frequency must equal 1. Finally, by the principle of equivalence, we concluded that the probability of the certain event also must be 1. In this way, a logical chain of reasoning led from the first expression for the sum of all the component probabilities (3.8) to the conclusion that this sum must be equal to 1, since it could be interpreted as the probability, 1, of the certain, inevitable event.

Thus, we discovered two ways in which a sum such as that given in (3.8) could be understood. (Its numerical value was seen to be 1,

[8]You can verify this assertion by writing out the expression for the probability of that composite event, using the "direct" procedure. You will obtain a sum of six probability values, similar to (3.4) or (3.5); if you compare your sum with the sum (3.9), you will see that these two sums are the same.

no matter which of the two approaches was used.) In the first analysis we evaluated the sum principally by an argument based on the analysis of *frequencies*—as in (3.9) and (3.10). In our second approach, we identified the same basic sum in (3.8) with the probability of a *composite event*, and went on to consider the nature and the characteristics of that event. The arithmetical procedures were almost identical in these two studies of (3.8), but the way in which we viewed these procedures, and thus the meaning of a sum, differed conceptually. This aspect of mathematics is called the "interpretation" of mathematical material, and refers to alternative ways in which a given mathematical expression can be conceptually connected to empirical issues in the physical world. We encountered an example of interpretation during the discussion of the probability of composite events when we interpreted a numerical value (3.2) in two conceptually different ways: as a probability calculated according to basic definitions, and as a sum of three probabilities. Interpretation occupies an important position in mathematics. In the last chapter, it will be examined further in the context of so-called Bayesian approaches.

Complementary Events

We will next briefly consider a concept that we shall use on occasion. Let us continue to use our familiar illustrative example, the die. As we know, that statistical situation is composed of a certain number of elementary events, namely, the six faces. One, and only one, of these must occur on a given roll of the die.

We can arbitrarily divide these six simple events into two groups, A and B, placing one or more events into one group and the remaining events into the other. Many different pairs of groupings (41, to be exact) can be obtained by this procedure. Eight different examples of such group pairs are shown in table 3.2. With *any one* of the 41 possible different arrangements of simple events, we can always associate two events in the obvious way—namely, one event that is constructed from the elementary events (or elementary event, if there is only one) in group A, and the second event, that constructed from group B. That is, one event will be the event, "one of the simple events in group A occurred," and the other event will be "one of the simple events in group B occurred." One, and usually both, of these events will be a composite event. Table 3.3 illustrates eight pairs of these two types of events; each pair corresponds to one of the groupings in table 3.2. A pair of such events is called a pair of *complementary events*.

Table 3.2

Examples of group pairs

Pair no.	Group A	Group B
1	ace	deuce, trey, four, five, six
2	four	ace, deuce, trey, five, six
3	deuce, six	ace, trey, four, five
4	ace, four	deuce, trey, five, six
5	deuce, trey, five	ace, four, six
6	ace, trey, six	deuce, four, five
7	ace, deuce, trey, four, six	five
8	ace, deuce, four, five, six	trey

Table 3.3

Examples of complementary pairs of composite events

Pair no.	Event A	Event B
1	ace	deuce or trey or four or five or six
2	four	ace or deuce or trey or five or six
3	deuce or six	ace or trey or four or five
4	ace or four	deuce or trey or five or six
5	deuce or trey or five	ace or four or six
6	ace or trey or six	deuce or four or five
7	ace or deuce or trey or four or six	five
8	ace or deuce or four or five or six	trey

We say of such pairs that the event A is complementary to event B, and vice versa. For example, for the fourth pair of events illustrated in table 3.3, we would say that "ace or four" is complementary to "deuce or trey or five or six," and vice versa. The salient characteristic of such pairs of events follows from the procedure that was originally used to divide the simple events into two sets: between them, any given pair of complementary events contains each of the simple events once, and only once. That is, each simple event appears only in one or the other of a pair of complementary events; and no simple event is omitted from a given complementary pair.

There is an alternative way of speaking about such event pairs. Consider the pair of complementary events "ace or trey or six" and "deuce or four or five" (the sixth pair in table 3.3). We could call the first event, "NOT the second event," and vice versa. Thus, we could define or identify *either* event in a complementary pair in terms of the other. The first event, in our example, "ace or trey or six," could equally well have been called, "NOT deuce or four or five," and the reverse is also true.

We now ask: for a given pair of complementary events, is there any particular relationship between the corresponding two probabilities? As a result of our previous work it will be easy to demonstrate that a simple relationship must always hold between the probability of an event A and the probability of its complement, the event $NOT\ A$. We shall discover that when we are adding two such probabilities, we are in fact adding together *the probabilities of all the elementary events*. We are really forming a sum such as that expressed in (3.8), although it may not be immediately obvious that we are doing so. A specific example will illustrate the point. Suppose we would construct the following complementary pair A and $NOT\ A$: A is the event, "ace or trey or six"; $NOT\ A$, therefore, is the event "deuce or four or five." By our "direct" method, we know that the probability of A can be obtained by adding the probabilities of the constituent elementary events, as in (3.4) or (3.5):

$$\begin{aligned} \text{probability of } A = &\ \text{probability of "ace"} \\ &+ \text{probability of "trey"} \\ &+ \text{probability of "six."} \end{aligned} \tag{3.11}$$

In order to facilitate the writing of such terms involving probabilities, we shall use a standard abbreviation. We will write the probability of an event such as "ace" by using the symbolic notation, p(ace) for the more cumbersome "probability of ace." For example, we may rewrite (3.11) as

$$p(A) = p(\text{ace}) + p(\text{trey}) + p(\text{six}). \tag{3.11a}$$

In this notation, then,

$$p(NOT\ A) = p(\text{deuce}) + p(\text{four}) + p(\text{five}). \tag{3.12}$$

Adding (3.11) and (3.12), we obtain

$$\begin{aligned} p(A) + p(NOT\ A) &= [p(\text{ace}) + p(\text{trey}) + p(\text{six})] \\ &\quad + [p(\text{deuce}) + p(\text{four}) + p(\text{five})]. \end{aligned} \tag{3.13}$$

The order of addition of the right-hand side in (3.13) does not affect the value of the sum. We can therefore rearrange the terms and place the six terms in their "natural" order shown in (3.8):

$$p(\text{ace}) + p(\text{deuce}) + p(\text{trey}) + p(\text{four}) + p(\text{five}) + p(\text{six}).$$

We already know from our previous discussion the value of that sum: it is 1. Therefore, the value of (3.13), and thus the sum of the probabilities of two complementary events, is 1 as well.

Our example has illustrated that when one adds the probabilities of an event and its complement, one is actually adding all the probabilities of the simple events in a given probabilistic situation (although one is not necessarily adding them in their natural order). Thus, we infer that the sum of the probability of an event and the probability of its complementary event must always equal 1.

Summary of Results

We have used simple empirical approaches to introduce certain probabilistic concepts. Before we continue with a brief illustration of a theoretical approach, let us collect the principal results of our previous work.

1. The value of the probability of any event is given by the relative frequency obtained from a series of trials, and vice versa (the "principle of equivalence").

2. A probability may have any numerical value between 0 and 1, inclusive.

3. The probability of a composite event can be calculated directly by adding together the probabilities of the simple component events that constitute the composite event. Alternatively, one may calculate the probability of a composite event by using basic definitions and procedures (frequencies, relative frequencies, and the principle of equivalence).

4. If we add all the probabilities of the elementary (noncomposite) events that constitute a given experimental situation, we obtain a value of 1, exactly.

5. The sum of the two probabilities of any complementary pair of events equals 1, exactly.

A Theoretical Approach

We will conclude this chapter with a simple example of those approaches that use logical principles, formal axiomatic methods, and similar abstract mathematical tools.

In many common games of chance such as card games, roulette, or tossing coins, the players believe that various events have certain definite probabilities. Usually, players do not obtain these probabilities empirically (for example, by counting frequencies or by using the principle of equivalence). Rather, players' assumptions are intuitively based on logical principles. If we were to examine the bases of these or similar kinds of beliefs, we would discover a common element: the probabilities are usually obtained by a line of reasoning (or, frequently, by a tacit, unexamined understanding) that assumes certain events to be *equally probable*. For example, if we are rolling a "fair" die, we assume "fair" means that all the faces have an equal chance of occurring. How do we move from that assumption to the calculation of actual probabilities? We apply the general principle that the sum of the probabilities of all simple events in a given situation must be 1, exactly. We have six die faces, and six probabilities. If these probabilities are to be equal and also add to 1, each obviously must be 1/6 or 0.16666.... Similarly, each suit in a standard, well-shuffled deck must have a probability of 1/4; each slot of an unbiased 30-slot roulette wheel must have a probability of 1/30, and so on. More generally, if a probabilistic situation consists of N equally probable events, then the probability of each one of those events must be $1/N$. This statement is sometimes called the *principle of indifference*; the premise that N events should be treated as equiprobable implies that in those cases nature is "indifferent"—no preference is shown.

This simple example of a "theoretically based" approach may seem innocuous and obvious, but the principle of indifference is very useful in a variety of situations; it can be used to solve some quite complex problems. For instance, in some involved games of chance it can be used to help one discover a sound strategy of play. It is important in more serious contexts as well, such as in certain branches of physics, engineering, or industrial quality control.

The principal purpose of this presentation was to demonstrate that one can use logical approaches based on simple principles to obtain probabilities of events without invariably having to resort to empirical measures and procedures. Our illustrative example, the principle of indifference, can be relied on only if an assumption of equal probabilities has a valid, sound basis. If we are in a crooked game, or if we otherwise abuse the principle, our conclusions will of course be questionable.[9]

[9]For example, one might erroneously believe that two composite events such as one of the pairs in table 3.3 may be considered to be equiprobable; one might conclude that since they were just "two events," the probability total of 1 ought to be divided equally between them. One would not be likely to commit that kind of an obvious error in the present example, but as statistical situations become more complex and obscure, this or similar kinds of fallacious reasoning become less obvious and less easy to identify.

PROBLEMS

3.1 Define and briefly discuss the following terms and concepts, giving examples: trial or observation of an experiment; event; favorable event; complementary event; composite event; frequency or observed frequency; relative frequency; probability; the principle of equivalence; and the principle of indifference.

3.2 On any given day, the probability that it will rain is 0.15. According to the principle of equivalence, how many rainy days would be expected each year? [Hint: see footnote 3.]

3.3 An event occurred 750 times in 1,200 trials. What is its probability? Justify your answer.

3.4 A person concluded that because an event had been observed 10 times, its probability must be 0.10. Comment on that conclusion.

3.5 A student invokes the principle of equivalence, and calculates the probability of winning a scholarship to be 3.42. What does that result imply?

3.6 In 4,000 draws from a standard deck of cards, 900 clubs, 750 diamonds, and 1,210 hearts were obtained. From these data, calculate the probability of obtaining a spade; a black card.

3.7 The slots on a roulette wheel are numbered from 0 to 29 in unit steps. What is the probability of obtaining the slot numbered 10? Support your answer. Why might your answer be wrong?

3.8 Consider the following events:

(a) it will snow tomorrow;

(b) a face card will be drawn from a standard deck of cards;

(c) oil will be found when drilling a well;

(d) team A wins a football game;

(e) a coin that has been tossed will stand on edge.

For each of these events, describe the corresponding complementary event in two different ways.

3.9 Using the data in table 3.1, calculate the probability of each of the two composite events "NOT an ace," and "NOT a deuce" in at least two different ways. Why is the sum of these probabilities greater than 1? [Hint: write out and analyze that sum.]

3.10 In a particular psychiatric population, a patient is classified as psychotic, neurotic, or borderline. (Each person receives only one diagnostic label.) Diagnosing one patient constitutes an event.

(a) If the relative frequencies of classifying a patient as neurotic and as borderline are, respectively, 0.470 and 0.323, what is the probability that a patient will be classified as psychotic?

(b) What is the probability of the composite event "neurotic or psychotic"? How else could that event be described?

(c) What is the relative frequency of the event: "NOT borderline"?

CHAPTER 4

Discrete Random Variables

Our introduction to RV concepts will continue to rely largely on an intuitive, empirically based approach rather than on one that is mathematically formal and rigorous. We shall develop the key ideas concerning RVs in the context of certain simple physical models. In chapter 3, we introduced probabilistic concepts principally by means of "empirical" models that were simple also—tossing a coin, drawing a card, or rolling a die—yet they nevertheless could illustrate the subject matter adequately and parsimoniously. Similarly, we shall now introduce the principal RV concepts in terms of simple physical mechanisms that embody certain essential formal characteristics. Superficially these stark illustrative models will bear little if any resemblance to realistic experiments; actually, however, they will exemplify major formal features of typical experimental studies, as we shall eventually come to recognize.

Probability Functions

So far, we examined two sets of concepts separately, one set pertaining to outcomes (chap. 2) and another pertaining to probability (chap. 3). We are now ready to combine these two groups of ideas within one framework. We shall integrate these two sets in the context of a roulette wheel, a device that incorporates the salient features of each. Most of us are familiar with these kinds of mechanisms. Typically, a roulette wheel has a definite number of slots; each slot is numbered; on each turn of the wheel, one, and only one, of these numbers is obtained; prior to that turn, the number that will result is, of course, uncertain; and the wheel can be turned one or more times.

We see that the characteristics of this kind of a device can be considered either from the perspective of chapter 2 or from that of chapter 3. On the one hand, the roulette wheel displays a potential outcome set—specifically, one that is discrete, and limited in range. Thus, the concepts of chapter 2 apply to the numbers that label the slots. On the other hand, in terms of the framework developed in chapter 3 the numbered slots can be characterized as a set of simple events. Trials, frequency counts, relative frequencies, and the other related probabilistic concepts developed in that chapter will therefore apply.

In order to integrate these two sets of concepts within a single formal framework, we will now take a seemingly simple and obvious step.[1] We shall formally identify a potential outcome set with a group of simple events and their associated probabilistic framework. To illustrate the procedure and its implications, let us develop it in terms of a specific illustrative roulette wheel. For that purpose, the particular wheel that we select as an exemplar would make little difference. We could equally well choose a wheel having any number of slots and using any reasonable scheme for numbering these. We shall arbitrarily select a roulette wheel that has 10 slots that are numbered from 0 to 9 in unit steps.

In order to "identify the potential outcome set with a group of simple events and their associated probabilistic framework," we shall simply assign *one particular probability value* to *each one* of the 10 *outcome values* in the potential outcome. From the point of view of mathematics, by taking this step we thereby specify a *function*. Roughly speaking, that concept connotes a rule or prescription according to which one set of values is assigned to another set.[2] In our case, the two kinds of numbers are *probability values* and *outcome values*; the function provides the rule that tells us the probability value that is to be assigned to a given

[1]From a formal, mathematical standpoint, this step is anything but insignificant or conceptually trivial. Technically, it is a matter of moving from one kind of a mathematical "event space" to another, a new space (see Freeman, 1963, pp. 16-17).

outcome value in the potential outcome set. (We shall illustrate this procedure shortly with several specific examples.) We shall refer to this kind of a specification or assignment by various equivalent terms, such as "attaching probabilities to outcomes," "making an assignment of probability values to outcome values," or "coupling probabilities and corresponding outcomes."

The particular type of function that performs this specific kind of an assignment (attaching probability values to outcome values) is called a PROBABILITY FUNCTION. *It is the basic mathematical representation of a discrete RV*. Indeed, for the time being we shall treat "discrete RV" and "probability function" as equivalent concepts. A probability function completely describes the mathematical, formal characteristics of a discrete RV.

Let us, then, construct a probability function for our 10-slot wheel. We have ten actual outcomes or simple events; one, and only one, of these must occur on a turn of the wheel—on a "trial of the experiment." We need to assign one specific probability value to each one of these ten outcome values. We have a wide latitude in making this kind of an assignment, but the probability values must be assigned in a way that will conform to the general requirements stipulated in chapter 3. For example, each probability value must lie in the numerical range between 0 and 1, inclusive; the sum of the probabilities of all the simple events must add to 1, exactly; and so on.

We shall specify a simple probabilistic situation for our first example of a probability function: a "fair" wheel, that is, one that has equiprobable outcomes. We have ten possible outcomes in the potential outcome set and thus are speaking about ten equally probable simple events. By the principle of indifference, we know in that case each event must have a probability of 1/10 or 0.10. Accordingly, the probability function in this instance will assign a probability value of 0.10 to the outcome value 0, a probability

[2]The concept of a function is basic in much of mathematical work. It can be developed in a rigorous manner (see, for example, MacLane and Birkhoff, 1967), but that approach is clearly beyond our scope. We shall learn enough for our purposes by examining various specific mathematical functions as we encounter these in the material that follows.

value of 0.10 to the outcome value 1, and so on for the other outcome values in the potential outcome.

We can exhibit this situation graphically. Figure 4.1 shows the ten possible outcome values (the potential outcome set) on an outcome axis, a procedure familiar from chapter 2. The ten corresponding probability values (in our example, each equal to 1/10) are shown as heights of vertical lines at each outcome value. The height of a line (the ordinate of its upper end point) represents the probability value. Figure 4.1, then, is the *graph of a probability function*. We can see that whereas we had needed only *one* axis, one dimension, to represent a set of *outcome values* (see figs. 2.1 to 2.3), we now need *two* axes, two dimensions, to represent a probability function. This illustrates geometrically a major formal point that we should always remember about probability functions and thus about the mathematical properties of discrete RVs. There always are *two* sets of numbers involved—outcome values and probability values. This may seem simple, but as the situation becomes complex it can become confusing.[3] I wish to emphasize that in every case involving a discrete RV, we must keep the presence of these two sets of numbers firmly in mind. This is an example of "a simple fundamental" that one can all too easily lose sight of as new complexities are introduced.

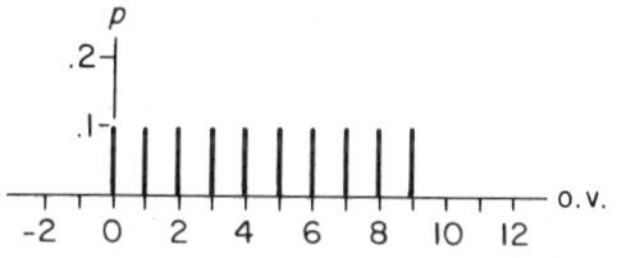

FIGURE 4.1 An unbiased probability function
Note: For abbreviations used in this and all following figures and tables, consult List of Abbreviations and Symbols.

At any rate, figure 4.1 shows that for each point on the outcome axis that is contained in the potential outcome (that is, for each one of the ten possible outcome values), the probability function

[3]For example, confusion can arise when the outcome values themselves are probability values—as of course they can be, just as they can be any other kind of a value—or when we are considering more than one probability function at a time, as we shall in part V.

specifies a corresponding probability value—in this case, since we have a "fair" wheel, the same value, 0.10. Colloquially, we speak about "the *value* of the function at a point" instead of the more formal and complete "the value of the probability assigned by the probability function to a point (or to a value) on the outcome axis." In the informal, colloquial terminology, we would say about the probability function illustrated in figure 4.1 that, for instance, "the *value* of the function *at* 3.0 *is* 0.10," instead of the more formal "the *probability value* assigned *by* the probability function *to* the outcome axis point (or outcome value) 3.0 *is* 0.10."

Bias

Suppose we were to alter the probabilistic properties of our roulette wheel so that it would no longer be "fair." How would such a change be reflected in the probability function (and thus in the mathematical properties of the RV)? As long as we had the same wheel, the potential outcome set would remain unchanged, of course; it would still comprise the same ten numbers. What would be altered, however, would be some or all of the ten previously equal probability values. I will now present several examples of a biased wheel.

Table 4.1

A biased probability function

Outcome value	Assigned probability
0	0.02
1	.05
2	.08
3	.15
4	.20
5	.20
6	.15
7	.08
8	.05
9	.02

As a first example, consider a wheel having outcome values that are more likely in the mid-range of the potential outcome than at either end of that set. Probabilities in this instance might have the values listed in table 4.1. This table describes or defines a probability function, because it shows the "rule" according to which ten particular probability values are assigned to the ten outcome values. (We see that these probability values continue to meet the stipulated requirements; for example, each value lies between 0 and 1, and the sum of all the probabilities attached to the ten simple events is 1.) The graph of this probability function is shown in figure 4.2. The probabilities at each end of the potential outcome region have decreased from their previous value (fig. 4.1) of 0.10, while those in the midrange have increased over that value. In general, any changes in the probability values assigned to one sector of the potential outcome must be compensated by some offsetting changes in another sector or sectors so that the total probability sum can continue to be equal to 1, as required. The changes in probability values reflect, of course, changes in the likelihood of obtaining specific outcomes on any one turn of the wheel. The principle of equivalence continues to apply, so that a change in the probability value assigned to an outcome implies a corresponding change in frequency and relative frequency in a set of repeated trials.

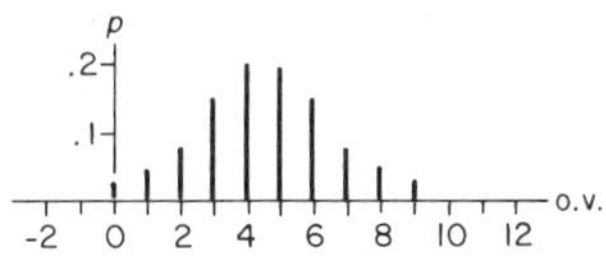

FIGURE 4.2 A probability function with more probable midrange

A second possibility might be that the even numbers and zero were slightly more likely outcomes than the odd numbers. That kind of bias is sketched in the graph of the probability function shown in figure 4.3.

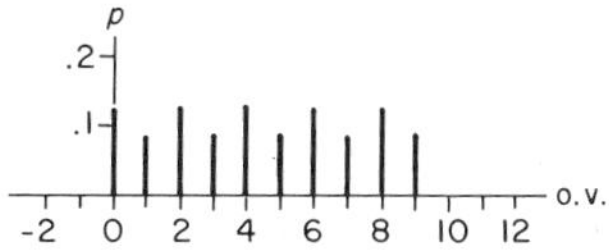

FIGURE 4.3 A probability function with even outcome values more probable

A third, more extreme bias would result from "fixing" the wheel so that only a few outcome values could possibly occur. Figure 4.4 shows that kind of a situation. The graph of that probability function represents a situation where one could obtain only the numbers 0, 3, 6, and 8. This specification implies that the probabilities, and thus the frequencies, of the remaining six numbers must be zero, as shown.

FIGURE 4.4 A highly biased probability function

Each new bias implies and defines a corresponding new probability function, and there are endless possibilities for redefining the ten assigned probability values. We say that the graphs of different probability functions, such as those shown in figures 4.1 through 4.4, exhibit different *forms* or *profiles*. If we connect the tips of the vertical lines with a smooth curve, we obtain a defining outline that encloses or envelops the collection of vertical lines. Such an outline shape is called an *envelope* in mathematics. We shall frequently have an occasion to refer to envelopes of probability functions, and will use the terms profile, form, or envelope interchangeably. In figure 4.5, the envelope for the graph of figure 4.2 is shown as a dotted line.

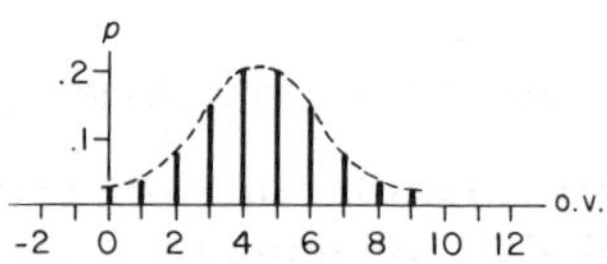

FIGURE 4.5 An envelope of a probability function

Probability in Regions

We have been considering specific outcome values and their associated probabilities. These pairs of numbers are defined by the probability function, which thus directly provides the answer to the question, "What is the probability of obtaining any one particular given outcome value?" One simply "reads off" the probability value corresponding to that outcome value, using either a table such as table 4.1 or a graph such as figure 4.2.

Suppose that we now ask this question instead: "Given a probability function, what is the probability of obtaining *an outcome that lies in some specified numerical region or range of outcome values*?" (To avoid cumbersome verbiage, we will often refer to "the probability of obtaining an outcome that lies within a specified range of the outcome axis" simply as "*the probability of*—or *in*—*the range*," or, "*the probability of the region*.") For example, we might wish to know: what is the probability of the outcome range 1.5 to 5.5? Let us discuss this question in terms of the roulette wheel mathematically defined by the probability function of table 4.1 or figure 4.2. Since the numerical outcome range from 1.5 to 5.5 contains the four possible outcome values 2, 3, 4, and 5, and only these, our question about the probability in the range from 1.5 to 5.5 is equivalent to asking, what is the probability of obtaining a 2 or 3 or 4 or 5 on a given turn? We now recognize that we are considering the probability of a *composite event*. Rather obviously, the event is "2 or 3 or 4 or 5." The original question concerning the probability of an outcome falling into a specified *outcome range* has now been shifted to the parallel question of finding the probability associated with a specific composite event. That is, "the outcome lies between 1.5 and 5.5" is seen to refer to the same event as "2 or 3 or 4 or 5 occurred."

We have already learned how to calculate the probabilities of these kinds of events in chapter 3, and therefore can obtain the result immediately from the data of table 4.1. We can use the "direct" method demonstrated in that chapter, and simply add the four probabilities associated with the four outcome values in the specified range to obtain the answer 0.63. That value, 0.63, then, is the probability that an outcome will fall into the range from 1.5 to 5.5. Incidentally, that is also the probability value assigned to *any* outcome region that contains these same four outcome values, and only these. For example, a range such as from 1.900 to 5.001, or from 1.002 to 5.999, would also have a probability of 0.63.

The same approach would be used to find the probability of any other specified region of the outcome range. The method would also remain the same in principle were one dealing with some other probability function—for example, one that had a different potential outcome, or a different set of assigned probability values from those specified in table 4.1.

The concept of *probability associated with a segment of the outcome region* is extremely important in statistics, and will recur in many guises and many contexts throughout this work. The probability of a region will prove to be particularly important for statistical inference (part IV).

In chapter 3, I presented another concept that is relevant to calculating probabilities in ranges, namely, the concept of complementary pairs of events. We have just considered the outcome axis range of 1.5 to 5.5 and calculated its probability (again, strictly speaking, "the probability of an outcome falling within that range"). We can also consider a second closely related outcome range, namely, the portion of the outcome axis that lies *outside* the range 1.5 to 5.5. Let us call the first range, 1.5 to 5.5, the range A, and the second range, B. What is the probability of B, of finding an outcome within that range? Since B is specified as that portion of the outcome axis that lies outside A, it means the numerical range "less than 1.5 and greater than 5.5." It thus obviously contains six possible outcomes values: 0, 1, 6, 7, 8, and 9.

We have already seen that the composite event "an outcome lies in the range A" is equivalent to the composite event "2 or 3 or 4 or 5." Analogously, the composite event "an outcome lies outside A" (i.e., "an outcome is in B") describes the event "on a turn of the wheel, one of the outcome values 0 or 1 or 6 or 7 or 8 or 9 is obtained." If we now look at these two composite events more closely, we see that they form a pair of *complementary events*. Between them, these two events contain each simple event or simple possible outcome exactly once.

It is instructive and easy to discover the geometrical implications of complementarity. On an outcome axis, the geometrical representation of a pair of complementary events is a pair of segments having the characteristics shown in figure 4.6. That figure displays the outcome axis segments corresponding to the numerical ranges A and B. We see that geometrically, a pair of complementary events implies two outcome segments that together cover the *total potential outcome range*, exactly, and *without overlap*.

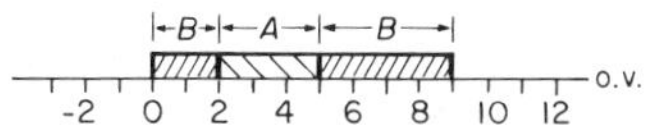

FIGURE 4.6 Complementary segments of a potential outcome

We know from our previous work that the sum of the probabilities of complementary events is 1. Therefore, the probability of finding an outcome in range A and the probability of finding an outcome in range B (or not A) must add to 1. We have already calculated the first probability, and found it to equal 0.63. The probability of B obviously must be 0.37. To check our calculations, we can calculate the latter probability also by our familiar "direct" method. We merely add the six probabilities assigned to the six simple outcomes in B. From table 4.1, the six pertinent probability values are 0.02, 0.05, 0.15, 0.08, 0.05, and 0.02; their sum is 0.37, as expected.

This example illustrates a general fact of some importance. If we know the probability of obtaining an outcome lying within some specified outcome range, we thereby immediately know the probability associated with the remainder of the outcome range (whether or not it is limited). These two ranges encompass a pair of complementary events, and the two associated probabilities must add to 1, exactly.

The Cumulative Distribution Function

We have been introduced to the basic mathematical description of a discrete RV, the probability function, and to its graphical representation. We will now consider an equivalent, second method of describing a discrete RV. This second kind of a function is called a CUMULATIVE DISTRIBUTION FUNCTION. It is convenient to introduce it in the context of discrete RVs, but its full importance will begin to emerge only after we will have introduced continuous RVs.

We will illustrate the concept by using the familiar biased probability function defined in table 4.1 and shown graphically in figure

4.2. Let us implement the following procedure. We will start at the extreme left end of the outcome axis, and begin to move toward the right. (Of course, we cannot really begin "at the extreme left end," since an outcome axis extends without limit in both the positive and the negative direction. We can, however, begin in a range of "very high" negative values—for instance, at a value of minus one billion.) As we move from left to right, successively passing over all the values in the outcome axis, we will acquire a *running total*. That cumulative sum will be obtained by adding *the probability values* that we encounter in our traversal. That is, as we move from left to right, covering the entire axis, we will be passing various outcome values that have been assigned probability values by a probability function. As we pass over each of these kinds of points on the outcome axis, we will add the *attached probability* to our accumulating sum. Let us note that once again we are dealing with *two* different kinds of numbers, outcome values and corresponding probability values.

By following this procedure, we shall be forming a running total that at *any point* along the outcome axis will contain *all* the probability (i.e., the sum of all the assigned probabilities) that exists or lies to the *left* of that point. Those probabilities to the left are the constituents of our accumulating sum.

Let us implement this procedure for the particular RV represented by the probability function presented in table 4.1. We will begin with any point in the very far negative (left) region of the outcome axis, for example, the point −1,000,000. How much probability lies to the *left* of that point? That is, how much probability would we have accumulated at the point −1,000,000 by moving *to* that point *from* the extreme negative regions of the outcome axis? We know that in our example all the available probability lies in the range 0 to 9, inclusive. The ten probability values assigned to the ten outcome values in that range add to 1, the maximum permissible total. Therefore, the probability *anywhere else* along the outcome axis (strictly speaking, "assigned to any other point on the outcome axis"), either to the left or to the right of the range 0 to 9, must be 0. Outside the range 0 to 9, there is colloquially speaking "no probability left" to be assigned. By this reasoning, we see that we could not have accumulated any probability by traveling from the left up to the point −1,000,000. We should have been traveling only over outcome regions that have 0 probability—thus, there could not be a cumulative sum other than 0.

We have presumably arrived at the point −1,000,000 and our accumulated probability is 0. Let us continue to move toward the right. Suppose we arbitrarily pause at the outcome value −10.5 and ask again, how much probability have we accumulated now, i.e., how much probability lies in the whole region to the *left* of −10.5? The earlier answer has not changed. The accumulated total probability must still be 0, by the previous reasoning. Obviously, this situation will remain unchanged as long as one is still moving in the outcome region that lies to the left of the first, smallest outcome value that is in the potential outcome—in our present example, the value 0. As long as we have not reached that first value, we cannot accumulate any probability, and the accumulated sum must remain at 0. Although in the present case the region we are speaking about happens to be the region of negative outcome values, one must not conclude that this characteristic has any particular significance. There is no reason why a probability function could not assign a probability value to negative outcome values, for example, to the outcome value −5.8. It may even happen that a potential outcome will in a given instance lie entirely in the range of negative outcome axis values. In our illustrative case, the fact that the probability function does not assign any probability to negative outcome values is thus just an accidental, insignificant feature.

Let us continue to move to the right, in the direction of increasing outcome values, and pause, again arbitrarily, at the point +0.01. What is the situation at that outcome value? Have we accumulated any probability? Or, equivalently, does any probability lie to the left of 0.01? We *have* accumulated a contribution to our sum, and there *is* probability attached to the region to the left. (That, of course, is the reason why we have been able to accumulate some probability.) The outcome value of 0 is in the potential outcome. It has an associated probability value of 0.02, as we see from table 4.1 or figure 4.2. Therefore, as we moved from the left past the outcome value 0, we suddenly accumulated the probability value attached to that outcome: we added 0.02 to our previous sum, 0. At the point 0.01, the accumulated total probability now is 0.02.

We continue to move toward the right along the outcome axis, pausing wherever we like to record our accumulated probability total. In this fashion we obtain for *any* selected outcome axis value a corresponding cumulative probability total. Table 4.2 shows the result of this process for a number of typical, arbitrarily selected values along the outcome axis. We can plot these data. We will show the outcome values on an outcome axis, as usual, and the corresponding accumulated probability total along the vertical axis. Figure 4.7 shows the points sampled in table 4.2.

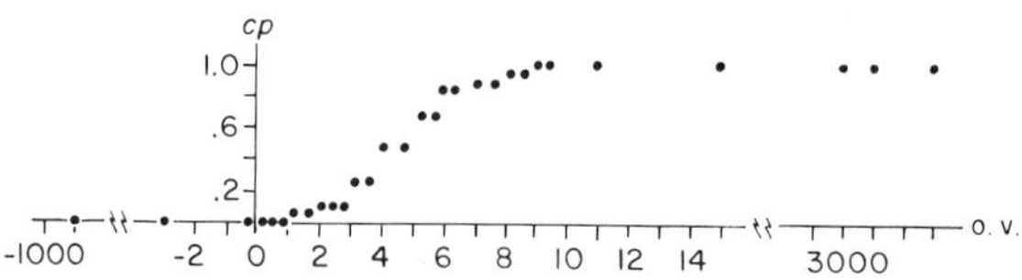

FIGURE 4.7 Cumulative probabilities

Table 4.2

Cumulative probability (*cp*)

o.v.	*cp*	o.v.	*cp*
−1,000	0	5.3	.70
−3	0	5.7	.70
−0.01	0	6.01	.85
+0.01	0.02	6.4	.85
.6	.02	7.05	.93
.9	.02	7.9	.93
1.1	.07	8.2	.98
1.8	.07	8.7	.98
2.01	.15	9.001	1.00
2.6	.15	11.0	1
3.2	.30	15.0	1
3.8	.30	⋮	⋮
4.1	.50	5,000	1
4.9	.50	↓	↓

Figure 4.7 illustrates the main characteristics of our cumulative procedure. We see that first of all, the cumulative probability is 0 in the regions to the left of the first (smallest) outcome value, 0, as it should be for our particular probability function. Then, every time we move past an outcome value that has an associated probability, the cumulative total is increased stepwise; it is increased, of course, by exactly the amount of that attached probability value. For example, we see that just after we have passed over the outcome value 2, the accumulated probability has been increased from its previous total of 0.07 to a new value of 0.15. Obviously, it has been increased by just the amount of probability attached to the outcome value 2, namely, 0.08. We also see that at this point our cumulative probability total of 0.15 is precisely equal to the sum of all (in this case, three) probabilities attached to outcomes that lie to the *left* of our present location.

We have seen what happens as we pass over an outcome value that has an attached probability. What about the outcome regions *between* any neighboring pair of such values, that is, regions such as "greater than 5 and less than 6"? We cannot increase our probability sum as we move within such regions, for the obvious reason that there isn't any assigned probability there to accumulate. The probability sum therefore must remain constant as we travel over any of the outcome regions that lie between neighboring outcome values in the potential outcome.

What happens to the cumulative probability after we have traversed the last outcome value (in this case, 9) that is contained in the potential outcome set? What is the total probability that lies to the left of, for example, the outcome value 9.01? It must be 1 (see chap. 3). Furthermore, since that is "all the probability there is," the probability function cannot assign a probability to any outcome value greater than 9. Thus, as we continue to move to the right along the outcome axis, the cumulative probability must remain constant at 1, no matter how far we continue to move.

We conclude that there are three kinds of outcome regions in which the cumulative total does not change: (1) the entire region that lies to the *left* of the smallest possible outcome value in the potential outcome; (2) the kind of region that lies *between* any two neighboring possible outcome values in the potential outcome;

and (3) the entire region that lies to the *right* of the largest possible outcome value in the potential outcome. These general conclusions are reflected in the pattern of the data shown in figure 4.7.

Had we sampled more outcome values than those shown in table 4.2 as we moved from left to right, the resulting data would have clustered together more closely, but would still have continued to follow the pattern that can be seen to emerge in figure 4.7. Intuitively, we can see that were we to calculate the cumulative probability value at more and more outcome values, we should eventually approach the situation shown in figure 4.8. The data points are now so densely clustered that they form continuous horizontal lines in each one of the three types of outcome regions in which the cumulative probability does not change. The only places along the outcome axis where the cumulative probability can and does change are those places that are in the potential outcome, and that consequently have a probability value assigned by the probability function. These places are, of course, the ten outcome values 0, 1, 2, . . ., 9. At these outcome locations, the accumulated probability sum exhibits a discontinuous jump in value. The probability attached to the possible outcome values is added "suddenly" and that implies a sudden increase in the accumulating sum. In figure 4.8, we see these jumps in the graph of the cumulative distribution function. A function that has this kind of a graph is sometimes referred to as a "staircase" or a "step" function, for obvious reasons.

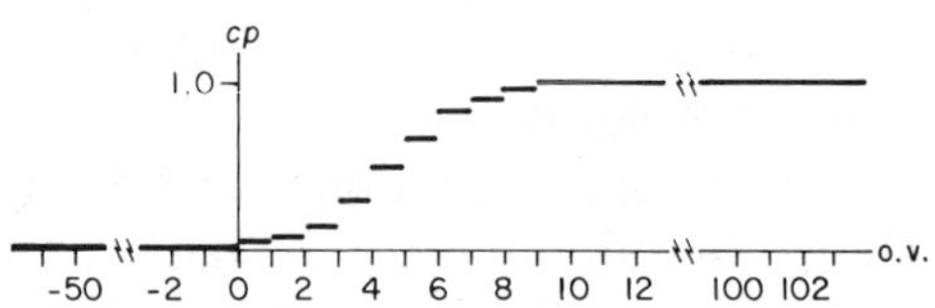

FIGURE 4.8 Graph of a cumulative distribution function

Thus, finally, as a result of performing the movement from left to right together with the corresponding cumulative addition of probabilities, we have obtained another function, the cumulative distribution function. It provides a rule that specifies for *any* one point on the outcome axis a corresponding value that is a probability sum—specifically, the sum of all the probabilities that have been assigned to outcome values lying to the left of that outcome point. *The cumulative distribution function is the function whose value at any point on the outcome axis is the accumulated sum of the probabilities*. For example, in figure 4.8, the value of the cumulative distribution function at 2.50 is the probability total 0.15.

A function that is constructed according to the procedures just described must exhibit certain properties. These reflect the fact that we are adding or accumulating probabilities, quantities that as we know are numbers that must conform to certain special requirements. Thus, our function, the cumulative distribution function, and its graph, always must have the following features:

1. At the extreme left regions of the outcome axis, the value of the function is 0.
2. At any point on the outcome axis, the value of the function, and thus the height of the graph, specifies the total amount of probability lying in the whole region to the *left* of that point.
3. Since we have constructed the function by adding *probabilities* (and these must be nonnegative, i.e., 0 or greater), its value of any outcome point can never be less than 0, and its graph can thus never fall below the outcome axis.
4. For the same reason, the value of the function, and thus the height of the graph, cannot decrease as we move from left to right.
5. As we continue to move toward the right, the function reaches a value of exactly 1 as its maximum, and remains at that value for the rest of the outcome region. That is so because as we move toward infinitely large outcome values, sooner or later we shall have passed over all (or "almost" all) the potential outcome regions that have associated probabilities; these probabilities must add to 1.

A probability function and the corresponding cumulative distribution function form a unique pair, in the sense that given either one of these, the other is rigidly specified. Although we shall not pursue the point here, one can always recover a probability function from a cumulative distribution function, and vice versa. One only needs to apply simple logic to obtain one from the other. Since each function in an associated pair uniquely determines the other, either of these can be used equally well to provide a complete mathematical description or representation of a specific discrete RV. In other words, a particular RV is strictly defined by either a probability function or the corresponding cumulative distribution function.

We will now consider briefly one typical and important application of a cumulative distribution function. We will see how one can use this kind of a function to obtain the probability associated with any specified *region* of the outcome range. We have already learned procedures for finding this kind of a sum (see "Probabilities in Regions"); why should we consider another method? It is true that for discrete RVs, the new procedure does not offer a significant advantage over the old. Its usefulness and importance will become apparent, however, as we begin to study continuous RVs.

Let us consider a specific example of using the cumulative distribution function of figure 4.8 and table 4.2 to find the probability in an outcome region. (We remember that this cumulative distribution function defines the same RV as table 4.1 or figure 4.2.) Suppose we wish to find the probability that an outcome will lie in the range 6.2 to 8.4. From our previous discussions we know that we could add the two probabilities that are assigned in that range (0.08 and 0.05) directly to obtain the desired probability, 0.13. We can equally well use the cumulative distribution function in the following way. In figure 4.8, we see that the two values of that function at the outcome locations 6.2 and 8.4 are, respectively, 0.85 and 0.98. These two values of the function represent, respectively, the total probability lying to the left of 6.2 and the total probability lying to the left of 8.4. Therefore, the *difference* between the two probability sums at these two outcome locations *must* represent the probability contributed by the region between 6.2 and 8.4. That is, this region must contain exactly the amount of probability that was added to the cumulative total as one moved from 6.2 to 8.4 along the outcome axis. Therefore, by subtracting one cumulative probability from the other, one recovers the amount contributed by the region lying between the two specified outcome points: $0.98 - 0.85 = 0.13$.

Thus, one can find the probability over an outcome region either by the "direct" method of adding the appropriate probability values obtained from a probability function, or by calculating a difference between the values of a cumulative distribution function. The latter procedure, as I have mentioned, has certain advantages—indeed, as we shall see, for a continuous RV it frequently is the only practical one available.

Extending the Range

The last topic that we shall consider in this chapter is the case of a discrete RV that has a *not* limited potential outcome range. The basic RV characteristics that we have just presented will remain unchanged or require only minor modification.

We can use our familiar roulette wheel as a point of departure. Suppose we imagine a larger wheel, that is, one that has more slots. Obviously, this implies that the potential outcome set has been changed; the number of possible outcomes has increased. For example, we now could have a 20-slot wheel, with outcomes numbered 0, 1, 2, . . . , 19. Are there any other consequences of increasing the number of slots? An important consequence of adding more slots, and thus more possible outcome values in the potential outcome, is that, by and large, the probability associated with a typical slot must now be less than it was before. The sum of all the associated probabilities must remain constant at 1; we now have more terms in the sum of probabilities; and obviously, on the whole, the more terms there are, the smaller they must be. The "by and large" and "on the whole" qualifiers refer to the fact that while a typical probability value associated with an outcome *must decrease* as we *add* slots to the wheel, one or several of the individual probabilities could remain unchanged or even increase, thereby going against the general trend. This case is illustrated in figure 4.9. Probability functions of a 10- and 20-slot wheel are compared. We see that in this particular hypothetical example, one of the outcome values, 3, has a greater probability in the 20-slot case than it had in the 10-slot case. On the whole, however, the assigned probability values in the second probability function are smaller (averaging about 0.05) than in the first function (averaging about 0.10), as they should and must be.

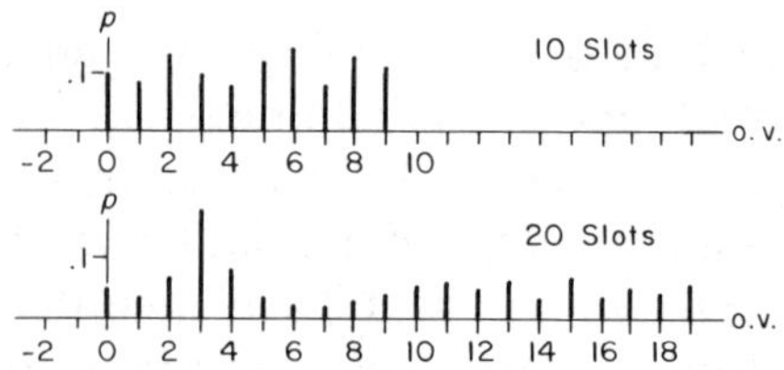

FIGURE 4.9 Probability functions of two roulette wheels

Suppose we keep adding more and more slots. Of course, we cannot continue indefinitely in this fashion with real roulette wheels. We can, however, continue *ad infinitum* conceptually, and would eventually arrive at a convenient mathematical fiction. We can envision a roulette wheel that had an "infinite" number of possible outcomes. For example, we could imagine a wheel numbered from 1 through "all" the integers. This kind of a wheel, although impossible to realize physically, can be mathematically useful. There are certain situations where it is convenient, and accurate enough, to treat a potential outcome set that has a limited but very wide range as a potential outcome that is not limited in range.

We have conceptualized a roulette wheel that has infinitely many slots and thus infinitely many outcome values in the potential set. One thing we can demonstrate about this situation is that in principle, such a wheel cannot be a "fair" or unbiased device. Having an unbiased wheel implies by definition that each one of its outcome values has the same assigned probability value. In the present case, it is not difficult to show that no matter how small that probability would be, there are now so very many possible outcome values, and thus so very many assigned probability values, that the cumulative probability must exceed the specified value, 1, at *some* point along the outcome axis.

We shall demonstrate this informally. Suppose that we were to attach a probability of only one billionth to each outcome value of a wheel numbered from 1 to "infinity" in unit steps. Surely one billionth is a very small probability value. Yet, it is not small enough. We see that the total probability attached to the first billion outcome values would be 1. The subsequent outcome values (i.e., those greater than one billion) would continue to contribute to the probability total, thus causing that total to exceed 1. This must not happen (see chap. 3). The same reasoning would apply for *any* other probability value that we might propose—one billionth of a billionth, etc. The cumulative probability would always exceed its stipulated limit of 1, provided one would include a sufficient number of outcome values. Sooner or later, the cumulative probability would exceed 1 (or any other fixed number, for that matter). Since an unbiased wheel that has an infinite number of slots violates the basic properties of probabilistic situations, it cannot be a valid mathematical concept.

If, as I have claimed, one cannot have equal probabilities (a "fair" wheel) for RVs that are discrete and not limited in range, how could one then assign to the unlimited number of outcome values a correspondingly unlimited number of probability values that would still add up to 1, exactly, as required? There are a number of available schemes, and they all involve assigning probabilities that decrease in value as one moves along the outcome axis. I shall illustrate the approach in terms of one simple scheme. Let us consider a discrete, not-limited-in-range potential outcome such as the set of positive integers—in other words, a roulette wheel whose slots are numbered 1, 2, 3, and so on. We shall assign a probability value to each one of these infinite number of outcome values in the following manner. To the first outcome value, 1, we shall assign a probability value of 1/2. To the second outcome value, 2, we shall assign a probability value that is one half of the previous probability value: 1/2 of 1/2, or 1/4. To the third outcome value, 3, we shall again assign one half of the previous probability: 1/2 of 1/4, or 1/8, and so on.[4]

Table 4.3 shows the first few values of a probability function and corresponding cumulative distribution function that have been constructed according to this procedure. The two graphs are shown in figure 4.10; it will be instructive to compare these, since they exhibit a certain complementary relationship. On the one

[4]You have probably learned about this kind of a numerical sequence and its sum in a high school mathematics course. It can be shown that provided certain requirements are met, the sum of a geometrical sequence approaches a limiting value more and more closely as one adds more and more terms. In our case, it can be shown that the limiting sum is 1.

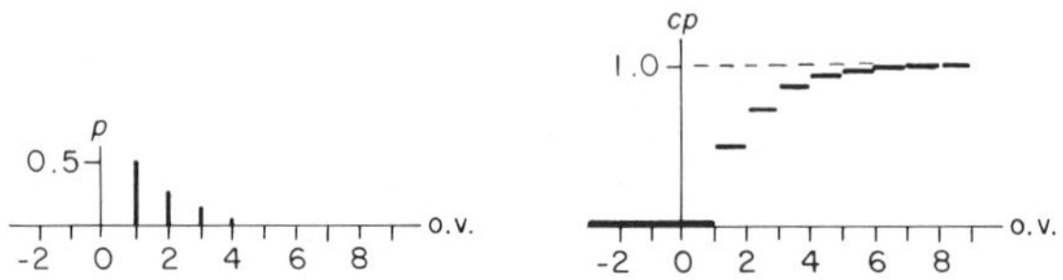

FIGURE 4.10 A not-limited-in-range discrete RV

Table 4.3
Data for figure 4.10

O.V.	Assigned p	cp
1	1/2	1/2
2	1/4	3/4
3	1/8	7/8
4	1/16	15/16
5	1/32	31/32
6	1/64	63/64
↓	↓	↓
N	$(1/2)^N$	$\frac{(2^N - 1)}{2^N}$
↓	↓	↓
∞	0	1

hand, we see that the probability values assigned by the probability function rapidly become very small for higher outcome values. This must be the case, of course, so that the probability total will not exceed 1, its stipulated value. On the other hand, we see correspondingly that the cumulative distribution function rapidly approaches its ultimate value, 1, and then changes little in that value as one continues to move to the right along the outcome axis.[5] The cumulative distribution function changes but little in

[5]We see that the graph of the cumulative distribution function approaches a horizontal line that has the probability value 1, but never quite reaches it. We say of that kind of situation that a graph approaches a line "asymptotically," or that the limiting line is the "asymptote" of the graph.

these regions of large outcome values because, as we have seen, the probability values assigned to these regions are very small. Thus, as one traverses these kinds of outcome regions, one cannot add significant amounts of probability to the cumulative sum; in general, small probability values "go with" small changes in the cumulative distribution function, and vice versa.

We can find probabilities of regions in substantially the same ways for the not limited as for the limited case. The difference is that now some of the probability assignments may involve outcome segments that are not limited in range, and this is a new situation. Consider, for instance, the probability function shown in table 4.3. Suppose one were asked to calculate the probability assigned to the region from 1 to 5, inclusive. This would pose no new problems. As we have seen, we can obtain that probability by the direct method; we only need to add the probabilities assigned to the five outcome values that lie in that outcome axis segment. Suppose, however, that one were asked instead to calculate the probability for the outcome region "greater than 5." The direct method now must fail, since it would require the actual addition of an unlimited number of probability values. That cannot be done, of course, by finite arithmetical methods. We can, however, obtain the probability of that not-limited-in-range region provided we recognize that the two composite events "5 or less" and "6 or greater" are a complementary pair. Thus, since we know or can easily compute the probability of the first of these two regions, we can also thereby immediately obtain the probability of the second region (see chap. 3). We see from table 4.3 that the probability of the range "5 or less" (i.e., the range from 1 to 5, inclusive) is 31/32; we therefore immediately know that the probability assigned to the second region, "6 or greater," must be 1/32, exactly.

Incidentally, we could have obtained an excellent approximation to that latter probability value by calculating the probability of only a limited portion of the not-limited range "6 or greater." That kind of a procedure would provide a good approximation of the actual probability value, 1/32, because, as we already know, the probability values assigned to the higher outcome values rapidly diminish in magnitude as one moves to the right along the outcome axis. Thus, probabilities attached to higher outcome values cannot contribute greatly to the cumulative sum. Let us illustrate this situation by actual numerical examples.

Consider the limited range from 6 to 20, inclusive. By actual addition, one finds that the probability of that range is only *one millionth less* than 1/32, the probability assigned to the entire range "6 or greater." (Correspondingly, the sum of the probabilities attached to all outcome values greater than 20 must be approximately only one millionth—a vivid proof that the probabilities attached to the more remote outcome axis regions cannot contribute significantly to a probability sum.) By this estimate, then, we should be making a very small error that would be insignificant in most practical situations. If we wish, we could even decrease that error, making it as small as we please, by simply using a wider, but still limited, outcome span. For example, if we were to use the range from 6 to 100, inclusive, we should find that the assigned probability for that range is only about 10^{-31} less than 1/32. That is an unimaginably small error.

There are still a number of other matters that could be considered in regard to discrete RVs that are not limited in range. For instance, we have not examined the case of a discrete potential outcome that is not limited in either direction of the outcome axis. We have learned enough, however, to enable us to move to the next major topic, namely, random variables whose potential outcomes are continuous rather than discrete. As we shall see particularly in the discussions that begin in part IV, this class of RVs is of great importance in many applications of statistics to the behavioral disciplines.

PROBLEMS

4.1 What are the two kinds of numbers involved in every probability function?

4.2 You are told that three slots on a particular roulette wheel are labeled with the outcome values 5, 7, and 10, and that these have assigned probabilities of 0.2, 0.1, and 0.4, respectively. Are you able to say how many slots the wheel has? Why, or why not? What *can* you say about the wheel?

4.3 In general, what happens to the probability values associated with each actual outcome value as one considers roulette wheels that have more slots (outcome values)? Less slots?

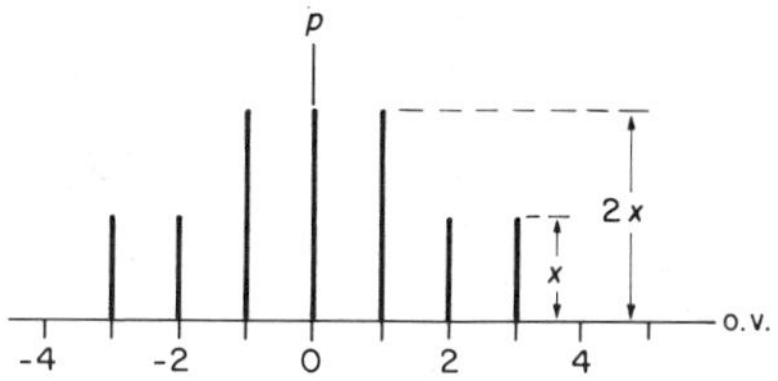

FIGURE P4.1

4.4 Consider the probability function shown in figure P4.1.
   (a) What is x?
   (b) Calculate the values of the corresponding cumulative distribution function, and draw its graph.
   (c) Calculate the probability assigned to the outcome axis region "greater than -2 and less than 3" by the direct method.
   (d) Verify your answer to (c) by using the cumulative distribution function to find the probability in that region.
   (e) If you spin a roulette wheel that has the probability function shown in figure P4.1 20,000 times, how many times would you expect to obtain outcome values that lie between -2 and 3, *inclusive*?

4.5 Repeat problem 4.4 for the probability function shown in figure P4.2.

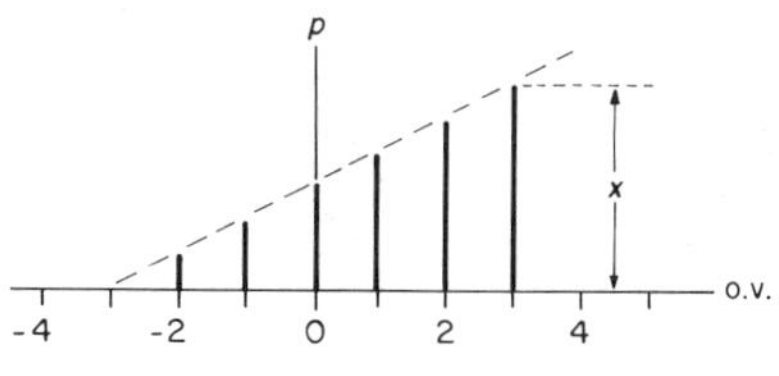

FIGURE P4.2

4.6 A discrete RV has the cumulative distribution function shown in figure P4.3. (The three incremental steps are of equal magnitude.) Recover the corresponding probability function, and sketch its graph.

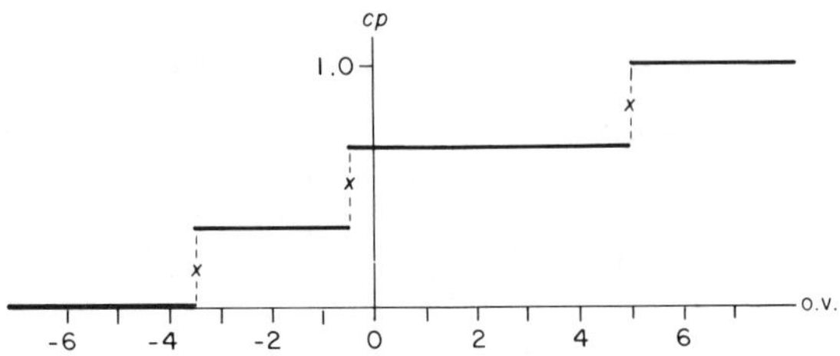

FIGURE P4.3

CHAPTER 5

Continuous Random Variables

In this chapter we shall consider RVs that have continuous rather than discrete potential outcomes. Since we already have learned quite a bit about the discrete case, we shall use it as a point of departure; the concept of a continuous RV will emerge as the result of a process that begins with a discrete RV.

The first continuous RV that we shall seek to develop will be one that is unbiased and limited in range. No particular significance should be attached to the specifics of this continuous RV. The example merely provides a convenient introduction, and the basic results obtained will apply generally to continuous RVs.

Let us begin with an unbiased, 10-slot roulette wheel whose slots bear numerical labels that lie in the range between 0 and 10. We shall place each slot within one of the ten one-unit-long outcome axis segments 0 to 1, 1 to 2, . . ., 9 to 10. Let us arbitrarily select the midpoints of each of these segments, and label the slots 0.5, 1.5, 2.5, . . ., and 9.5. Since we are postulating that the wheel is unbiased, each slot is equiprobable and, by the principle of indifference, has an associated probability value of 0.10.

One of the principal distinguishing features of a continuous potential outcome is that it has an infinite number of densely spaced outcome values in its range. It would therefore seem reasonable to suppose that if we wish to develop a continuous from a discrete situation, we should need to introduce more outcome values within the range of a discrete potential outcome set. Let us then double the number of slots between 0 and 10. We now have 20 equiprobable outcome values located, say, at 0.25,

0.75, 1.25, 1.75, . . ., and 9.75; each outcome value will have an assigned probability of 1/20 or 0.05.

Let us continue in this fashion, and implement a series of similar steps. At each step, we shall double the previous number of slots in the range from 0 to 10, and relabel the possible outcome values in some reasonable fashion. Furthermore, each time we double the number of slots, we shall need to halve the probability values assigned to the individual outcome values. The first four steps of this process are illustrated by the four graphs in figure 5.1. These represent the probability function for a 10-, 20-, 40-, and 80-slot wheel, respectively. In order to show the process more clearly, figure 5.2 displays for each of these probability functions a magnified view of a typical one-unit-long outcome axis segment. The interval from 6 to 7 has been arbitrarily selected. This magnification of a portion of the outcome axis will enable us to follow the details of the process better.

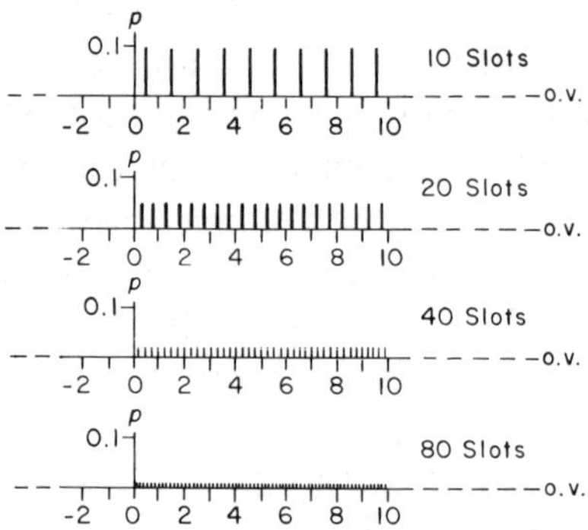

FIGURE 5.1 Adding slots within a fixed-outcome segment

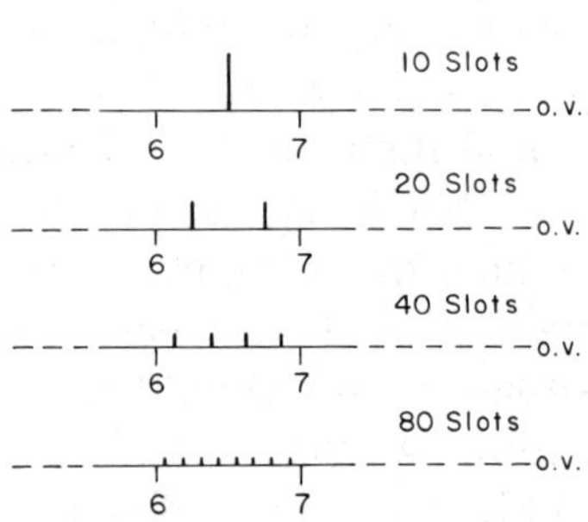

FIGURE 5.2 Close-up of a unit outcome axis segment

Suppose that we were to continue in this fashion indefinitely, hoping thereby to arrive at a continuous rather than a discrete outcome situation. We should be disappointed. We would find that no matter how many times we repeated the step of doubling the number of slots and halving the associated probability values, we still would be faced with a situation that has the same basic logical or formal features—incrementally spaced outcome values and definite, though smaller and smaller associated probabilities. In other words, we still would have a discrete RV represented by the familiar kind of a probability function. It would seem that we are at an impasse; how are we to accomplish a transition from discrete to continuous outcomes and RVs?

We shall need a new concept, and the preceding steps hold a clue. Let us consider the length of a typical outcome axis segment that contains only *one* of the actual outcome values in the potential outcome. As we see in figure 5.2, for a 10-slot wheel, a segment that contains only one possible outcome value is one outcome axis unit long; for a 20-slot wheel, a segment that contains only one possible outcome value is now 0.5 outcome axis units long; for a 40-slot wheel, a similar segment is 0.25 outcome axis units long, and so on. Thus, doubling the number of slots in the range from 0 to 10 has two consequences. We have seen that each time we double the number of slots, we must halve the value of the probability value assigned to each slot; now we notice that we also must halve the length of each typical outcome axis segment that contains one, and only one, of the values in the potential outcome. Thus, each of these two quantities is reduced by the same proportion as the number of slots increases. The reason is simple: we are dividing two constant entities—the total probability, 1.0, in one case, and the total potential outcome length, 10 outcome axis units, in the other case—by the same quantity, namely, the number of slots or actual outcome values of the wheel.

Accordingly, if we at each step compute the ratio or quotient between the *probability value assigned to any one slot* and the *length of any typical outcome axis segment that contains one, and only one, actual outcome value*, we should find that this ratio remains *constant* from step to step. That ratio, then, is independent of the number of slots in the range. It would not matter whether we had a wheel with 40 or 40,000 slots in the range from 0 to 10; the ratio between an assigned probability value and the length of any outcome axis segment that contains one possible outcome *must* remain constant because both quantities vary according to the same factor, the number of slots on a wheel. Table 5.1 shows this situation for five versions of a roulette wheel (a 10-, 20-, 40-, 80-, and 10,000-slot wheel).

Table 5.1

A constant ratio

Number of slots	Probability of each slot	Length of segment containing 1 slot	Ratio of probability to segment length
10	0.10	1.0	0.10
20	.05	0.5	.10
40	.025	.25	.10
80	.0125	.125	.10
10,000	.0001	.001	.10

Density

We have just identified a particular kind of constant ratio situation. An analogous situation is well known in the natural sciences and in engineering. Let us see how these disciplines have dealt with a parallel phenomenon.

Consider a *uniform* block, that is, a piece of material that has the same consistency throughout. Let us say that it has a mass of 1,000 kg. and a volume of 10 $m.^3$ In science, the DENSITY of matter is defined as the *ratio* of *mass* to *volume*, as you probably know. In our example, the density of the material of the block therefore is 1,000 kg./10 $m.^3$, or 100 kg./$m.^3$

Let us next consider some smaller portion of the block—for example, a piece one tenth of the total block. That segment could be obtained from *any* region of the original block. In this smaller sector, what is the density of the material? Our smaller segment has one tenth of the original mass (1/10 of 1,000 kg., or 100 kg.) and one tenth of the original volume (1/10 of 10 $m.^3$, or 1.0 $m.^3$).

Therefore the density of the material is *still* 100 kg./m.^{3}; it has the same value for a small segment of a block as it had in the complete block. What would happen to the density were we to consider smaller and smaller segments? Obviously, the decreases in mass and volume would continue to offset one another exactly, so that the density, ratio of mass to volume, would remain the same for any small segment, regardless of its size (or location). For example, were we to consider a region one tenth of the previously considered sector, its mass would be 10 kg., its volume, 0.10 m.^{3}, but its density would still be 10/0.10 or 100 kg./m.^{3} This would be true regardless of the region of the original block one was considering.

Thus, it would seem that we could continue to calculate the density for smaller and smaller, arbitrarily located sectors of the original block; we would always obtain the same answer, 100 kg./m.^{3}, for the density of such segments, regardless of their size or location. Scientists have carried this process to its logical limit and created a highly useful mathematical fiction. One speaks of the MASS DENSITY of a point volume. That is, at each and every location throughout a block of material, one now conceptualizes a miniscule point segment, a volume of "zero space"—but a segment that, even though it now has *zero mass* and *zero volume*, still has a *density*! Furthermore, since it was previously found that the magnitude of the density was unaffected by segment size, it is now argued that one can consider the density of this "zero" segment as still having the same numerical value as the density of any tangible, actual segment of our sample block.

The concept of the "density of a point segment" is mathematically valid and a practically useful concept. It is based on a logical line of reasoning that begins with an unproblematic definition of the density of an extended, tangible block of material, and by mathematical means extends that concept to vanishingly small regions within a block. The critical step involves the argument that, since the density in a uniform material always remains at a constant value regardless of the size of the region that one is considering, the density will continue to remain at that same value even for a "vanishingly small" segment.

To summarize the argument thus far: the density of a uniform block remains at the same value at every point throughout the material; a tiny piece that has essentially zero mass and zero volume will still have the same density as the total block—in our example, 100 kg./m.^{3}

We can invert the process we have been considering, and apply the concept of density in the reverse direction. Suppose we have a piece of uniform material whose *mass* is unknown. If we know the *density* and *volume* of the piece, we can obtain its *mass*. We only need to add together, as it were, all the zero-volume, zero-mass pieces that exist throughout the block. The appropriate arithmetical operation is multiplication. We obtained the *mass density* by *dividing mass* by *volume*; accordingly, to obtain *mass from volume* and *density*, we *multiply* these two latter quantities. In simple algebraic notation, if we let d, m, and v represent density, mass, and volume of a block, respectively, then if $d = m/v$, $m = d \times v$.

In terms of a numerical example, if a uniform material has a density of 100 kg./m.^{3}, and if we have a piece whose volume is 0.65 m.^{3}, then the mass of that piece is the product of density and volume: (100 kg./m.^{3}) $\times$ (0.65 m.^{3}), or 65 kg. We can recover the quantity of mass of a specified volume of uniform material, if we know the material's density.

Probability Density

You may be wondering by now what blocks have to do with roulette wheels. The crux of the matter is this. We can identify formal parallels, or mathematical analogies, between these two situations. In each case, there is a kind of *entity* that is distributed over a *region* of *space*. For the block, there is *mass* distributed over a *volume* (a region of three-dimensional space); and for the roulette wheel, there is *probability* distributed over an *outcome axis region* (a region of one-dimensional space). Furthermore, in each case we were able to identify a ratio that remains constant over smaller and smaller regions. For the block of material, it was the mass density, the ratio of mass to volume, that remained constant. For the roulette wheel, it was the ratio between the probability value assigned to an individual slot and the length of an outcome axis segment that contained one, and only one, slot.

On the basis of these analogies, it seems reasonable to extend the concept of density, and to introduce it into the RV framework. We shall introduce it in the obvious fashion. We shall suppose that were we to continue to place more and more slots (i.e., possible outcome values) into the outcome region between 0 and 10, we should eventually be able to represent the situation in terms of a useful mathematical fiction: we could ultimately say that the outcome axis region between 0 and 10 contains infinitely many slots, each lying within a "zero-length" segment of the outcome axis, and each having an assigned probability value of *zero*. Furthermore, we could assume that for each of these infinitely many outcome values and associated outcome axis segments, the *ratio* of probability to length would retain its previous value (in our example, 0.10—see table 5.1). We have, in essence, applied the same kind of argument that was advanced earlier for a "zero mass/zero volume" block segment.

Because of its obvious conceptual kinship to the density of physical materials, this ratio of *probability* to *outcome axis segment length* is called the PROBABILITY DENSITY. We have arrived at a concept that is central to the idea of a continuous RV: there is something called a "probability density" that is assigned to each one of the infinite number of densely spaced outcome values that lie within the potential outcome range.

Probability Density Functions

We have, then, a probability density value assigned everywhere, to each point, in the outcome region (in our example, the region from 0 to 10). We can once more speak of a function, a mathematical system that assigns numerical values to some second set of numbers. Let us recall our previous encounter in chapter 4 with a probability function. That function assigned probability values to discrete outcome values at selected locations on the outcome axis. Now we are assigning probability densities to outcomes; we naturally call a function that accomplishes this kind of an assignment a PROBABILITY DENSITY FUNCTION. A probability density function will be our principal formal mathematical representation of a continuous RV.

It should already be apparent that there are two major differences between probability functions and probability density functions. First, there is the matter of the difference in the kinds of entities assigned to outcome values by these two kinds of functions. A probability function assigns a probability to an outcome value, while a probability density function assigns a probability density to an outcome value. We have said that at a given outcome value, the *value* of a probability function is the *probability* assigned by the function to that outcome point; correspondingly, the *value* of a probability density function at a given outcome value is the *probability density* assigned by that function to that outcome point. (In our present example, that value of the probability density function is the *same* value, 0.10, everywhere in the potential outcome range.)

The second difference between a probability function and a probability density function arises from the difference between a discrete and a continuous potential outcome. We saw in chapter 4 that, since a discrete RV has a discrete potential outcome, a probability function assigns values (probabilities) only at certain outcome values.[1] A probability density function, however, is the mathematical representation of a *continuous* RV and thus is a continuous potential outcome situation: the probability density function assigns a probability density everywhere in its range—to each of the infinite number of possible outcome values that lie in the potential outcome. A probability density function has a value everywhere in its potential outcome, while a probability function has a value (other than zero) only at certain discrete locations on the outcome axis.

We can graph a probability density function. Figure 5.3 shows such a graph for the probability density function of an unbiased continuous roulette wheel whose potential outcome spans the range from 0 to 10. The potential outcome is shown, as usual, as a portion of the horizontal outcome axis; the value of the probability density function, the probability density, is plotted along the vertical axis. Properly speaking, we no longer have a roulette wheel, a device characterized by a discrete potential outcome set

[1]One can, if one wishes to do so, use a mathematical artifice and say that a probability function also assigns values everywhere; one merely says that the function assigns a value of zero to those outcome values to which it does not assign nonzero values.

(that is, having a specified number of slots). Now we have a different device. On any one trial or turn of the wheel, *any* one of the infinite numbers between 0 and 10 could occur. That kind of a device is more appropriately called a "spinner" rather than a roulette wheel (see problem 2.3).

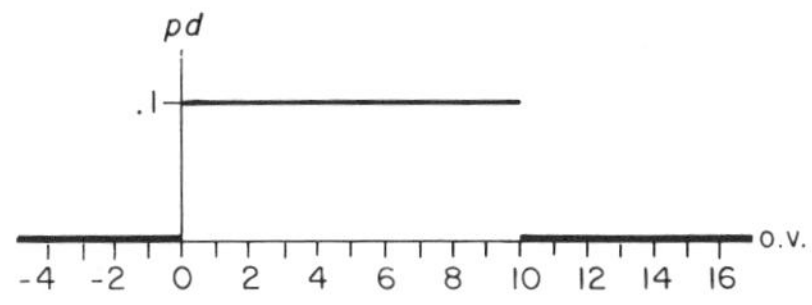

FIGURE 5.3 A uniform probability density function

If we compare the graphical representation of an unbiased roulette wheel (fig. 5.1) with that of an unbiased spinner, we can see the mathematical differences between a probability function and a probability density function reflected in these graphs. First, the value of a probability function is a probability, while that of a probability density function is a probability density. Accordingly, the vertical axes of the two types of graphs should be labeled with these different terms, respectively. Second, a probability function has a value only at specified, selected outcome locations; its graph consists of a series of vertical lines. The probability density function, however, has a value everywhere in the potential outcome. Therefore, it must be represented by a continuous curve (in our present case, a straight horizontal line) in that outcome range; the height of the curve in that range defines the value of the function (the probability density) at every outcome point—for our spinner example, every number between 0 and 10.

There also are similarities. Both graphs have an outcome axis, of course. Furthermore, the *envelopes* of the probability functions in figure 5.1 are horizontal lines, and the graph of the probability density function in figure 5.3 is a straight horizontal line. This similarity reflects our assumption that the roulette wheels represented in figure 5.1 and the spinner represented in figure 5.3 all are unbiased devices. Probability density functions that have a graph such as that represented in figure 5.3 are called *uniform*, *rectangular*, or *flat*. Another similarity concerns the *algebraic sign* of the numbers assigned by both types of functions to outcome values. In each instance, these assigned numbers must be nonnegative, since they are either probabilities (in the case of a probability function) or stem directly from probabilities (in the case of a probability density function). Thus, the graphs of either of these kinds of functions can never fall below the horizontal axis, the line that represents zero probability or probability density.

Probability in Regions

The use of a probability density function parallels that of a probability function in a number of important respects. One very important use of a probability density function is in finding the probability assigned to any specified outcome axis span by a continuous RV. Perhaps we should remind ourselves of the empirical implications of that concept. The probability assigned to a specified outcome region still retains its familiar empirical connotations (see chaps. 3 and 4). It still refers to the probability of obtaining on any trial an outcome value that falls within the specified region. Thus, the probability assigned to a specified outcome axis range (colloquially, "the probability in the range") still invokes the familiar set of pertinent empirical concepts—repeated trials, frequencies, relative frequencies, the principle of equivalence, etc.

We remember that in the case of discrete RVs we had several alternative methods for obtaining the probability assigned to a specified region by a given discrete RV. We developed a "direct" method based on a simple addition of probabilities; we used the concept of complementary outcome pairs; and we used the cumulative distribution function. All these methods were predicated on the addition of probability values attached to corresponding outcome values in the specified outcome range. Now, however, we no longer have a probability function; thus, we now have neither probability values attached to outcomes nor a set of discrete, possible values in the potential outcome set. Instead, we have probability density values that are assigned to an infinite number of outcome values in the continuous potential outcome (in the range from 0 to 10, in our example). Consequently, we cannot use our previous approaches to finding probabilities in outcome regions; these approaches must be modified. Unfortunately, these modifications are a bit intricate. They will therefore be presented only in broad outline. Additional details will be introduced as we return to the question of the probability in regions in a variety of contexts.

We are seeking a method that will allow us to find the probability in a specified sector of the potential outcome of a uniform probability density function. The task is formally similar to that of finding the mass of a designated volume of uniform material knowing the mass density of that material. We learned that in order to accomplish this latter task, we only needed to *multiply* the *density* (mass per volume) by the designated *volume* (spatial dimension). The process for recovering probability given a probability density over a specified outcome region is entirely analogous. To find the probability (analogous to mass) of a specified region or length of the outcome axis (analogous to volume), we multiply the *probability density* (probability per unit of length of the outcome axis) by the *length of the specified segment*. The result is the probability in that region.

We can apply this general procedure, this "product rule," to our example of a uniform probability density function that assigns a probability density value of 0.10 throughout the outcome axis region from 0 to 10. Suppose we would like to find the probability in the region from 3.4 to 6.7, for instance. The length of that designated span is 6.7 − 3.4, or 3.3 outcome axis units. Therefore, the probability of that segment is (0.10) × (3.3), or 0.33. That is the probability that on any one turn of our unbiased spinner we would obtain an outcome value that lies within the outcome region from 3.4 to 6.7.

The principle of equivalence continues to apply. A probability of 0.33 implies an equivalent relative frequency of 0.33. Thus, in any repeated set of observations with our spinner, we should expect that about 33 out of every 100 outcome values, or 33% of the resulting outcomes, would fall within the specified range. The other 67% of outcome values would of course fall within the remaining portions of the potential outcome range of 0 to 10, the range "0 to 3.4 and 6.7 to 10."

The finding that we can recover probability by multiplying

probability density with outcome axis segment length has several important implications. One of these concerns the probability of obtaining any *one* specified outcome axis value, for example, the outcome value 5.6. To find the probability assigned by our probability density function to that value, we ask ourselves: "How long is the outcome axis 'segment' that *is* the single outcome axis value 5.6?" It is of course 0 outcome axis units long; a point or single outcome value is a "zero-length" line. Therefore, by our principle that probability may be recovered by a multiplicative operation, we can immediately conclude that the probability assigned to any one specified single outcome value by a probability density function is *0*.

The result is paradoxical. On the one hand, for a continuous RV the probability of obtaining a single, specified outcome value on a trial is zero, as we have just concluded. On the other hand, we of course do obtain *some* number in the potential outcome, some actual outcome, from a trial—yet, prior to the trial that number had a zero probability of occurring. In that sense, it was an "impossible" result. This is a peculiarity of continuous RVs, and is of more theoretical than practical consequence. In practice, we shall always be considering probabilities of outcome *ranges* of continuous RVs, and such probabilities are not at all paradoxical.

In a way, we should have anticipated this result. We had developed the concept of probability density in the first place by postulating that a "zero-length" outcome axis segment, i.e., a point on the outcome axis, would have an assigned probability of zero. Our development has now come full circle and returned us to that postulate: we now find that if an RV assigns a probability density to a potential outcome set, then the probability assigned by that probability density function to *each point* in that set will be zero.

We have learned the principle that we can obtain the *probability* assigned to a specified outcome range by a uniform RV by *multiplying* the *span of the specified range* by the *assigned probability density value*. This arithmetical product can be given an extremely important and illuminating geometrical interpretation, to be presented next.

The Area Under a Curve

We are about to consider what it means in geometrical terms to multiply the span of an outcome region by a probability density value. The geometrical framework for the discussion is provided by the graph of the probability density function. We know that on such a graph the value of a probability density is represented by the height of the graph above the outcome axis. Of course, the magnitude of a specified outcome span, the difference between two outcome values such as 6.7 and 3.4, is geometrically represented as the length of that segment on the outcome axis. Thus, these two kinds of arithmetical quantities, a difference between two outcome values and a probability density value, are represented on the graph of a probability density function as a length and a height, respectively. We already know that their product is the probability associated with the specified outcome axis segment. We can also see, however, that from a geometrical point of view, that same product represents an *area*—specifically, a rectangular area such as the one shown in figure 5.4. It is this kind of an area, then, that is implied by the product of outcome axis segment and probability density. Therefore, *the probability assigned to an outcome axis region implies, and is represented by, that kind of an area.*

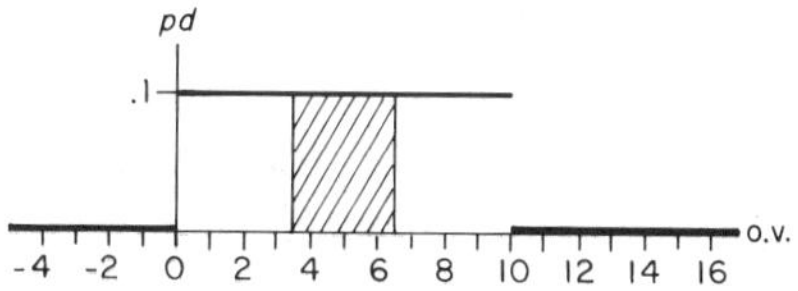

FIGURE 5.4 An area under the curve

The area in figure 5.4 is an example of an AREA UNDER THE CURVE BETWEEN TWO OUTCOME VALUES. (In our case, the "curve" is a straight horizontal line.) It is an area defined by four boundaries: the outcome axis segment; the graph of the probability density function ("the curve of the graph"); and the two vertical lines erected at the end points of the specified outcome axis segment.

We can say, then, that the probability of finding an outcome between any two specified outcome values is given by the area under the curve between these two values. We have demonstrated this principle informally for a rectangular or uniform probability density function. It will play a major role in the remainder of this text, and will be developed considerably further in a number of specific contexts.

An important related concept and term is the TOTAL AREA UNDER THE CURVE. That term refers to the area under the graph of a probability density function between the two extremes or end points of the *whole potential outcome* set. In our case, it would be the area under the curve between the outcome values 0 and 10. We know in general, without even considering probability densities, that the whole potential outcome is the composite event that must occur on a given trial of an RV. It is the certain event, because it is the event that contains all the possible elementary events, that is, all the possible outcome values—that had been our definition of the potential outcome (see chap. 2). Thus, if we ask: "How frequently will we obtain a number that lies within the potential outcome?" the answer is, on every turn of the spinner. From our discussion in chapter 3, we know that the probability assigned to that certain event is 1.0, exactly; therefore, that is the probability that must be assigned to the whole potential outcome set.

We can now verify this conclusion reached by a general argument by using our "product rule" to find the total area under the curve, i.e., to find the area associated with the whole potential outcome. In our example, that area obviously is (0.10) × (10.0), or 1.0, as it should be. This particular example is a special instance of a general principle: the total area under the graph of a probability density function is always the area associated with the certain event, and therefore is *always* equal to 1.

Biased Spinners

We so far have been considering a continuous RV with a rectangular probability density function. As we know, this kind of a uniform, rectangular, or flat profile represents an unbiased spinner, just as the corresponding "flat" envelopes of probability functions represented an unbiased roulette wheel in chapter 4. As one might expect, many statistical situations arise that do not display this "fair" behavior and consequently cannot be properly represented mathematically by a rectangular RV. We have already illustrated and briefly discussed the departures from a "flat" envelope for discrete RVs in chapter 4. Just as curved envelopes of probability functions correspond to biased roulette wheels, so do curved graphs of probability density functions correspond to biased spinners. Thus, envelopes of probability functions such as those shown in figures 4.2 to 4.4 have counterparts in biased probability density functions. Figure 5.5 illustrates the graphs of three probability density functions whose biases roughly correspond to those of the three probability functions in figures 4.2, 4.3, and 4.4.

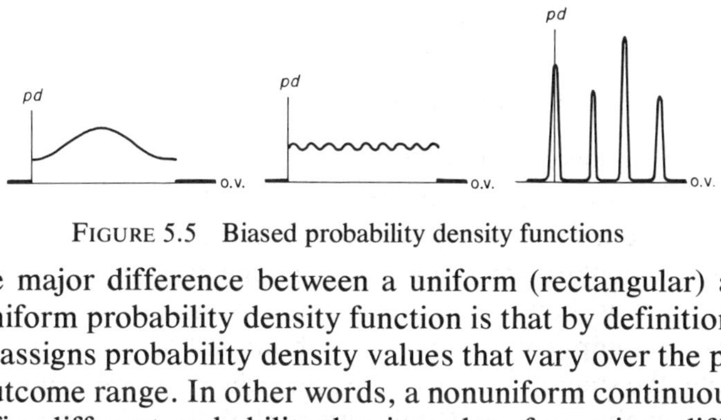

FIGURE 5.5 Biased probability density functions

The major difference between a uniform (rectangular) and a nonuniform probability density function is that by definition, the latter assigns probability density values that vary over the potential outcome range. In other words, a nonuniform continuous RV specifies different probability density values for various different outcome values. Therefore, a nonuniform continuous RV can no longer be defined or described simply by stipulating a single probability density value that holds everywhere in the outcome region. We can no longer just say as before, "the probability density value is 0.10 everywhere in the outcome region from 0 to 10," for example. Some other methods of describing these functions must be found. The general problem of specifying RVs will occupy us in part II. For the present, we shall rely primarily on graphical representations.

The matter of the probability assigned to outcome regions by nonuniform RVs is a topic that will occupy us frequently and in considerable detail in subsequent chapters. We will now introduce it briefly with reference to a typical graph of a nonuniform, continuous RV that is limited in range. Suppose we wanted to find the probability in some outcome region such as that lying between the points labeled *a* and *b* of the graph of the nonuniform probability density function shown in figure 5.6. The principle developed for the special case of a uniform continuous RV continues to apply: *the probability between any two specified outcome values in the potential outcome of a probability density function is still represented by the area under the curve between these two outcome values*. We shall frequently have an occasion to use this very important and basic principle.

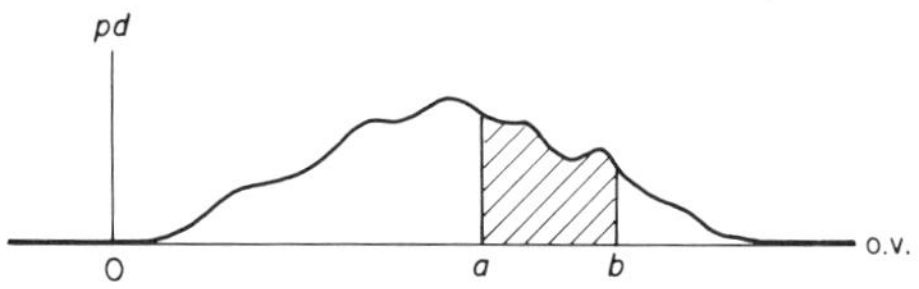

FIGURE 5.6 An irregular probability density function

It had been easy to find an area under the curve as long as we were dealing with uniform probability density functions. In those cases, the "curve" of the graph was a straight line, and we only needed to calculate areas of a simple geometrical shape, namely, a rectangle. Now, however, we have a new situation; we are dealing with more complicated, irregularly bounded areas, such as, for example, the shaded area in figure 5.6. How could we compute the value of such areas, and thus the probability of outcome axis regions such as the span from *a* to *b* in figure 5.6? A number of different methods may be used. For certain kinds of continuous RVs, areas under graphs may be found by the methods of calculus. In other cases one may have to resort to approximate numerical methods. For example, one could divide an outcome axis region such as the span from *a* to *b* in figure 5.6 into contiguous narrow vertical strips, as illustrated in figure 5.7. If one uses sufficiently narrow strips, then the value of the probability density function will vary but little over the width of any one strip. Accordingly, one may treat each strip as a rectangle and obtain a close approximation to its actual area by a simple calculation. One then obtains an approximation to the area under the curve in a specified outcome axis region by summing the areas of all the narrow rectangular strips in that region. Appendix A demonstrates the details of a very similar numerical method.

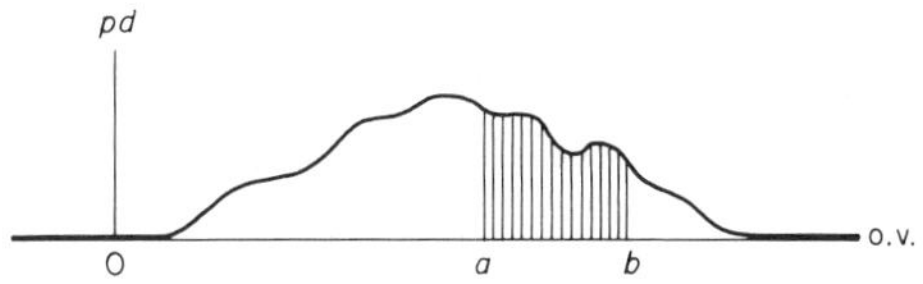

FIGURE 5.7 Dividing an outcome axis segment into strips

These considerations suggest that it may sometimes be quite tedious to obtain an area under a segment of an irregularly shaped probability density function. In order to avoid that kind of laborious effort, one can define and use a cumulative distribution function, an entity introduced in chapter 4 for discrete RVs. Except for some relatively minor details, a cumulative distribution function for a continuous RV is basically the same kind of a function as that developed for a discrete RV.[2] It exhibits substantially the same formal properties, and can be used in much the same way to find the probability in a specified outcome region.

The graph in figure 5.8 shows the cumulative distribution function that corresponds to the probability density function shown in figure 5.6. Let us see how we would use this cumulative distribution function to find the probability in the region between the outcome values a and b in figure 5.6. The two values of the cumulative distribution function at the outcome points a and b are shown in figure 5.8 as the cumulative probability values p and q, respectively. According to the basic definition of a cumulative distribution function, the value of that function at any one outcome value is equal to all the probability lying to the left of that

[2]The principal difference is that the cumulative distribution function of a discrete RV has "steps," while that of a continuous RV is generally smooth (compare figs. 4.8 and 5.8). That kind of difference reflects the fact that in the discrete case, the cumulative distribution function can acquire probability only at selected values along the outcome axis and thus "grow" at only those isolated values, while in the continuous case, the function is constantly accumulating probability and "growing" as one moves from left to right in its potential outcome region. (See also problem 5.3.)

point. Accordingly, p and q represent all the probability lying to the left of the outcome values a and b, respectively. The difference in the two cumulative probability values must represent the probability assigned to the outcome span between a and b. Therefore, if we subtract p from q, we immediately obtain the desired probability in the region between a and b. Of course, this probability value is also the value of the shaded area in fig. 5.6.

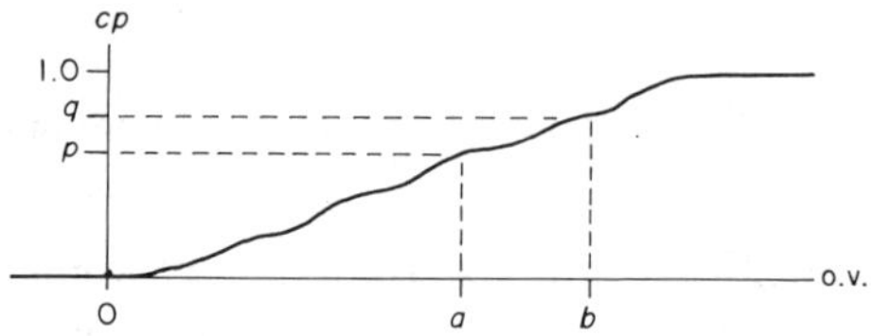

FIGURE 5.8 Finding the probability of an outcome axis segment

There is still the unanswered question of how one could obtain a cumulative distribution function from a probability density function in the first place. For profiles that have relatively simple geometrical shapes, the process is easy. For probability density functions with more complex profiles, however, one needs to use more advanced mathematical procedures. In some cases, one may have to resort to using computers. The point is: for any given probability density function, one needs to compute the corresponding cumulative distribution function only *once*. Subsequently, once the cumulative distribution function is available, one can find the probability assigned to *any* specified portion of the outcome axis by the straightforward procedure just described. One merely uses the cumulative distribution function to obtain two cumulative probability values, one for each of the two end points of the specified outcome axis segment, and then subtracts one probability value from the other. The difference is the desired probability value.

We now may see why the cumulative distribution function is important and useful. In chapter 4 it had been of relatively little computational use because probabilities in regions could be obtained easily from probability functions. Now we can see that a cumulative distribution function promises to be useful in situations where probabilities in regions cannot be obtained easily from a probability density function.

Extending the Range

The last case to be explored in this chapter is that of a continuous RV whose range is not limited. This kind of a probability density function may have a potential outcome that is not limited in the positive direction of the outcome axis, or the negative direction, or in both directions. Examples of these three cases are presented in figure 5.9.

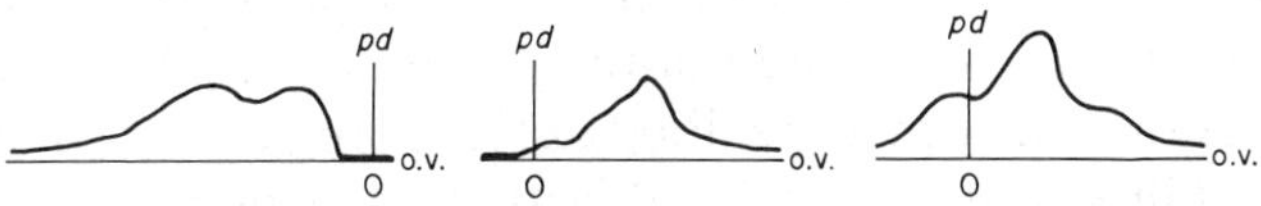

FIGURE 5.9 Not-limited-in-range continuous RVs

The general properties of these kinds of probability density functions are very much like those of probability density functions that are limited in range. Some new considerations may arise, however, in computing the area under a curve. Previously, for a continuous RV that was limited in range, these kinds of areas always had two definite vertical boundaries, one at each end of the specified outcome axis segment (for instance, at the points a and b in fig. 5.6). Thus, in principle, the "area under a curve" always had a clear, definite meaning. Now, however, since the potential outcome is not limited in range, it may happen that one of these vertical boundaries no longer exists for a specified region; in that case, the meaning of "area under the curve" would not be quite so obvious. For example, consider the probability density function sketched in figure 5.10. If we wished to calculate the area under the curve between the outcome values r and s, that would present no new conceptual problems. That area is basically the same kind of an area as the region between a and b in figure 5.6. If, however, we were asked to compute the area under the curve to the *right* of s, or to the *left* of r, we should have to compute an area of an unbounded region, one that lacked one (or even both) of the usual two vertical boundaries.

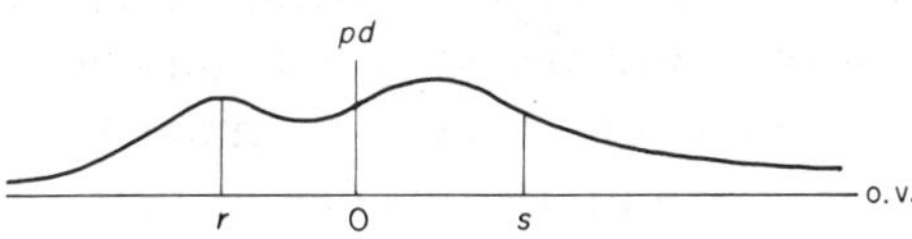

FIGURE 5.10 Bounded and unbounded areas

The general methods used to deal with these kinds of situations are very similar to those that were applied in chapter 4 to the parallel discrete case, the not-limited-in-range probability function. The approaches introduced for the discrete, not-limited-in-range case included the use of the concept of complementary outcome pairs and the use of approximation methods.

We will not consider these issues in detail at the present time, but only mention a few particularly important points. One basic characteristic of a not-limited-in-range, continuous RV is that the area under the curve in a specified outcome region is still equal to the probability value associated with that region, even if that outcome region is not limited in range. The basic relationship between a probability assigned to a region and the area under the curve continues to hold.

Another important point is that the total area under the curve still must equal 1, exactly. Even though the potential outcome is not limited in one or both outcome axis directions, that outcome axis range always stands for the *certain* event, and that event always has a probability of 1.

A continuous RV that is not limited in range cannot be uniform or "flat"; it cannot have a constant probability density value, no matter how small, over the entire, unlimited range. We can demonstrate this through a simple argument that essentially repeats the argument presented for the parallel discrete case in chapter 4. Let us assume that we could have a *uniform* RV that was not limited in range. By definition, it would have some *constant* probability density value over the *unlimited* potential outcome. Let us say that this probability density value would be some very small number represented by the value a. We have an unlimited outcome range available (by our assumption), so we can always find a segment that has a length $1/a$. The area under the curve within this segment is $(a) \times (1/a)$, or 1, exactly. But we know that since our RV is presumed to be not limited in range, the segment that we are considering is only a portion of the whole potential outcome. Therefore, there are additional outcome regions under the curve; these would add to the area under the curve, and the area under the curve would thus exceed its permissible total of 1. This must not happen. Our assumption that a uniform, not-limited-in-range RV can exist has led to an untenable situation and must be rejected.

We can illustrate this general demonstration by a numerical example. Suppose that the probability density value a would be only one *millionth*—surely a fairly small constant value. Then, an outcome axis segment of $1/a$ would be one *million* outcome axis units long. The area under the curve of that segment would be equal to one millionth times one million, or 1. We see that one portion of the not-limited potential outcome range would already have contributed a probability of 1 to the area under the curve. Obviously, other portions of the remaining potential outcome region would make further contributions to that area, bringing the total above 1. As a matter of fact, if we did have a uniform, not-limited-in-range probability density function, the area under the curve would exceed *any* specified numerical value; this can be demonstrated by a simple extension of the previous argument.

As we shall see later, a not-limited-in-range continuous probability density function *must* approach the outcome axis more and more closely (*asymptotically*; see chap. 4, n. 5) so that the total area under the curve does not exceed 1.

This completes our initial presentation of RV concepts. We will next address the matter of describing various properties of probability functions and probability density functions. That is, we shall study general procedures for mathematically specifying the profile characteristics of these kinds of functions. These issues are the province of descriptive statistics, the topic of part II. I wish to conclude this part with several observations concerning the basic terminology of our framework.

Terminology

We have been introduced to three mathematical concepts and their geometrical representations: probability functions, probability density functions, and cumulative distribution functions. You should be aware that these entities do not have a completely standard terminology. Each may be called by a slightly different name by various authors. It is important when reading the literature to recognize which of these three entities is being considered at any one particular time.

Another caution might be voiced. Writers are not always careful (and not always correct) in the matter of the *values* of these kinds of functions. Correspondingly, they are not always careful with graphical representations; in particular, the vertical axes are frequently mislabeled, or even not labeled at all. You need to remember the points that I have emphasized continually: the value of a probability function is a *probability*; that of a probability density function is a *probability density* (and therefore *not* an entity such as a probability, frequency, relative frequency, or the like); and finally, the value of a cumulative distribution function is always a *probability*—specifically, a cumulative or accumulated probability.

Some authors at times use one single generic label for any one of these three kinds of functions, and that can be very convenient. They call any or all of these functions PROBABILITY DISTRIBUTIONS when they are speaking generally, or when the usage is unambiguous. We shall use this general term when it is appropriate and convenient.

It is also convenient to abbreviate the names of these three principal functions. We shall be using the terms probability function, probability density function, and cumulative distribution function a great deal, and it will therefore often be convenient and helpful to abbreviate these by pf, pdf, and cdf, respectively.

PROBLEMS

5.1 What are the two kinds of numbers involved in every probability density function?

5.2 Consider an unbiased roulette wheel whose potential outcome spans the range from −6 to +2.

(a) For a 30-slot wheel, what would be the length of an outcome axis segment that contains 1 slot? For a 100-slot wheel? For a 1,000-slot wheel? What would be the corresponding probability values?

(b) For each of the three roulette wheels, calculate the ratio of assigned probability to one outcome segment length. Does it remain constant? Why, or why not?

5.3 We can use the cdf of a discrete RV to deepen our understanding of the cdf of a continuous RV.

(a) Sketch the three cdfs corresponding to the pdfs of the 10-, 20-, and 40-slot unbiased roulette wheels shown in figure 5.1.

(b) You should be able to discern a trend from your results. Discuss what happens as the number of slots in the outcome axis region from 0 to 10 increases.

(c) Carry your inference to its logical conclusion, and discuss what happens to the cdf when you have an "infinite" number of slots, i.e., when you have the spinner whose pdf is shown in figure 5.3. Sketch the graph of its cdf.

5.4 The potential outcome of a spinner spans the range from -10 to $+5$. In the range between -10 and 0, the probability density is constant and is equal to 0.07. What is the probability assigned to the outcome region from 0 to 5? Can you draw the complete pdf? Why, or why not?

5.5 In problem 5.4, assume that the probability density is constant in the region from 0 to 5.

(a) What is the value of that probability density?

(b) Draw the graph of the pdf of the spinner.

(c) What is the probability assigned to the outcome region from -2 to 3?

(d) If you spin the spinner 30,000 times, how many outcome values would you expect to find in the range from -2 to 3?

5.6 Construct the cdf for the pdf in problem 5.5. [Hint: Either use simple algebra to relate a typical outcome value x to the corresponding cumulative probability, or else obtain a sufficient number of sample points from the pdf so that the pattern of the cdf becomes obvious.]

5.7 The triangular pdf of a spinner is shown in figure P5.1.

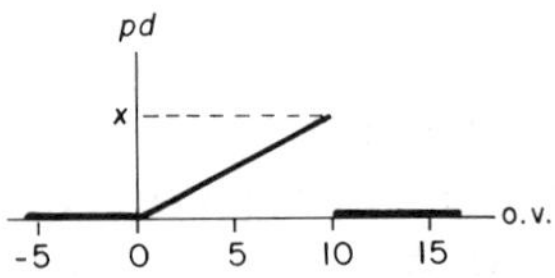

FIGURE P5.1

(a) What is the probability density value x?

(b) Find the probability density values at these outcome values: 0, 0.5, 1.0, . . ., and 10.

(c) What are the probabilities in the 20 one-half unit outcome axis segments?

(d) Use your data to sketch a graph of the associated cdf.

(e) Calculate the probability assigned to the outcome axis region between 4.5 and 6.0 directly by finding the appropriate area under the curve of the pdf; verify your answer, at least approximately, by using the sketch you have constructed for the corresponding cdf.

PART II

Overview of Descriptive Statistics

CHAPTER 6

Approaches to Description

We have already seen in several contexts that probability distributions (our generic term for probability functions, probability density functions, and cumulative distribution functions) can have very different features. We have classified RVs into discrete or continuous, limited- or not-limited-in-range, and fair or biased, categories. These are rather coarse descriptive classification schemes that ignore other differences that may exist between RVs of the same subtype. For example, the three probability functions in figures 4.2 to 4.4 would all be classified as discrete, limited in range, and biased or nonuniform, yet there are obvious differences between them. How might one describe RVs further so that these additional characteristics would be specified? Part II will explore that question. We will present a very general introduction to some of the concepts and descriptive methods that we shall study in more detail in subsequent chapters.

General Features

There are other very general descriptors in addition to those just mentioned. One of these concerns symmetry. Some probability distributions are symmetrical about an outcome value (fig. 6.1), while others are not (fig. 6.2). An unsymmetrical profile is

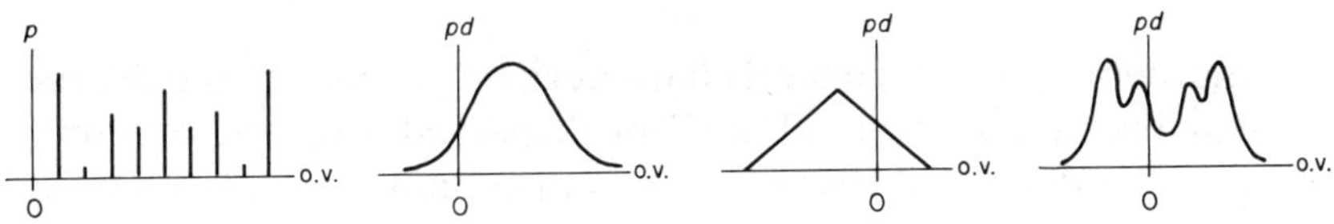

FIGURE 6.1 Symmetrical probability distributions

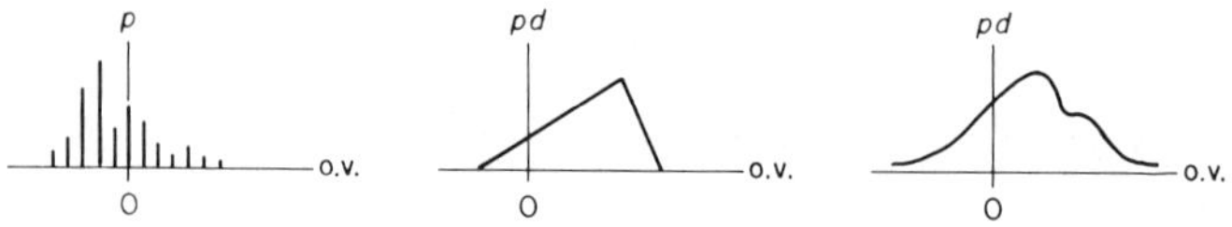

FIGURE 6.2 Unsymmetrical probability distributions

said to be positively skewed, or skewed to the right, if the "tail" of the profile extends in the right direction along the outcome axis, and negatively skewed, or skewed to the left, in the opposite situation. Figure 6.3 illustrates these definitions.

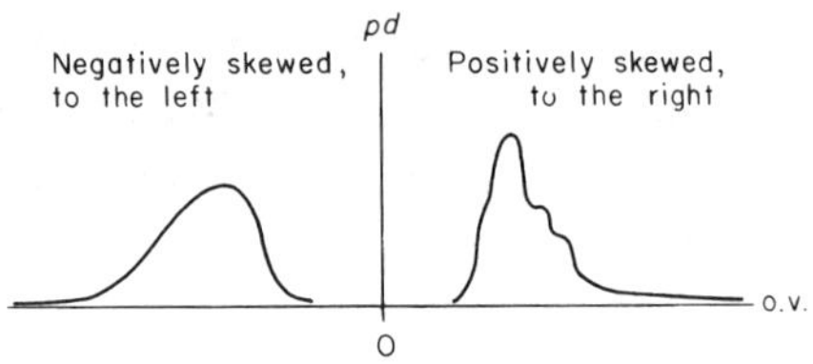

FIGURE 6.3 Skewed probability distributions

Different probability distributions can be centered at different regions of the outcome axis. That is, the location of the outcome range which contains most or all of the area under the curve might be different for different RVs. Figure 6.4 shows three pfs that differ from one another only in their general location along the outcome axis. We refer to this feature as the "central tendency." It is an important general property of a given probability distribution, and can be specified more precisely by quantitative means.

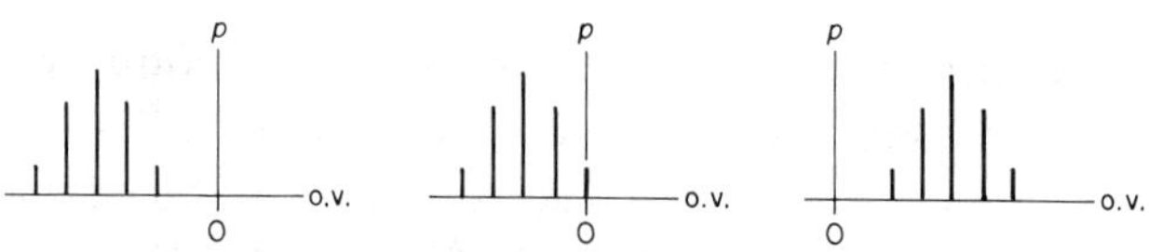

FIGURE 6.4 Differences in central tendency

Another important general characteristic pertains to the degree to which an RV is "spread out," or dispersed, over the outcome range. The degree of dispersion can also be described quantitatively. It tells us how much variation or spread in outcome values one might expect to obtain in a *set* of numbers generated by repeated trials of a given RV.

Data Points

We know that in mathematical terms, pfs, pdfs, or cdfs are first of all, functions. Each one is a mathematical system that assigns probabilistic values, that is, probabilities or probability densities, to outcome values. In chapters 4 and 5 we briefly discussed two very common ways of specifying probability distributions, namely, *graphs* and *tables*, of these functions. These methods are used so frequently that the distinctions between an RV and its graph or table tend to become blurred. For example, we often speak of "the profile of the RV" when the correct but more cumbersome terminology would be, "the profile of the graph of the RV." Strictly speaking, an RV is a function, and thus a mathematical entity or system. A graph is a *picture* of that function, and thus not really the function itself. We will be casual in these matters most of the time, since the inexact terminology does not introduce conceptual difficulties.

Although tables and graphs are often very convenient, they may be less than ideal for some particular purposes. For instance, they are sometimes difficult to use in theoretical work. Therefore, other descriptive methods have been developed. The first of these alternative approaches is the familiar use of an algebraic equation to define a mathematical function.

Equations

The algebraic method is so commonplace that it is the method that usually comes to mind when one refers to a mathematical function. It is a symbolic, abstract method that uses an equation to define the functional relationship between two sets of numbers (the familiar x and y). Elementary equations typically contain polynomial (powers of the variables), trigonometric, exponential, or logarithmic expressions. In each case, an equation provides a mathematical "recipe" that defines the association between two sets of numbers. We know that in statistics, these two sets of numbers are *outcome values* and *probabilistic entities*. For our applications, then, an algebraic equation would be used to specify a probability or a probability density for a given outcome value in the potential outcome set.

Algebraic methods can be very convenient and precise. Unfortunately, one cannot always resort to them. For example, a probability distribution may have a highly irregular shape or envelope that cannot be accurately described by a simple algebraic equation (see fig. 5.6). For this and other reasons, statisticians have developed alternative, more general, descriptive methods.

Average or Expected Values

We will now introduce a basic approach to describing RVs that is important theoretically as well as practically. The approach is very general in that it can be used to describe any kind of a probability distribution. It is also very flexible, because it can provide any desired degree of precision; it can be used to describe an RV very broadly, or very specifically, or to some intermediate degree of specificity. The approach involves some subtle concepts, and is best presented through actual examples (chaps. 7 and 8). The present discussion will only outline the ideas in general terms.

The approach is based on the simple and familiar arithmetical procedure of averaging. We remember that the average of any set of numbers is the sum of these numbers, divided by the number of terms contained in that sum. We shall see in chapter 7 that a probability distribution can yield a whole family of averages. In fact, it can yield an infinite number of certain kinds of averages. Conversely, such a *set* of averages can be used to describe an RV. The flexibility of this descriptive methodology derives from the fact that we can use either some or all of these numbers to describe an RV. If we provide all of these descriptors, if we furnish "the complete family," we thereby define an RV precisely and uniquely. If, however, we provide only a partial set, only some of these numbers, we may correspondingly provide only an incomplete description or specification of an RV; yet, such a partial description may be quite adequate for certain purposes.

In this family of descriptors, there are two particular numbers that provide important although partial information about a given probability distribution. One of these averages quantifies the *cen-*

tral tendency, and the other number quantifies the degree to which a probability distribution is *dispersed* about its central location. These two descriptors, the two particular averages, are called, respectively, the *mean* and the *variance*. We shall have considerably more to say about them.

The infinite set of descriptors that is generated by this averaging process has other names as well. This family of numbers is sometimes called the set of "expected values"; that term refers to "expectation" in a particular, mathematical sense, as we shall later see. The descriptors are also sometimes called "moments"—the first, second, third, etc., moment—because of their close mathematical kinship to a concept developed in physics. In that discipline, "moment" refers to the twisting action (torque) of a force or a mass about a fixed point. Both of these concepts, expected value and moment, will be considered further in the next two chapters.

Guessing and Error

Prior to an actual trial, we cannot know the actual outcome that will be observed; we can, however, make a guess about that value. Now, strange as it may seem, we can define certain descriptors in the context of making such guesses. The procedure will be clarified when it is applied to several situations in the next two chapters, and I will here once again only sketch the approach.

Let us imagine that we are about to perform a trial, and that we guess a number, some outcome value, in advance. The result of the trial is an actual outcome value; usually, it will be a different value from our prior guess—sometimes very different, sometimes reasonably close. Thus, there is an *error* associated with *each* trial and guess. We would like to make the best guess each time we perform a trial, naturally, but what is the "best" number to guess? The answer is, it depends. It depends on the particular criterion that we choose to define "best." Different criteria could lead to different numbers that were "best guesses," just as different criteria for "the best place to live" could lead to different locales, for example. That is, in asking, what is the best place to live, we may get different answers depending on whether we rate a locale on the basis of job opportunities, climate, housing, schools, cost of living, etc. Different criteria may lead to different selections. In a similar way, there are several ways of defining "best" in the guessing situation. For a given criterion, one can identify a specific, associated outcome value that is the best guess according to that criterion. Furthermore, as we shall see, a guess that is "best" according to one criterion may be a very bad guess according to another.

This chapter has surveyed the principal approaches that are used in describing probability distributions and RVs. The next two chapters will examine descriptive statistics in greater detail.

PROBLEMS

6.1 Discuss the differences between an algebraic equation for a pf and for a pdf. Are there any similarities?

6.2 What does the term "value of a function" mean? What is the value of a probability function? Of a probability density function? Of a cumulative distribution function? [See also chaps. 4 and 5.]

6.3 Why are general descriptors such as those pertaining to symmetry characteristics, central tendency, or dispersion less than completely adequate for describing an RV?

6.4 Describe the process of finding the average of a set of numbers.

6.5 Suppose you had a set of five numbers. What might the term "average of the squares" mean? Illustrate your answer with the set 2, 3, 6, 7, and 12.

CHAPTER 7

Description: Discrete Random Variables

This chapter will present some specific procedures that are used to describe a discrete RV. The descriptive methodologies will be examined in terms of a pf shown in figure 7.1. The choice of that particular RV is arbitrary; any other comparable RV (discrete and limited in range) could have been used just as well to illustrate the descriptive methods.

The Mean

The pf shown in figure 7.1 is biased; in the terminology of chapter 6, it is negatively skewed, or skewed to the left. The pf could represent a biased roulette wheel having six slots labeled from -2 to 3 in unit increments.

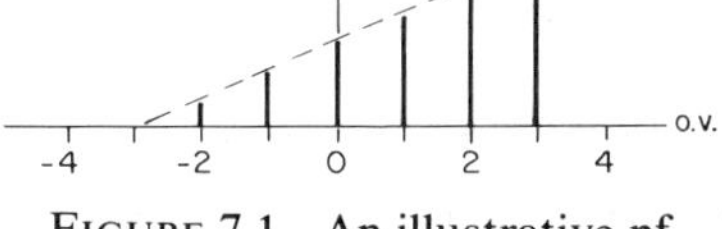

FIGURE 7.1 An illustrative pf

Let us assume that we had performed 21 trials and obtained the results shown in table 7.1. We would like to compute the average of these 21 actual outcome values. We follow the procedure mentioned in chapter 6: the average of any set of numbers is obtained by adding these, and dividing the resulting sum by the number of terms in that sum. To find the *average* or *mean* of the 21 values listed in table 7.1, then, we only need to add these values and divide the sum by 21:

$$\frac{\begin{array}{l}(2)+(0)+(2)+(1)+(-1)+(3)+(3)+(1)+(3)+(-2)+(3)\\+(2)+(-1)+(3)+(0)+(2)+(1)+(3)+(1)+(0)+(2)\end{array}}{21}. \quad (7.1)$$

Table 7.1

Hypothetical data: 21 trials with pf in figure 7.1

Trial no.	Outcome value	Trial no.	Outcome value	Trial no.	Outcome value
1	2	8	1	15	0
2	0	9	3	16	2
3	2	10	−2	17	1
4	1	11	3	18	3
5	−1	12	2	19	1
6	3	13	−1	20	0
7	3	14	3	21	2

The number we obtain, $1\frac{1}{3}$, is the *simple average* or *mean* of the 21 actual outcome values. We shall see, however, that this numerical value represents much more than that. Additional meanings of the quantity called the mean will emerge as we explore various aspects of the RV formal framework; our conception of the mean will grow throughout this book. The following discussion is only a first introduction.

Let us put (7.1) into a different form. As a first step, we shall group like terms in the numerator:

$$\frac{\begin{array}{l}[(-2)]+[(-1)+(-1)]+[(0)+(0)+(0)]\\+[(1)+(1)+(1)+(1)]+[(2)+(2)+(2)+(2)+(2)]\\+[(3)+(3)+(3)+(3)+(3)+(3)]\end{array}}{21}. \quad (7.2)$$

Each of the six pairs of square brackets contains a certain number of like outcome values. The number of times any one particular outcome values appears in a given bracket is, of course, the frequency of that outcome value in the 21 trials. We can therefore rewrite each of the six bracketed sums in (7.2) as a *product of an outcome value and its corresponding frequency*. We can write the expression for the mean as

$$\frac{\begin{array}{l}[(-2) \times (1)] + [(-1) \times (2)] + [(0) \times (3)] \\ + [(1) \times (4)] + [(2) \times (5)] + [(3) \times (6)]\end{array}}{21}. \tag{7.3}$$

Finally, if we distribute division over the six terms of the sum, we obtain the following sum:

$$\begin{gathered}\left[(-2) \times \left(\frac{1}{21}\right)\right] + \left[(-1) \times \left(\frac{2}{21}\right)\right] + \left[(0) \times \left(\frac{3}{21}\right)\right] \\ + \left[(1) \times \left(\frac{4}{21}\right)\right] + \left[(2) \times \left(\frac{5}{21}\right)\right] + \left[(3) \times \left(\frac{6}{21}\right)\right]\end{gathered} \tag{7.4}$$

In this new form of the expression for the mean, we should recognize that in each one of the six product terms the number that multiplies the outcome value is the corresponding relative frequency. The principle of equivalence now allows us to equate each of these six relative frequencies with a probability value. We can therefore rewrite (7.4), using the symbolic notation introduced in chapter 3 for representing probability terms:

$$\begin{array}{l}[(-2) \times p(-2)] + [(-1) \times p(-1)] + [(0) \times p(0)] \\ + [(1) \times p(1)] + [(2) \times p(2)] + [(3) \times p(3)].\end{array} \tag{7.5}$$

This expression states that the mean can be calculated as the sum of six terms, one for each outcome value in the potential outcome set. Each term consists of the product of an outcome value and its corresponding probability. Each of the six terms is of the form (outcome value) × (corresponding assigned probability).

Our starting point had been a set of 21 actual outcome values obtained by repeated trials (table 7.1). We calculated their mean according to the usual mathematical procedure (7.1) and then, by a series of arithmetical steps and by applying the principle of equivalence, obtained an equivalent expression for the mean (7.5). The difference between (7.1) and (7.5) is highly significant conceptually. The sum (7.1) was constructed from *actual outcomes*, from data, and thus had immediate, close conceptual ties to empirically obtained results. It contained all 21 actual outcome values obtained by 21 repeated trials, explicitly. Now, however, (7.5) defines the *mean* only in terms of entities that are *constituents of a discrete RV*—outcome values in a potential outcome set and corresponding assigned probability values. An explicit, direct connection with empirical data is no longer visible. The expression (7.5) contains only six terms (not 21), one for each of the possible outcome values in figure 7.1: the 21 actual outcome values obtained from repeated trials are not in evidence. In essence, "experimental data" (actually, in our case, hypothetical data) have been replaced by general terms that refer to RV concepts only.

This difference is significant conceptually. It is evident that (7.5) would allow us to compute the mean *solely* from information furnished by a *pf*; the expression implies that everything that we need to know in order to compute a mean is specified by an RV: the outcome values in the potential outcome set, and corresponding probabilities. There had been nothing particularly special or idiosyncratic about our illustrative discrete RV. Therefore, since the pf was quite representative, we may infer that we could immediately calculate a mean, without reference to repeated trials and actual outcomes, for *any other* comparable RV as well. We thus have moved from a concept that concerned *data*—the average of a set of actual outcomes—to a concept that concerns only *probability distributions*. We might therefore say that a general expression such as (7.5) defines the *mean of an RV* or of a probability function, although we do not yet quite know what the term or concept "mean of a random variable" implies.

The two other previously mentioned alternatives to the term "mean," the terms "expected value" and "moment," have implications that can illuminate the relationships between a pf and its mean. Let us examine these terms. Taken literally, the term "expected value" would suggest that an outcome value is "expected," i.e., obtainable. In our specific example, the value of the mean is $1\frac{1}{3}$. We see from figure 7.1 that this value is not in our potential outcome; that set contains only the six values −2, −1, 0, 1, 2, and 3. Therefore, in our particular example we shall never obtain the "expected value" as the actual outcome of a single trial involving our RV. In that sense, "expected value" seems to be a misnomer.

We shall see presently how this apparent contradiction can be resolved. Initially, we had obtained a value for the mean by averaging 21 actual outcomes (7.1). We then demonstrated informally (steps 7.2 through 7.4) that the same value could also be obtained directly by a procedure that invoked only quantities specified by a probability distribution (7.5). That simple demonstration was possible because the hypothetical data in table 7.1 had been carefully selected to ensure that in this instance, the two values of the mean—that obtained by averaging a small set of outcomes (7.1) and that obtained from an RV alone (7.5)—would be equal to one another. This was a convenient artifice for first introducing the concept of the mean. As we shall see considerably later (part IV), however, in an actual experiment it would seldom if ever happen that these two values would indeed be equal. Nevertheless, our approach is not altogether artificial, because there *is* a sense in which the mean of an RV defined in terms of probability distribution, like (7.5), and the mean conceptualized as an average computed from data are equivalent to each other. The missing ingredient is the concept of the *long-term* average. If one repeats more and more observations or trials with an RV, obtaining more and more outcome values—considerably more than the 21 values in table 7.1—and if one continues to average these, then, as more trials are performed, this "long-term" average will tend to approach more and more closely the same value as the mean defined in terms of the RV. It is in this sense that the mean of a given RV is an "expected value": it is the value we should "expect" to obtain from the long-term average of data—from an average of very many actual outcome values acquired from many repeated trials of that pf. Thus, two apparently different conceptions of "the mean of an RV"—(1) the entity specified in terms of an RV by the procedure exemplified by (7.5); and (2) the value obtained from the long-term average—ultimately do converge on the same numerical value in any given RV situation.

Let us now examine the other term, moment. We know from chapter 6 that this alternative term is adopted from physics, where it pertains to masses and twisting forces about a fixed point such as the fulcrum of a lever. In physics, the mathematical treatment of situations involving moments is virtually identical to certain treatments of averages and probabilities found in statistics. Once again, as in chapter 5, formal analogies can be identified between physical systems comprising masses and distances and statistical "systems" (RVs) comprising probabilities and outcome values ("distances" on the outcome axis). For example, in physics a moment is defined as a product involving a mass and physical distance. That product has the same mathematical form as the typical product term in (7.5), the product of a probability and an outcome value. That is only one of several formal similarities that demonstrate the formal analogies between certain physical and statistical concepts. We cannot pursue these analogies in depth; that would take us too far afield. We can, however, show their plausibility by means of a simple example.

Consider the probability distribution shown in figure 7.1 and a physical system, shown schematically in figure 7.2, which consists of a set of masses located along a "balanced yardstick"—a lever. If we compare figures 7.1 and 7.2, we can see some obvious similarities. There are six masses in the physical system, and six possible outcome values in the pf. We also can see that the quantity of mass assigned to each of these physical bodies, and the location of each body on the yardstick, correspond, respectively, to a probability and an outcome value of the pf.

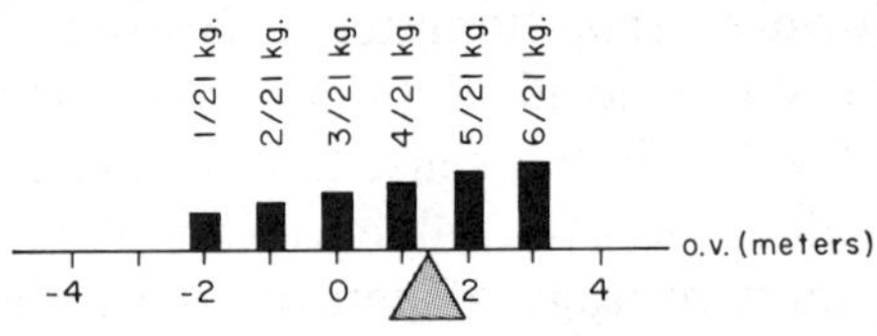

FIGURE 7.2 A physical system of masses

The system of masses in figure 7.2 will balance at some particular point along the lever. That point is located at the value $1\frac{1}{3}$ on the "yardstick"; it has the same numerical value as the mean of the pf—see (7.1) through (7.5). In physics, that kind of a balance point is called "the center of mass of the system," and it describes some important physical and mathematical properties of such a system. Likewise, in statistics, the mean describes some important empirical and theoretical properties of probability distributions. There are, of course, many mass systems that would balance at the same point, $1\frac{1}{3}$; correspondingly, there are many different types of probability distributions that would have a mean of $1\frac{1}{3}$. Nevertheless, this single descriptor does provide important although partial information about probability distributions, as we shall see in parts IV and V. At any rate, the mean can now be given a physical interpretation. It is that location or value on the outcome axis where a pf would "balance" if each probability value were considered to be a quantity of mass. This interpretation implies one sense in which the mean is a measure of central tendency—intuitively, we can appreciate that such a balance point would indicate something about the region in which a probability distribution is centered. The mean of an RV is an important enough descriptor to warrant a special symbol: the Greek letter μ (mu).

We learned in chapter 6 that the mean can also be viewed in the context of a particular "best guess" criterion. We shall return to that subject briefly at the end of this chapter, after we have considered the other members in the family of descriptors—the set of "higher moments."

The Variance and Other Averages

We have introduced one RV descriptor, μ, and found that its value for the pf shown in figure 7.1 is $1\frac{1}{3}$. We also noted that while μ does describe some important properties of any one RV, it falls short of describing a probability distribution completely; there are infinitely many different RVs that all have the same mean. Thus, the mean leaves many mathematical characteristics of a pf undefined. The mean provides only a very partial, incomplete description of a given probability distribution. Therefore, to describe a given pf unambiguously, other, additional descriptors will be needed. We shall introduce these now, still in terms of the probability function illustrated in figure 7.1. In our presentation, we shall use an approach that parallels the approach used previously to introduce the mean. It will be convenient and simple first to introduce these descriptors as various averages derived from a set of 21 numbers. Next, we shall invoke the kinds of steps represented by (7.1) through (7.5) to support the claim that each of these new descriptors can be obtained *directly* from a pf, rather than from a limited set of data. Last, we shall explore a second, equivalent specification for each of these descriptors, the kind of definition that is based on the concept of the long-term average.

Let us start by converting the 21 actual outcome values in table 7.1 to a simply related set of 21 other, "datalike" values. These numbers, the so-called *deviations from (or about) the mean*, will be derived according to the following procedure. We obtain for each outcome value in table 7.1 a corresponding deviation about the mean simply by substracting the value of the mean, $1\frac{1}{3}$, from that outcome value. (We know the value of μ for the particular pf in figure 7.1 from our earlier calculations, of course.) For example, if on a particular trial we obtain the outcome value 2, then the corresponding deviation from the mean for that trial is $[(2) - (1\frac{1}{3})]$, or 2/3; had we obtained the value (-1) instead, the corresponding deviation from the mean on that trial would have been $[(-1) - (1\frac{1}{3})]$, or $-2\frac{1}{3}$, and so on. Thus, one can compute one deviation about the mean for each of the 21 actual outcome values listed in table 7.1. These 21 corresponding deviations from the mean are shown in the second column of table 7.2.

Before proceeding, we might note that the sum of these 21 deviations, and therefore their average, is exactly 0. This must always be the case, as a simple algebraic argument will demonstrate (see problems 7.2 and 7.3).

The next step will be to raise the 21 deviations from the mean to various higher *powers*; we shall square them, cube them, raise them to the fourth power, etc. (raise them to various *degrees*—second, third, fourth, . . .). Corresponding to *each* particular power or degree, there will be *one set of 21 new terms*. Table 7.2 shows five sets of such 21 new values derived from the first five powers of the deviations about the mean. We could of course continue in this fashion and obtain more and more of these sets, without limit. For *each power*, from one to "infinity," we would generate *one* corresponding set of 21 values by raising each one of the 21 deviations from the mean to that power.

Table 7.2

Averages of powers of the deviations about the mean

	o.v.	(o.v. − 4/3)	$(\text{o.v.} - 4/3)^2$	$(\text{o.v.} - 4/3)^3$	$(\text{o.v.} - 4/3)^4$	$(\text{o.v.} - 4/3)^5$
	2	2/3	0.44	0.30	0.20	0.13
	0	−4/3	1.78	−2.37	3.16	−4.21
	2	2/3	0.44	0.30	0.20	0.13
	1	−1/3	0.11	−0.04	0.01	−0.00
	−1	−7/3	5.44	−12.70	29.64	−69.16
	3	5/3	2.78	4.63	7.72	12.86
	3	5/3	2.78	4.63	7.72	12.86
	1	−1/3	0.11	−0.04	0.01	−0.00
	3	5/3	2.78	4.63	7.72	12.86
	−2	−10/3	11.11	−37.04	123.46	−411.52
	3	5/3	2.78	4.63	7.72	12.86
	2	2/3	0.44	0.30	0.20	0.13
	−1	−7/3	5.44	−12.70	29.64	−69.16
	3	5/3	2.78	4.63	7.72	12.86
	0	−4/3	1.78	−2.37	3.16	−4.21
	2	2/3	0.44	0.30	0.20	0.13
	1	−1/3	0.11	−0.04	0.01	−0.00
	3	5/3	2.78	4.63	7.72	12.86
	1	−1/3	0.11	−0.04	0.01	−0.00
	0	−4/3	1.78	−2.37	3.16	−4.21
	2	2/3	0.44	0.30	0.20	0.13
Sums:	28	0	46.67	−40.33	239.56	−484.69
Averages:	28/21 = 4/3	0	46.67/21 = 2.22	−40.33/21 = −1.93	239.56/21 = 11.40	−484.69/21 = −23.08

As we remember, we averaged the original outcome values by adding them and dividing the sum by 21—(7.1). The basic method used to calculate averages remains unchanged for our next development. We shall average each of our columns of new "data" (the squares, cubes, fourth powers, etc., of the deviations from the mean). We follow our standard rationale and procedure to compute these averages. For example, to find the average of the 21 numbers obtained by squaring the 21 deviations from the mean (the third column of values in table 7.2), we would, as usual, add these numbers and divide the resulting sum by 21. This particular average would be called, for obvious reasons, *the average of the squares of the deviations from the mean*. In exactly the same fashion, we could obtain "the average of the third power of the deviations from the mean," "the average of the fourth power . . .," etc. By this procedure we could obtain an "infinite" number of averages—*one for each power of the deviations from the mean*. Each number would be one additional descriptor. The five averages for the first five degrees are shown in table 7.2.

This is the approach, then, that can provide us with an infinite set of descriptive numbers that define a particular RV. Although it is far from obvious, a *given family of such descriptors specifies a probability distribution uniquely*; conversely, *a given probability distribution will generate a unique infinite set of such descriptors*. The mathematical methodology that analyzes and elucidates the formal relationships between a probabiliy distribution and its corresponding family of descriptors is quite advanced and beyond our scope (see Freeman, 1963, pp. 32-33).

We recall that the mean was called, equivalently, an expected value, or a moment. The averages of the various powers of the deviations from the mean are also referred to as expected values and moments. The terminology is now modified appropriately, however, to reflect that, first, we are speaking about *deviations from the mean* (and not simple outcome values), and second, that we are calculating averages of numbers that have been raised to some *power* (not to the first degree). Thus, the average of the squares is called "the expected value of the squares of the deviations from the mean," or, "the second moment about the mean"; similarly, the average of the cubes is called "the expected value of the third power (or the cube, the third degree) of the deviations about the mean," or, "the third moment about the mean"; the terminology for the other, higher moments follows in the obvious fashion.

We shall next move from this first conceptualization of a higher moment about the mean as an average calculated from a limited set of data (table 7.2) to a definition based solely on a probability function. To accomplish this reconceptualization, we rely on a series of steps very similar to those performed in transforming the first expression for the mean, the simple average specified in (7.1), into the redefinition that relied only on a probability function, not data, i.e., (7.5). For example, to show that the second moment about the mean can be defined solely in terms of information contained in an RV, we first write the expression for that descriptor in a form analogous to (7.1); we would specify that moment as an average of the squares of 21 deviations about the mean. Next, we would perform a series of simple manipulations of that sum, essentially repeating the arithmetical procedures exemplified by (7.2) through (7.4). Last, we would invoke the principle of equivalence, and write the expression for the second moment about the mean in a form that parallels (7.5):

$$\begin{aligned}&\{[(-2) - (1\tfrac{1}{3})]^2 \times p(-2)\} + \{[(-1) - (1\tfrac{1}{3})]^2 \times p(-1)\}\\ &+ \{[(0) - (1\tfrac{1}{3})]^2 \times p(0)\} + \{[(1) - (1\tfrac{1}{3})]^2 \times p(1)\}\\ &+ \{[(2) - (1\tfrac{1}{3})]^2 \times p(2)\} + \{[(3) - (1\tfrac{1}{3})]^2 \times p(3)\}. \end{aligned} \tag{7.6}$$

Parallel expressions could be developed for any one of the other higher moments about the mean. In each case, the descriptor would be specified as a sum of six product terms. The only difference between (7.6) and the expression for any of the other higher moments is the power or degree to which the deviations about the mean are raised in a given instance. For the second moment, each of the six deviations about the mean in (7.6) was raised to the second power; for the third moment, they would each be raised to the third power, and so on.

We can apply this general procedure to other discrete RVs, of course. In a given instance, we would merely use the appropriate outcome values and assigned probabilities and form sums such as those in (7.5) and (7.6). For a given discrete RV, the mean would be calculated from a sum of terms according to the procedure illustrated in (7.5); each term would be of the form [(outcome value)] $\times$ p(outcome value). Any one of the higher moments would be calculated by means of an equation similar to (7.6). Each term in the sum would be of the form [(outcome value) $-$ (mean)]^n $\times$ p(outcome value), where n would be the degree of the specified moment; for the second moment, n would be 2, for the third, 3, and so on. One other characteristic should be noted. For a given pf, the *number* of terms in the sum used to compute any one of the moments would be equal to the *number of outcome values* in the potential set. In our example, there were six possible outcome values in the potential outcome of the pf in figure 7.1; hence, there are six terms in (7.5) and (7.6).

We have now achieved the specification of each member of the family of moments solely in terms of a probability function. This provides the first of two equivalent approaches to defining these members of the descriptor family. The other, second approach is by way of *long-term averages*, as before. The approach parallels exactly that used earlier to define μ in terms of a long-term average. Therefore, we shall not repeat the details. The approach should be obvious. Were one to perform many repeated observations with the pf shown in figure 7.1 and consequently obtain many more outcomes and associated deviations from the mean, one would obtain tabulations similar to tables 7.1 and 7.2. The only difference would be that one would have hundreds or thousands of entries rather than, as previously, 21. These data would provide the basis for a set of long-term averages, one average for each of the moments. In the long run, for very many repeated observations, the numerical values obtained in this fashion would agree with those obtained by procedures such as (7.5) or (7.6).

The preceding discussions have relied on intuitive, informal arguments, in accordance with our usual practice. The conclusions, however, can be reached also by more formal procedures, and are valid. For a given discrete RV, each member of the family of moments can be defined in terms of an expression that invokes only information contained in that probability function; alternatively and equivalently, each descriptor can also be conceptualized as a particular long-term average, an average of very many—indeed, infinitely many—actual outcomes obtained from repeated trials. The two approaches lead to the same set of descriptors for a given probability function.

Some Special Descriptors

We have said that one can calculate various averages and use these in a family of numbers that describe an RV uniquely and completely. Each one of this infinite number of descriptors, each average, provides partial mathematical information about a given probability distribution. For example, we have learned that the first descriptor in this family, the simple average or mean, provides important partial information about a pf: it gives the "center of mass" of that probability distribution (as well as other information yet to be presented).

Similarly, the second descriptor, the second moment about the mean, is highly important in statistical work. We learned in chapter 6 that it has a special name, *variance*. The descriptor is represented by a special symbol, σ^2, the Greek letter sigma, squared. The variance provides a measure of the degree to which a probability distribution is spread or "dispersed" about its mean. In general, the larger the variance, the greater the dispersion.

In statistics, the *positive square root of the variance* also plays an important role. Accordingly, it, too, is given a special name, *the standard deviation*, and a special symbol, σ (the Greek letter sigma). We shall examine these special quantities in a number of different contexts and in considerable detail in later sections of this book.

Errors and Criteria

Let us return to table 7.1. We presumably performed 21 trials and obtained the 21 actual outcomes listed in that table. Let us now assume that before performing each trial, we would have made a guess or prediction concerning the anticipated actual outcome value. We shall consider two different criteria that lead to two different "best guesses." First, suppose that we would wish to guess the number that will result in the greatest number of correct guesses in a given set of repeated trials. What number should we choose? We should like to choose that number which we would expect to appear most often. Which outcome value should appear most frequently in a series of repeated trials? "Most frequent" implies "greatest relative frequency," which in turn implies "highest probability," as we should recognize from previous discussions. Accordingly, for our particular example, we should each time choose the value 3. If we examine figure 7.1, we see that this is the outcome value that has the largest assigned probability.

The outcome value associated with the highest assigned frequency in a pf is called the *mode*; it represents the best guess if our goal is to be *precisely correct* as often as possible in a given series of repeated trials. In our example, the data listed in table 7.1 show that had we used the mode, 3, as our guess, we should have been correct 6 times out of 21 trials—we would have obtained a greater number of correct guesses using that outcome value than any other.

The mode is that number which gives the greatest number of correct guesses, but we may have a different goal or criterion in mind. We might not wish to be strictly correct, most frequently; rather, we may instead seek to minimize our mistakes in some other fashion. "Mistakes" imply errors, and we therefore must define that term more closely.

The error associated with each trial can be defined in various ways. One of the these defines the *signed error*, the *algebraic difference* between the *actual obtained outcome* and our *guessed value*: (actual obtained value) − (guessed value). For example, had we predicted the value 3 and obtained the actual outcome value 1, the signed error would be [(1) − (3)], or −2 for that particular trial. Thus, in general, if an actual outcome is greater than the prediction, the error will have a positive sign; if the actual outcome is smaller than the prediction, the error will have a negative sign; and, if the prediction is correct, the error is zero.

In our hypothetical set of repeated trials, then, 21 observations and accompanying predictions will generate 21 associated signed errors. Suppose we would wish to minimize the average of these errors. What number should we predict on each trial? The answer is the mean, μ. In our example, had we guessed $1\frac{1}{3}$ on each trial, we should have obtained the 21 signed errors shown in table 7.3—one error for each trial. We see that the average of these errors is 0.[1] The mean is the best number to predict if we wish to minimize the average signed error in a series of repeated observations; we have demonstrated this only informally, by way of a specific example, but the conclusion is generally valid.

[1]The average of these 21 signed error terms is 0 because, in the present example, we had arranged the average of the hypothetical data in table 7.3 to have the same value as the mean of the RV that presumably had generated that set of actual outcome values. This is an artificial situation that one would hardly ever encounter in an actual experiment. Usually the average of a set of data obtained by repeated trials of an RV will be different from the mean of that RV. (This is a matter we shall consider in detail in parts IV and V.) Consequently, the average of a set of signed error terms computed from a set of data will seldom if ever be exactly 0, if we use the RV mean as our predicted value.

Table 7.3

Signed errors

Trial no.	o.v.	Error	Trial no.	o.v.	Error	Trial no.	o.v.	Error
1	2	2/3	8	1	−1/3	15	0	−4/3
2	0	−4/3	9	3	5/3	16	2	2/3
3	2	2/3	10	−2	−10/3	17	1	−1/3
4	1	−1/3	11	3	5/3	18	3	5/3
5	−1	−7/3	12	2	2/3	19	1	−1/3
6	3	5/3	13	−1	−7/3	20	0	−4/3
7	3	5/3	14	3	5/3	21	2	2/3

This, then, is a third approach or definition that leads to the particular outcome value of a pf, the mean μ. We had previously explored an approach that specified the mean by an expression based on the pf—exemplified by (7.5)—and an approach based on the concept of the long-term average. We now see that the same quantity, the mean μ, can be defined in yet another way, in terms of a "best guess" criterion.

One point mentioned in chapter 6 may now assume more meaning. I mentioned that a prediction that is best according to one criterion may be a very poor guess according to another. We now have a suggestive example. If our goal would be to be absolutely correct as frequently as possible, the mean, a "best guess" according to one criterion, might be a very poor guess indeed. In our particular illustrative example, we should not be correct even once in a series of trials were we to guess the mean, since it is not even in our discrete potential outcome. Alternatively, if we wanted to guess a number that would minimize the average signed error in a number of repeated trials, the mode, a "best guess" according to another criterion, might in general be a very poor guess, although I have not demonstrated this in the discussion.

There are, as usual, many questions left unanswered and many issues that have been incompletely discussed. We shall, however, return to much of the material introduced in this chapter. Let us now consider the modifications in the descriptive methodology that are required as we move from the discrete to the continuous case.

PROBLEMS

7.1 Discuss the three approaches to defining the mean of a probability function.

7.2 Select any five numbers, and compute their mean. Form the five deviations from the mean. Construct the average of these five deviations, and analyze it in order to discover why it must be 0.

7.3 Generalize the result of problem 7.2 in two ways, using an algebraic approach. First, extend the analysis from five specific to *any* five numbers. [Hint: after you have represented the deviations and their average algebraically, regroup the terms in the sum that defines that average.] Second, extend the analysis from the set of any five numbers to a set of any N numbers, where N is any positive integer or whole number. [If necessary, consult Hays, 1973, p. 222.]

7.5 In general, how many descriptors from the family of moments would be required to uniquely specify a pf?

7.6 What can you say in general about the algebraic signs of the members of the family of moments? [Hint: examine table 7.2.] What would you say if someone claimed that the variance of an RV was -2.4?

7.7 Supply the intervening steps that lead from the average of 21 squares of the deviations about the mean (the numbers in column 3 of table 7.2) to the average expressed in (7.6). What is the principal conceptual difference between the beginning and final expression?

7.8 What does it mean if the variance of an RV is 0? [Hint: how can a sum of terms such as those in (7.6) be 0?]

7.9 One RV has a mean $\mu_1 = 20$ and a variance $\sigma^2_1 = 36$, while another RV has a mean $\mu_2 = -10$ and a variance $\sigma^2_2 = 100$. Discuss how these two pfs differ in central tendency and dispersion; make a rough sketch of two such RVs.

7.10 The standard deviation of a certain RV is 7.1. What is the variance of that RV?

7.11 The expression for computing the third moment about the mean is an expression analogous to (7.6). For the pf shown in figure 7.1 and specified in table 7.1, construct that expression, and calculate the descriptor. Use table 7.2 to check your answer.

CHAPTER 8

Description: Continuous Random Variables

We will conduct the discussion of descriptive methods for continuous RVs in terms of the probability distribution shown in figure 8.1. That pdf has a triangular profile that resembles the envelope of the pf used as the illustrative example in chapter 7 (fig. 7.1). We shall begin again by examining the concept of the mean.

FIGURE 8.1 A triangular pdf

Table 8.1

Hypothetical data: 21 trials with the pdf in figure 8.1

Trial no.	o.v.	Trial no.	o.v.	Trial no.	o.v.
1	2.64 . . .	8	1.41	15	−0.41
2	−2.51	9	0.31	16	2.78
3	0.04	10	2.47	17	1.69
4	−0.55	11	−0.33	18	2.37
5	−1.23	12	2.04	19	−1.72
6	2.83	13	1.37	20	1.80
7	1.74	14	0.68	21	0.71

The Mean

Let us assume, as we did in chapter 7, that we had performed 21 repeated trials. The hypothetical data are shown in table 8.1. We calculate the mean of these 21 data points as usual by forming the appropriate quotient:

$$\frac{\begin{array}{l}(2.64) + (-2.51) + (0.04) + (-0.55) + (-1.23) + (2.83) + (1.74) \\ + (1.41) + (0.31) + (2.47) + (-0.33) + (2.04) + (1.37) + (0.68) \\ + (-0.41) + (2.78) + (1.69) + (2.37) + (-1.72) + (1.80) + (0.71)\end{array}}{21}. \tag{8.1}$$

Next we should like to shift from the arithmetical concept of the mean as an average of a set of data to a more general, abstract concept of the mean as an average or expected value of an RV. We previously presented this kind of a conceptual shift in some detail in reference to a discrete RV (chap. 7). In that chapter, we accomplished our goal by a series of arithmetical manipulations—the steps leading from (7.1) to (7.5). By these steps, we transformed a simple average of actual outcome values to a more general expression that pertained to a mean of a probability distribution, the mean of an RV. Similarly, we would like to proceed from the mean of the 21 actual outcome values of a continuous RV, table 8.1 and (8.1), to an expression for the mean of an entire pdf. We would like to express that mean of an RV in terms of a general expression similar to (7.5). We wish to specify the mean of a pdf in terms of a potential outcome set and probability density values.

If we had a discrete RV, the next step would be to assemble like outcome values, as in (7.2). Now, however, we cannot do this. We have a spinner rather than a roulette wheel and the potential outcome set is not confined to a particular set of discrete values. Consequently, we would hardly ever obtain exactly the same outcome value even twice in a series of trials. This is illustrated in our hypothetical data. We see that in table 8.1, there are no identical values to be found among the 21 actual outcomes. Hence, there are no "like" terms to be grouped; we cannot take the step that would parallel the manipulations from (7.1) to (7.2).

There is yet another difference between the situation in chapter

7 and our present situation. In the course of demonstrating in chapter 7 that a moment could be computed directly from a probability distribution (rather than from a set of data), we viewed relative frequencies as probabilities; the principle of equivalence was invoked to move from (7.4) to (7.5). We cannot follow this procedure now, since we are dealing with a pdf, and thus with probability densities rather than probabilities. (The probability of obtaining any one outcome value is now 0; see chap. 5.) It seems that we cannot proceed further by simply following an approach paralleling that used in chapter 7. Apparently, an arithmetical average of 21 actual outcome values can no longer serve as the starting point from which the concept of a mean of a pdf could be developed.

How should we proceed? In certain situations, one can use calculus to find the mean and higher moments of an RV. There are many cases, however, where these methods are difficult to apply for one reason or another. At any rate, since calculus is outside our scope, we must seek an alternative approach. Chapter 7 holds a clue: we already know how to calculate the mean or any of the higher moments about the mean for a discrete RV—for a probability function. Therefore, if we were able to find a pf that would somehow be a suitable substitute for the pdf in figure 8.1, we could then proceed according to the methods introduced in chapter 7, and calculate any descriptor in the family of moments. Our aim, then, is to convert the "spinner" in figure 8.1 to an "equivalent" roulette wheel; we would like these two probability distributions to be equivalent in the sense that corresponding pairs of descriptors would have similar numerical values. For example, we would like the mean of the "equivalent" roulette wheel to have approximately the same value as the mean of the spinner.

What we shall do, roughly, is to reverse the steps we had followed in chapter 5 when we moved from a roulette wheel to a spinner. In that procedure, we "diluted" probabilities assigned to a limited number of outcome values into probability density values assigned to infinitely many outcome values in the same outcome axis span. Now we shall "coalesce" or "condense" probability density values assigned to infinitely many outcomes between -3 and $+3$ into a limited number of probability values assigned to a correspondingly limited number of outcome values in that same outcome axis region.

If we wish to construct a roulette wheel, we shall need to decide how many slots or outcome values our equivalent pf is to contain. In actual practice, we should probably choose a pf that has very many—perhaps thousands—of outcome values between −3 and +3. The use of many slots would provide a better approximation to a pdf. For our illustrative example, however, we shall select a wheel with only a relatively few actual outcome values so that the arithmetical calculations do not become burdensome. Let us, then, choose to approximate the pdf in figure 8.1 with a 12-slot roulette wheel, i.e., with a probability function that has 12 actual outcome values and a potential outcome span from approximately −3 to +3.

Since we are constructing a pf, we need to specify pairs of outcome values and associated probabilities (see chap. 4). We shall construct the desired pf in four steps. First, we shall *divide the outcome range* from −3 to +3 into 12 contiguous regions. We shall select 12 equal segments; each will span 0.5 outcome axis units.

The second step will be to *find the probability* assigned to these regions by the probability density function in figure 8.1. We can apply the methods used in chapter 5, since the areas under the curve have a simple geometry and are easy to calculate by elementary methods. The results are presented in table 8.2. We now have 12 probability values.

The third step is to *replace the continuous potential outcome* of figure 8.1 by a suitable discrete potential outcome. We shall accomplish this step by selecting *one* "reasonable" outcome value *within each strip* to represent the outcome range of that strip. What outcome number should we select to represent a given segment, a specific range of outcome values? For example, consider the first of the 12 strips, the strip containing the outcome axis segment from −3.0 to −2.5. We are attempting to replace that outcome region of the spinner by one roulette wheel slot, but what numerical label should we give that slot? For the calculations that we are about to perform, the particular choice will not make a great deal of difference. It will not affect our approximation

Table 8.2

Probabilities in 12 regions of a pdf

Outcome region		Probability in region
from	to	
−3.0	−2.5	1/144
−2.5	−2.0	3/144
−2.0	−1.5	5/144
−1.5	−1.0	7/144
−1.0	−0.5	9/144
−0.5	0.0	11/144
0.0	0.5	13/144
0.5	1.0	15/144
1.0	1.5	17/144
1.5	2.0	19/144
2.0	2.5	21/144
2.5	3.0	23/144

Table 8.3

Representative outcome values for 12 regions of a pdf

Outcome region		Representative outcome value
from	to	
−3.0	−2.5	−2.75
−2.5	−2.0	−2.25
−2.0	−1.5	−1.75
−1.5	−0.5	−0.75
−0.5	0.0	−0.25
0.0	0.5	0.25
0.5	1.0	0.75
1.0	1.5	1.25
1.5	2.0	1.75
2.0	2.5	2.25
2.5	3.0	2.75

significantly, although some choices would be better than others. Intuitively, we might expect that the midpoint of each outcome segment would be a reasonable value to choose for the "equivalent" slot value. Accordingly, we shall assign an outcome value of -2.75 to the first region, a value of -2.25 to the second, and so on. These 12 midpoint values are shown in table 8.3. We now have 12 slot labels, 12 discrete outcomes, in the range from -3 to $+3$. We have, in effect, converted the continuous potential outcome shown in figure 8.1 to the discrete potential outcome shown in table 8.3.

The fourth and last step is obvious. We shall *assign the probabilities* of the 12 outcome axis regions (table 8.2) to the corresponding 12 outcome values that represent those regions (table 8.3). By assigning probability values to outcome values, we are constructing a probability function, of course. That pf is defined in table 8.4 and illustrated in figure 8.2.

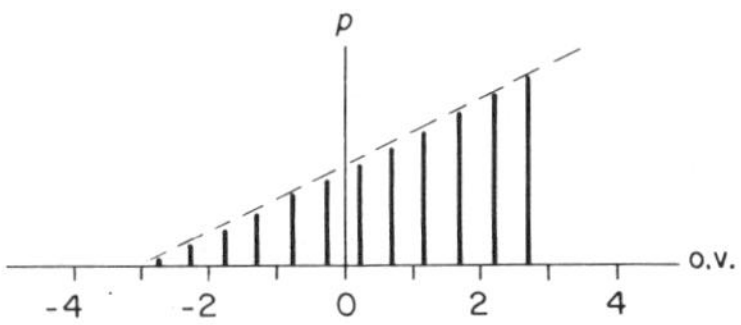

FIGURE 8.2 An equivalent pf

Table 8.4

An equivalent probability function

Outcome value	Assigned probability value
−2.75	1/144
−2.25	3/144
−1.75	5/144
−1.25	7/144
−0.75	9/144
−0.25	11/144
0.25	13/144
0.75	15/144
1.25	17/144
1.75	19/144
2.25	21/144
2.75	23/144

The moments of the pf that we have just constructed approximate the corresponding set of moments of the pdf in figure 8.1, although we shall not prove that equivalence. We can demonstrate it for the first two descriptors in the family of moments, however. By using the methods developed in chapter 7—see (7.5) and (7.6)—we find that the mean and variance of our pf are, approximately, 0.993 and 1.999, respectively. Let us see how close our approximations are. In this particular example, one can calculate the mean and variance of the pdf in figure 8.1 exactly by calculus. These are, respectively, precisely 1, and 2. We see that the approximations obtained by using our equivalent pf are quite good, at least for these first two in the family of moments.

We approximated the pdf in figure 8.1 by a 12-outcome pf. Had we selected some other comparable discrete RV, for example, a pf with 50 discrete values in the potential outcome range between -3 and $+3$, the details of the constructed pf would have differed from those of the pf specified in table 8.4; the basic approach, however, would have remained the same, regardless of the details of the roulette wheel. We should have followed the same four basic steps.

The family of expected values is an example of a family of *parameters*. We shall next examine the meaning of that important statistical term.

Parameters

A parameter is a number that furnishes either partial or complete information about the characteristics of a given mathematical entity such as a function or geometrical figure. For example, for a circle, the radius is a parameter; if we specify that value, we fully define a particular shape. For an ellipse, the two parameters that specify its shape are the lengths of the major and minor axes.[1]

There are two principal ideas concerning parameters that will be important to us. The first is that a parameter (or a set of parameters) selects one particular member from a set of similar entities. A particular radius value, for example, identifies one

[1] We are ignoring the specification of either the location or the orientation of a figure in the plane.

specific circle out of the whole family of circles; two specific numbers that specify a major and minor axis identify or select one particular ellipse from the family of all the possible ellipses, etc.

The second idea is that different categories of mathematical entities will require different numbers of parameters to define them fully. The two geometrical examples have provided a simple illustration. A circle required one number to specify it, while an ellipse required two.

A number of issues are related to these basic considerations, and we will briefly examine two of these. One concerns the matter of a partial specification of a mathematical situation. For example, let us reconsider the ellipse. We know that we need two numbers to fully define a specific elliptical shape. Suppose we were to furnish only one of these values, say, the length of the minor axis. What would that imply? The situation is illustrated in figure 8.3. Several ellipses are shown. One set consists of ellipses that all have the same minor axis; the other ellipses, shown by dotted lines, have minor axes of differing lengths. We see that by specifying only one parameter of the required two, we have selected a smaller from a larger family, i.e., one set of ellipses from the set of all possible ellipses. We might say that a partial specification has restricted or constrained the family, but has not achieved full specification.

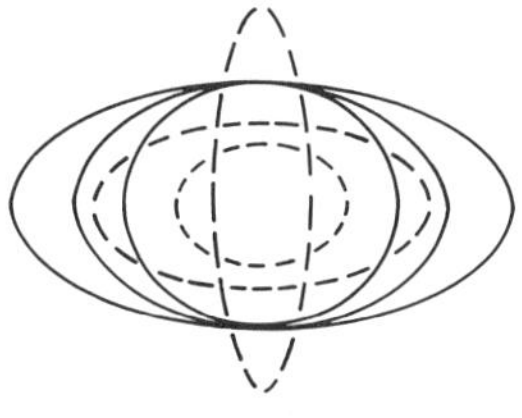

FIGURE 8.3 A family of ellipses

That conclusion is generally true. If a mathematical entity requires a certain number of parameters, for example, 20, to fully identify one specific member out of a family of related entities, then furnishing less than these 20 numbers will result in a specification of a "subfamily"—a family within the original family. In that respect, the example of the ellipses, although simple, is representative of that situation. By providing less than the required number of parameters, one partially defines an entity. I have alluded to this matter in the previous discussions concerning the mean; I noted that although many probability distributions could have the same mean, that value does provide some information, partial as it may be. In other words, by giving the mean of probability distribution, one narrows the range of options. One restricts the probability distribution to a subfamily, but in general, by specifying only the mean, one does not fully identify one particular, specific, probability distribution.

A second issue is closely related to the preceding considerations. It concerns the matter of how many descriptors or parameters would be required to uniquely specify one member of a particular family. Our previous examples illustrated this point; we saw that one kind of an entity, a circle, could be defined by a single number, whereas another kind of an entity, an ellipse, required two parameters. In statistics, different kinds of probability distributions will, in general, require a different number of parameters to fully define one specific member. Some families of probability distributions will require only one parameter to fully specify a member, while others will require very many parameters—perhaps an infinite number.

We have already encountered one basic set of statistical parameters, the moments. These specify a probability distribution uniquely. In many instances, however, they provide a kind of mathematical overkill. While one can always use this infinite set to describe a probability distribution, much simpler descriptions may be available for some particular types of distribution. An analogy can be drawn with a circle. We know that we can fully specify a circle by giving one number, the radius. We can, however, also specify a circle by defining an infinite number of points, its circumference. While this latter specification does define a circle uniquely, the former specification (the radius) is equally adequate and certainly much simpler. If we use the radius to define a circle, we need to specify only one parameter; if we choose to define the circle by defining all the points on its circumference, we shall require an infinite number of parameters. Similarly, for many kinds of probability distribution, there will be simpler ways of defining these parametrically than by using the full set of the infinite number of moments. We shall enlarge on the concepts associated with parameters when we examine specific probability distributions in parts IV and V.

Error Criteria

There are two descriptors that are frequently used in statistics that do not belong to the family of expected values. One of these is the *mode*, a descriptor that we have already met in chapter 7, and the other is the *median*. We will conclude our introduction to descriptive statistics by briefly examining these two descriptors in the context of "best guess" criteria. We had previously defined the mode as that outcome value that is the best guess in the sense of providing the greatest number of *exactly correct* guesses in a given number of repeated trials. We know, however, that for a continuous RV we are very unlikely ever to obtain the exact value we might guess prior to a trial, no matter what value we would choose. That is implied by the fact that the probability (and hence, the relative frequency and frequency) of any one outcome value for a continuous RV is 0 (see chap. 5). For a continuous RV we therefore cannot define the mode in exactly the same way as for a discrete RV. It can no longer be the value that we would expect to obtain most frequently, since we would seldom expect to obtain any one particular, specified outcome value even once in a series of trials. We will define the mode of a continuous RV as that outcome value that corresponds to the peak, the highest probability density, of a given continuous RV. There may be more than one peak in a pdf; in that case, an RV is called multimodal (bimodal if there are two peaks, etc.). Figure 8.4 shows several pdfs and their respective modes.

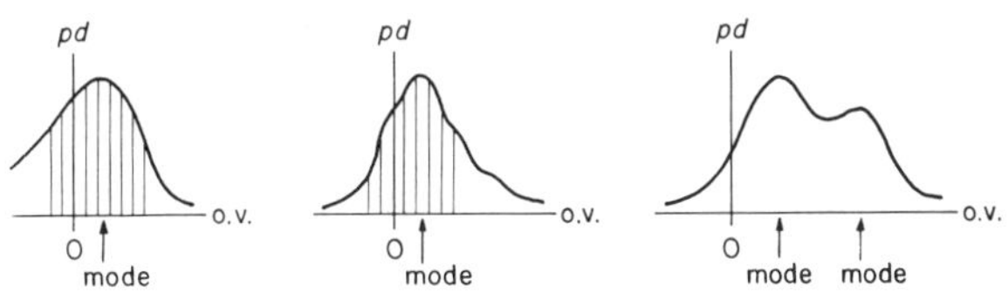

FIGURE 8.4 Modes

The mode now can be understood in terms of a best guess criterion. Let us divide a potential outcome set into many narrow segments of equal widths. For a unimodal pdf, the mode is the outcome value that will always lie within the strip that has the highest associated probability—within the tallest strip (see fig. 8.4). In a given number of repeated trials, a greater number of actual outcome values will probably lie within the strip containing the mode than within any other comparable strip. This concept can be readily extended to multimodal RVs.

We previously defined the mean in several ways (chap. 7). One of these definitions was couched in terms of a particular error criterion: the mean was defined as that outcome value that minimized the average *signed* error in the long run. (That definition continues to be valid for a continuous RV mean as well.) There is a closely related error criterion that leads to a slightly different descriptor, the *median*. The median is that outcome value that will minimize the average *unsigned* error—the average absolute value of the error—in the long run.[2] Although the median can be defined on the basis of that best guess criterion, it can equivalently be defined in terms of a probability distribution. In particular, the median is also that outcome value that divides the potential outcome region of a probability distribution into two equiprobable segments. Defined in this way, the median is the outcome value that divides the total area under the curve into two regions that each have an assigned probability value of 0.5. We may infer from the principle of equivalence that in a series of repeated trials, we should expect about half of the actual outcome values generated by those trials to lie on one side of the median, and half on the other side. For instance, if the median of an RV is the outcome value 9.5, and if we perform 100 repeated trials of that RV, we should expect about 50 outcome values to be smaller, and about 50 larger, than 9.5. (That property is *not* a characteristic of the mean. In general, unless an RV happens to be symmetrical,

[2]The absolute value of a number is the value that number has if we ignore its algebraic sign (plus or minus). It is represented by placing the number between vertical bars. Somewhat more formally: if a is a positive number, then $|a| = a$, and $|-a| = a$.

the mean does *not* divide the potential outcome of an RV into two equiprobable segments.)

It can be shown that the quantity defined in this probabilistic fashion and the quantity defined according to the previously stated "unsigned" error criterion both are the same parameter, the median (see Freeman, 1963, p. 34, problem 3.2, and p. 353).

We now have introduced a number of concepts and methods that are relevant to descriptive statistics. Next, we shall begin to consider experimental matters, issues that go beyond the strictly formal, mathematical RV characteristics that we have been considering to this point.

PROBLEMS

8.1 In a symmetrical pdf, can one identify the mean without performing any calculations? The median? Why, or why not?

8.2 What is the minimum number of parameters required to define a square? A triangle? A sphere?

8.3 Find the mean and the variance of the uniform pdf shown in figure 5.3. Use some reasonable number of outcome axis segments—say, 20—to construct an "equivalent" pf, and then use the methods developed in chapter 7.

8.4 Suppose that we know a pdf is uniform, and that it has a probability density value of 0.10 throughout its potential outcome range.

(a) Does that information uniquely define the RV? Why, or why not?

(b) Does that information uniquely define μ?

(c) Does that information uniquely define σ^2?
[Hint: remember that μ describes the central tendency; and σ, the dispersion about the mean.]

8.5 Consider two uniform RVs that have probability density values of 0.10 and 0.20, respectively, in their potential outcome range. What do you suppose will be the relationships between the two variances? Verify your guess by constructing two such RVs, computing their variances, and comparing these two parameter values (see problem 8.3).

8.6 Chapter 7 discussed the analogies between the mean of a probability distribution and the balance point of a system of masses. Use these analogies to explain why the mean of an RV does not necessarily divide the potential outcome into two equiprobable outcome axis regions. [Hint: In a physical system, what would correspond to such an equiprobable division?]

8.7 [Difficult.] We know that if a pdf is symmetrical, the mean and the median are both located at the axis of symmetry and therefore are equal to one another (see problem 8.1). Is the converse true? That is, if the mean and the median of a pdf have the same outcome value, is that pdf necessarily symmetrical?

PART III

The Origins of Random Variables

CHAPTER 9

Experiments

In the first two parts the basic concepts of the statistical RV framework were introduced in bold relief; real-world experimental issues that were not directly relevant to the essentials of that framework were set aside so that we would not be distracted from conceptual fundamentals. Accordingly, we identified and isolated for discussion the two major formal ingredients of RVs, probability and outcome, and constructed the RV concepts from these central constituents. As we began to consider descriptive statistics, we retained our focus on RVs *qua* RVs. Scarcely any reference was made to actual experimental issues other than to the "bare bones" models of the roulette wheel and the spinner.

Now, in order to proceed to other statistical topics, we must start to consider real experiments, at least to some extent. The introduction of additional perspectives and subject matter will necessarily introduce complexities that may tend to cloud and perhaps confuse the basic framework that was constructed in the preceding parts. In spite of their apparent diversity and complexity, all of the new concepts and issues will remain grounded in an RV framework; that basic conceptual system will continue to furnish the foundation and context for these other issues. It therefore remains vitally important to keep the essentials of the preceding material firmly in mind. We must continue to hold on grimly to the fact that probability distributions are functions that pair probabilistic and outcome values—*two* sets of values or numbers that must always be in the picture when a situation is conceptualized in terms of an RV framework. With these cautionary remarks, let us turn to experiments.

Experimentation is a wide subject that touches on many diverse issues. We shall mostly focus on certain central procedures that remain constant across a wide variety of experiments. In order to set these procedures into proper perspective, let us first take a panoramic view of the experimental process.

That process can be divided into four phases: preexperimental, preparatory, experimental (in the "narrow" sense), and postexperimental. The preexperimental phase can involve a very wide variety of concerns, ranging from the setting of priorities to questions of ethics and funding support. A central feature of this early phase is the definition of the *scientific question* (to be contrasted with experimental or statistical questions, as we shall presently see) that is to be experimentally investigated. Scientific questions might ask, for example, is a particular hormone implicated in schizophrenia; is one type of programmed intruction more effective than another; or are there personality differences between artists and scientists?

The second, preparatory phase is largely a planning phase. First, a scientific question must be cast into a suitable experimental mold. It must be translated into a specific, experimentally appropriate question (see Kirk [1972, pp. 127-130, 173-174, 177-185] for the distinctions between scientific and statistical questions). Thus, for the three previously mentioned illustrative scientific questions, one would construct corresponding experimental counterparts such as, will experimental animals injected with hormone X show disordered behavior on a learning task; will subjects taught by programmed instruction method Y achieve higher test scores than those by method Z; or are the Rorschach responses of the faculty members of a fine arts department different from those in physics, chemistry, and engineering departments? Subsequently, many other aspects of the experimental procedure must be selected, defined, organized, and integrated into an overall experimental plan. That plan will specify a set of experimental procedures—for example, how subjects are to be selected; what kinds of experimental *treatments* or *factors* are to be administered (kinds of hormones, diets, methods of instruction, etc.); what quantities or levels of these treatments are to be administered (how much of the hormone, etc.); how the results of these treatments are to be observed or measured, and the like. In addition, the overall plan will specify the mathematical aspects of the experiment—for example, how treatments and observations will be organized logically (Campbell and Stanley, 1963); how much data to gather; how these data are to be manipulated and processed; or the kinds of mathematical procedures that are to be used to analyze the results. Ideally, all facets of the general experimental design should interact in a manner that will produce a meaningful experiment whose conclusions are supported by sound methodological practice.

In the next phase, the experiment proper is performed. Data are acquired according to the methods, procedures, and plans developed in the preceding phase. These data are appropriately manipulated, reduced, and mathematically analyzed. One interprets the results of these analyses, and draws inferences about the experimental questions.

Finally, in the postexperimental phase, the answers to experimental questions are translated back into answers (or, usually, very partial answers) to the original, scientific question. The empirical implications of these answers are then worked out: appropriate decisions are made, appropriate actions implemented, etc.

Obviously, the entire process is complex (see Collateral Reading at end of part IV). Much of it is also largely beyond the scope of an introduction to statistics. As I have already mentioned, for our purposes we shall focus mainly on selected aspects that are of immediate relevance to our mathematical subject matter. Specifically, we shall attend primarily to certain mathematically specifiable features that are almost invariably present in the third phase, the experiment proper.

These features concern the raw, numerical data; their mathematical manipulation or reduction; the results and interpretations of these reductions; and the interrelationships between these three mathematical facets of the experimental process. In the next chapter, we shall begin to see what these features are, and it should come as no surprise that they will be conceptualized within an RV framework.

CHAPTER 10

Empirically Obtained Data and Their Mathematical Reduction

We are about to consider the principal ways in which experimental studies generate RVs. The discussion will necessarily remain at a general level, leaving questions unanswered and details unclarified. These unsettled issues will be resolved gradually as we begin to study specific quantitative methods and concepts in parts IV and V.

For the present, we shall primarily be interested in acquiring some general ideas about the experimental genesis of RVs. Let us develop these ideas in the context of a specific, illustrative, hypothetical experiment. We shall hypothesize a study that, although simple, is not altogether unrealistic. Suppose that a research group is interested in the effects of nutrition on learning. The members of this group believe that certain types of dietary deficiencies found in one geographic region may to some extent account for the generally poor academic performance of students from that region. The researchers translate this speculation into the following experiment: 100 newborn rats will be divided into two equal experimental groups. One group is to be raised on a normal diet; and the other, on a diet that is deficient in the implicated nutrient. At some time, the experimenters will measure the performance of each rat on some suitable learning task, thus obtaining one measure, one number, for each of the 100 animals. That measure might be the time taken to learn a particular task, for example.

Thus far the experiment has generated 100 numbers. Next, the experimenters must evaluate their empirical results. They must determine whether their measurements do or do not lend support to their premise that diet affects performance. In a typical experiment, they will not be able to evaluate this premise merely by examining the set of experimentally acquired data in their original form. In that form, the numerical results usually are unwieldy, unstructured, and obscure. In order to put these data into a form in which they can be used to evaluate the experimental premises, the experimenters frequently use a standard approach. They manipulate their original set of numerical data by some mathematical procedure or operation and obtain one "representative" number. In other words, the original numbers are reduced to one numerical index that presumably summarizes the quantitative experimental results and expresses them in a meaningful, tractable fashion. This procedure is indicated in figure 10.1.

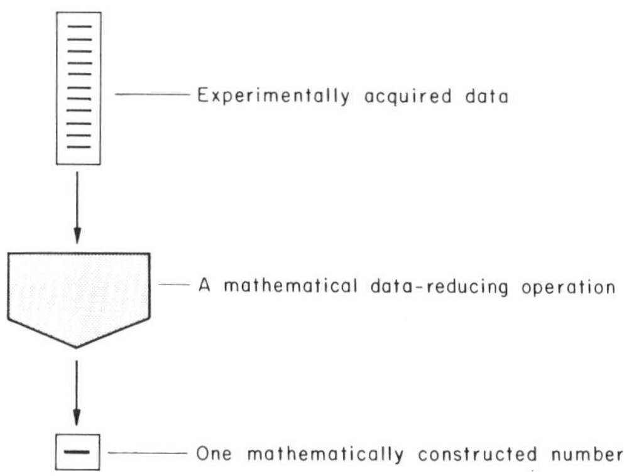

FIGURE 10.1 Reduction of data to a single number

We should not infer from that schematic representation, however, that there is only one mathematical procedure that can be used to reduce a set of empirical data to a single number. On the contrary; in general, the statistician has a wide variety of available data-reducing methods to choose from. One procedure is selected for a given experiment; different experimental circumstances and goals will dictate different choices, as we shall see in part IV.

Just how one selects a suitable mathematical procedure, how a single number is obtained, and how that single number is used to evaluate the results of an experiment are topics that will be considered in considerable detail later. The preceding discussion is only intended to illustrate two particular features of typical experiments or studies: (1) experimenters obtain a set of "raw" empirical data, e.g., 100 measures of the performance of rats on a learning task; and (2) these data are reduced or compressed to one "representative" number. Incidentally, these ideas were already broached in chapter 2. We are now ready to explore how these numbers can be conceptually placed within an RV framework.

RVs and Experimental Yields

We have seen that an experiment involves two kinds of numbers: (1) those obtained directly, by an experimental measurement or other similar procedure; and (2) those obtained indirectly, mathematically, from a set of the first kind of numbers. Numbers are numbers, of course, but we shall see increasingly clearly that the two kinds of numbers have very different theoretical and practical connotations.

In science, numbers, whether of the first or second kind, reveal little if any information until they have been placed within some conceptual framework. That is, numbers usually acquire scientific significance only when viewed within some theoretical system that makes them meaningful and useful.[1] In our situation, how should we view our numbers? Let us first consider the 100 empirically obtained numbers. In experiments such as those illustrated by our hypothetical study, the actual numbers obtained by measuring some attribute of a number of experimental subjects usually are unspecifiable in advance. Furthermore, we know that a given measurement procedure implies some particular potential outcome (see chap. 2). We thus have the two formal ingredients of an RV framework; we have numbers that can be conceptualized in terms of a potential outcome set, and associated uncertainty. Accordingly, from a mathematical point of view, it seems reasonable to treat these empirically acquired numbers as actual outcomes generated by 100 repeated trials of an RV "experiment."

[1]Placing data within a theoretical framework is such a commonplace step in scientific work that one tends to take it for granted, or even overlook it.

We shall do so. That is, we shall view these numbers as data generated by 100 turns of a roulette wheel or a spinner (see fig. 10.2). Which of these two kinds of devices we should choose for the mathematical framework in a given experiment would depend on the characteristics of the potential outcome set, and these would in turn depend on and reflect the formal features of a given measurement process, as explained in chap. 2. For the moment, let us be satisfied with understanding that numbers such as those actually obtained by a set of *empirical observations* are appropriately conceptualized, from a scientific point of view, as *repeated trials* of an RV situation.

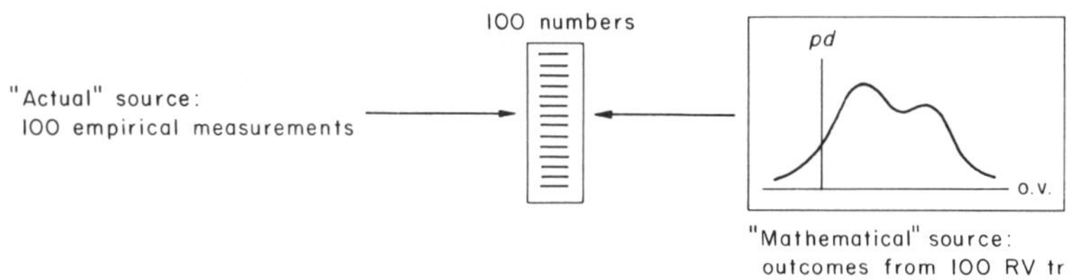

FIGURE 10.2 Two alternative conceptions of the source of empirical data

An RV that is mathematically conceptualized in conjunction with a given set of data, for example, an RV conceptualized as the "generator" of our 100 empirical measures, is sometimes referred to as an *underlying* RV. In any given experimental study, the RV conceptualized as underlying some set of numbers may be unknown, or partially known, or fully specifiable. That is not the issue. The point is that we may conceptualize *some* RV in conjunction with empirically obtained numbers. The reasons for, and the advantages gained by, this conceptual move will begin to emerge in chapter 12.

The same kind of conceptual approach can be applied to the second kind of a number, the number that in actuality is obtained by mathematically reducing a set of experimentally acquired numbers. This number, just as the numbers obtained by experimental measures, is unknown before an experiment is performed, and it, too, implies a potential outcome set (although we have not yet explored that aspect of reduced numbers). Therefore, it, too, can be viewed within an RV framework (see fig. 10.3). Specifically, we shall imagine that this kind of a number, a single number obtained by a data-reduction operation, is the number obtained by *one* turn of a roulette wheel or a spinner. For the purpose of mathematical analysis, then, this kind of a number will also be viewed as an outcome implicating an underlying RV.

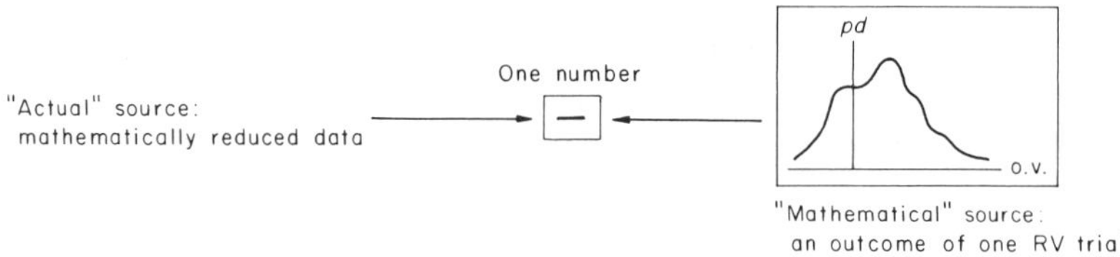

FIGURE 10.3 Two alternative conceptions of the source of a single reduced number

Thus far we have learned that both a set of 100 empirically obtained numbers and the one number mathematically derived from this set of empirical measures each can be conceptualized in terms of an underlying RV. As we shall begin to see in part IV, in a given experiment, these two different kinds of numbers will in general implicate two *different* underlying RVs.

Terminology

We have introduced the concept of an RV "underlying" a number or a set of numbers. In our framework and terminology we know that numbers "generated" by an RV situation are considered to be actual outcomes (part I). Thus, in identifying two different kinds of experimental sources of numbers we have also implied, correspondingly, two different kinds of actual outcomes. We shall now introduce a suitable terminology that reflects this distinction.

One of the two kinds of numbers that we have conceptualized as actual outcomes is the kind of a number that is acquired by direct experimental procedures, such as measurements or similar empirical observations. That kind of an actual outcome thus has close ties to experimental subjects. Traditionally, a set of such experimental subjects is conceptualized as a set of representative, sample entities drawn from a larger "population pool"; consequently, numbers obtained from such a set of experimental subjects are conceptualized as sample values representative of some attribute shared by a larger "underlying" population. For instance, according to that view, measurements such as those obtained in our hypothetical rat experiment would be conceptualized as sample measures or sample numerical values representative of the performance of a large "underlying" population. In other words, whereas we had been thinking about the 100 measures in mathematical terms as actual outcomes obtained by repeated trials involving an "underlying" RV, the more traditional approach, especially in elementary work, conceptualizes these kinds of numbers as sample values drawn from a population pool. That latter conceptualization implies, essentially, a lottery model—one draws numbers out of a hat, as it were. Thus, in this latter view, the "underlying" population plays the mathematical role, more or less, that we are assigning to an "underlying" RV (Hays, 1973, p. 261).

At any rate, since empirically obtained numbers and their mathematically conceptualized RV origins are so closely tied to the concept of an experimental population, we shall call an actual outcome that is this kind of a number a *population actual outcome* and, correspondingly, the RV that underlies these kinds of numbers a *population RV* or *population probability distribution*. We shall frequently use a subscript notation for these kinds of entities, identifying them as actual outcomes_P, RV_P, probability $\text{distribution}_\text{P}$, pf_P, or pdf_P.

In the more traditional, standard terminology, actual outcomes_P are called *sample values*, for the reasons mentioned above.

In figure 10.2, each of the 100 numbers is an actual outcome_P or a sample value; the underlying probability distribution is an RV_P (in this illustrative example, a pdf_P).

We still need to provide a similar suitable terminology for the second type of numbers, those obtained from a set of population actual outcomes by reducing these numbers mathematically to a single summarizing quantity. The mathematical origins of this kind of a number suggest that since it is indirectly obtained, that is, mathematically synthesized from data and in that sense derivative, it could appropriately be called a *derived actual outcome*. Correspondingly, the RV that underlies that kind of a number may be called a *derived RV* or a *derived probability distribution*. We shall use a second subscript notation in obvious parallel with the first, and label these kinds of entities with the subscript D, thus: actual outcome$_{D}$, RV$_{D}$, probability distribution$_{D}$, pf$_{D}$, or pdf$_{D}$.

The standard literature refers to this kind of a number, an actual outcome$_{D}$, as a *statistic*. That term reflects the mathematical use typically made of such numbers; in statistical work, actual outcomes$_{D}$ are principally used in conjunction with various kinds of evaluative, decision-making procedures that characterize the process of statistical inference. Furthermore, there are two broad classes of this kind of usage and thus, correspondingly two kinds of statistics: *sample statistics* and *test statistics* (Hays, pp. 262, 268, 374). This distinction is made on the basis of certain practical considerations that need not concern us. At this point we primarily need to recognize that in the experimental literature, the kind of a number that we have called a *derived actual outcome* traditionally is called a statistic. We shall use "derived actual outcome" and "statistic" interchangeably.

In figure 10.3, the single number obtained by processing the 100 actual outcomes$_{P}$ (sample values) is a derived actual outcome (actual outcome$_{D}$) or a statistic. The underlying RV is a derived probability distribution (RV$_{D}$ or probability distribution$_{D}$, or, in this particular illustrative example, a pdf$_{D}$).

Empirical Considerations

We have introduced the idea that an RV is conceptualized as the mathematical structure, the "statistical law," that underlies either an experimental measure (an actual outcome$_{P}$ or sample value) or a derived number (an actual outcome$_{D}$ or statistic). It might be helpful to remind ourselves in this context of some of the principal empirical implications inherent in such conceptualizations. We know in general that a probability distribution specifies probability or probability density values for a potential outcome set, and we also know that the principle of equivalence allows one to translate these mathematical specifications into empirically meaningful entities. Thus, an RV, a mathematical "system," prescribes empirical properties such as the frequency and relative frequency that an individual outcome value or outcome axis region will have in a given series of repeated trials. In the present context, then, when we say that from a mathematical point of view quantities such as either 100 experimentally acquired measures or a single reduced number can be viewed as numbers "generated according to an underlying RV," we are saying that the statistical behavior of such numbers reflects the usual empirical consequences implicit in an RV framework.

With respect to sample values, these matters are relatively straightforward. For instance, in our hypothetical experiment, saying that 100 measures of a test performance (e.g., the times required to perform some experimental task) have been "generated according to an underlying RV_P" amounts to saying that among this set of numbers (now conceptualized as repeated trials), the relative frequencies of outcomes in specified outcome regions will reflect the corresponding probabilities specified by the underlying RV_P. If that probability distribution specifies a probability of 0.25 for obtaining an outcome in the region between 1.5 and 3.5 seconds, for example, then the expected relative frequency of outcomes obtained in that range will also be 0.25; therefore, we should expect that about 25 of the 100 measured times fall within that outcome region.

Matters are somewhat different in the case of the other kind of a number, a derived actual outcome or statistic. We have stated that this kind of a number, too, can be considered as an actual outcome in an RV context. Specifically, I have claimed that a statistic can be viewed as an actual $outcome_D$ obtained from one trial involving an underlying probability distribution RV_D (see figs. 10.1 and 10.3). What does that mean in empirical terms? We are speaking now about only one number—an experiment produces *one* actual $outcome_D$. Yet, we are proposing to set that single number into a probabilistic framework, claiming that one can say that some RV_D "underlies" that single actual outcome.

One important meaning of that mathematical assumption is the following. We had obtained 100 experimental measures and reduced them to one number. If we were to *repeat the experiment* another time, with 100 different animals, we would almost certainly obtain 100 different numbers. After again reducing these to one number by our particular arithmetical procedure, we would also again obtain a single number; that number would probably be *different* from the corresponding single number obtained during the first experiment. A third performance of the experiment would probably yield yet another different set of 100 numbers and therefore yet another different single reduced number, and so on. Each repetition of the experiment thus will yield one statistic or actual $outcome_D$.[2] Therefore, for a number that is a statistic, empirical frequencies or relative frequencies implicate repetitions of a complete experiment. *For each "RV trial" involving an actual* $outcome_D$*, there must correspondingly be one entire experimental study.*

Thus, we may conclude that in one sense, the empirical connotations of an RV_P are different from those of an RV_D. For these two kinds of RVs, the concept of repeated trials will have different empirical implications. For an RV_P, the idea of repeated trials implies *repeated observations* made within one study, while for an RV_D, repeated trials imply *repeated experiments*. RV_P concerns the statistical pattern that will be exhibited by empirical measures (sample values or actual $outcomes_P$) that one obtains within a single experiment, while RV_D concerns the statistical pattern that will be exhibited by the "summarizing" numbers (the actual $outcomes_D$ or statistics) that would be obtained if one were to repeat the whole experiment a number of times—there would be one statistic corresponding to each experimental study.

This completes our initial overview of the experimental origins of RVs. We now are ready to see how this framework can be applied in statistical work to draw logical inferences from experimental results. This exploration will occupy us for the remainder of this work. The next section (part IV) will introduce a number of specific inferential methodologies, each in the context of a particular type of pdf or pf. The final section (part V) will extend the

[2]That is not always strictly true, as we shall see in later chapters. There are cases where several different data-reducing operations are applied to the same set of data (sample values) obtained in one experiment. That simple extension of the framework does not change the basic underlying concepts that we are developing here.

RV framework in a different direction. It will introduce a mathematical elaboration of our original concept of outcome (an extension to the so-called multivariate case), and will present certain inferential processes that derive from this widening of the conceptual horizons.

PROBLEMS

10.1 What is another name for "sample value"? For "statistic"?

10.2 What does "reducing a set of sample values to a statistic" mean?

10.3 In an RV framework, what is the mathematical source of an actual outcome$_P$? An actual outcome$_D$?

10.4 What is the empirical, actual source of a sample value or actual outcome$_P$? Of a statistic or actual outcome$_D$?

10.5 What does it mean to say that a probability distribution underlies an outcome value?

10.6 What are the kinds of probability distribution/outcome value pairs in an RV framework?

10.7 What does a set of statistics or derived actual outcomes imply? A set of sample values or population actual outcomes? (Discuss the mathematical as well as the empirical implications.)

10.8 An experiment begins formally with the administration of an intelligence test (the WAIS) to each of 25 subjects. How are the 25 test scores acquired by this procedure viewed in an RV framework?

10.9 Discuss and classify the potential outcome of the population probability distribution (RV_P) that underlies the 25 IQ measures in problem 10.9 (see chap. 2).

10.10 In the experiment described in problem 10.8, the experimenters computed the average of the squares of 25 deviations from the mean obtained from the 25 test scores. In an

RV framework, what kind of a number is that average, and what has "generated" it?

10.11 In part I, we learned that a probability distribution is a function that always involves two kinds of numbers. What kind of numbers have we been emphasizing thus far (problems 10.1 through 10.10)?

PART IV

Some Probability Distributions and Related Inferential Procedures

CHAPTER 11

The Formal Characteristics of the Normal Probability Distribution

In the preceding sections we examined various facets of RVs and closely associated concepts. We are now ready to assemble these facets, to integrate them, and bring them to bear on some of the more important topics that concern various branches of applied statistics.

In many of the previous discussions, the specifics of the profiles of probability distributions were largely irrelevant. Frequently, we merely sketched a distribution and did not worry about its precise shape. Where specific probability distributions were used, they were presented principally to illustrate and introduce various basic RV concepts. Therefore, those illustrative distributions mostly needed to have only simple profiles such as rectangular or triangular shapes. Now, as we begin to study the specifics of inferential processes and as the discussion becomes more quantitative, it will become necessary to consider a number of particular classes of probability distributions. In each case, a specific type of probability distribution will be introduced in terms of its formal, mathematical features. Next, we will illustrate one or more of its major applications to statistical inference, the process of working out the logical implications of the mathematical results of an experiment. Thus, we shall, on the one hand, become acquainted with some of the specific distributions that are important in the behavioral disciplines and, on the other hand, gradually unfold various facets of the process of statistical inference in the context of specific classes or categories of probability distributions.

We shall begin with the best-known distribution, familiar even to most people who lack formal statistical training. That distribution is, of course, the normal probability density function. It is also called "Gaussian" (after the mathematician C. F. Gauss, 1772-1855) or, colloquially, a bell-shaped curve. Its prominence stems from several factors. First, it has a profile that closely describes certain mathematical aspects of many different types of real-world statistical situations. It approximates the statistical properties of a variety of phenomena such as the distributions of heights or weights in populations, scores in academic tests, manufacturing errors in industry, and particle velocities in physics, among many others. One might say that it is one of the preferred shapes of nature.

Secondly, in addition to its importance as a mathematical descriptor of many situations in the real world, the normal pdf is also of major importance in statistics because it has certain special mathematical properties. We shall encounter some of these properties in subsequent chapters, although the full mathematical importance of the normal probability distribution becomes evident only in more advanced work.[1]

The Mathematical Specification

What is the normal probability distribution? Algebraically, it is simply a particular pdf specified by the formula

$$y = \frac{1}{\sqrt{(2\pi\sigma^2)}} \times e^{\frac{-(x-\mu)^2}{2\sigma^2}}, \tag{11.1}$$

where x is an outcome value and y is the corresponding probability density value.

Equation (11.1) may look formidable, but it is in principle no different from more familiar equations such as $y = x^2$. These kinds of equations are merely recipes that define, for any given value of

[1] For example, the normal pdf has certain special characteristics pertaining to independence (a concept we shall explore in chap. 20), and has a special place in theorems about "large numbers"—roughly, about outcomes of very many RV trials (see, for example, Freeman, 1963, p. 182; Hays, 1973, p. 305).

one set of numbers (outcome values in our case) a corresponding assigned value from another set of numbers (probability densities, in our case). In the familiar algebraic terminology, an entity that we are free to select, to "plug into" an equation, is called the *independent variable*; in (11.1), it is symbolized by x, and represents an *outcome value*. If we select a specific value of an independent variable, x, then (11.1) automatically specifies a corresponding value of a second variable, y—in our case, representing a probability density. Since the value of y will *depend on* the specific value that we select for x, y is called the *dependent variable*. In algebraic terminology, then, one says that an equation such as (11.1) defines a pdf by specifying for each value of the independent variable (for each outcome value, x) a corresponding, assigned value of the dependent variable (the probability density, y).

Equation (11.1) contains certain symbols other than the familiar x, y, square root sign, etc.: e, μ, and σ^2. The first of these, e, is an entity that, like π (pi) crops up in mathematics in many different contexts. Also like π, it merely represents a particular number (2.7813, approximately). The other two symbols, μ and σ^2, are *parameters* of the pdf. We have already met these symbols (part II) and know that in general they stand for the mean and variance of an RV, respectively. We shall presently examine them in greater detail in the context of the normal pdf.

If we observe (11.1) more closely, we can discern several general formal properties of that pdf just by inspection. First, since there is no indication to the contrary, we may suppose that x, the outcome value, can assume any numerical value. The implication is that the potential outcome set is therefore not limited in range in either direction along the outcome axis; x ranges from "minus infinity" to "plus infinity."[2] Next we observe that the equation contains parameters and we may infer that therefore it represents a family of pdfs, rather than only one specific profile (see the discussion concerning parameters in chap. 8). Furthermore, it appears that *two* parameters (μ and σ^2) are sufficient to define a specific member of this particular family of probability distribu-

[2]The quotation marks are there to remind us that infinity is not an actual number, but rather a numberlike concept.

tions. That is, given any particular values of μ and σ^2, (11.1) becomes completely specific and therefore fully defines and specifies one particular pdf. We shall return to this point presently when we examine the graphs of various specific normal probability distributions. A further characteristic can be observed on examination of (11.1). Since the independent variable, x, appears only in the form $(x - \mu)^2$, the pdf will be symmetrical about the value μ. That is, for any given values of the two parameters μ and σ^2, the probability density (y) will have the *same value* for any pair of outcome values (x) that are an equal distance away on either side of μ. For example, if μ equals 10, then y will have the same value for pairs of outcome values that are equidistant from 10, such as $x = 9$ and 11, 8 and 12, 5 and 15, 0 and 20, etc.[3] Let us next examine the quantitative aspects of a normal pdf.

Characteristics of the Graph

Let us examine the graph of one particular normal pdf. Figure 11.1 shows a graph of the normal probability distribution that has the values 10 and 4 for its two parameters μ and σ^2, respectively. We see that the curve is symmetrical about the outcome value 10, the mean, as anticipated. We also see that the range of the pdf is not limited; the curve continues indefinitely in both directions of

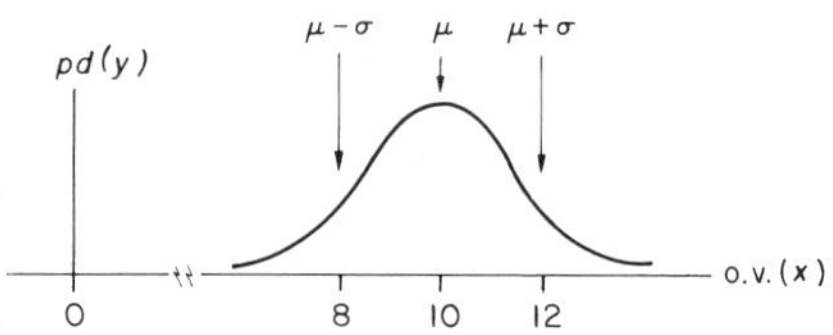

FIGURE 11.1 A normal probability density function

[3]If you like, you may convince yourself of this property even if you do not know how to calculate the value of the right-hand side of (11.1). First, select any values for μ and σ^2 (σ^2 must be nonnegative, of course); for example, select $\mu = 10$ and $\sigma^2 = 2$. Second, select any two outcome values x equidistant from your value of μ; in our example, you could select the pair 7 and 13, or the pair 5 and 15, etc. Third, write the term in the right-hand side of (11.1) for each of the two selected values of x, using these and your particular values of μ and σ^2. You will see that the resulting two numerical expressions for y are identical. That means that y, the probability density, has the same value for two outcome values that are equidistant from μ—in other words, the pdf is symmetrical about μ, as advertised.

the outcome axis, also as anticipated. The curve must therefore approach the outcome axis more and more closely in the more distant outcome regions so that the total area under the curve will be limited to 1, as required (see chaps. 4 and 5).

Any probability distribution that is symmetrical about some outcome value will have certain particular relationships between the median and the mean. In chapter 7 we learned that the "balance point" of a probability distribution is the outcome value that is the mean of that probability distribution. Obviously, the center of balance, and thus the mean μ, of a pdf that is symmetrical about an outcome value is that outcome value. For a symmetrical pf or pdf, then, the mean will occur at the axis of symmetry.

In addition, we know that the median is that outcome value that divides the total area under the curve into two equal parts (see chap. 8). We may infer that for a symmetrical probability distribution, the median must be located at the axis of symmetry (why?). Therefore, we can conclude in general that if a pdf or pf is symmetrical about some outcome value, then since the mean and median are always equal to that outcome value, they thus must also be equal to each other (see problem 8.1). For our illustrative pdf, then, the mean and median both have the same outcome value, 10. We also learned in chapter 8 that the mode of a pdf is the outcome value that has the highest assigned probability density value. We see by inspection that the mode of the pdf in figure 11.1 is also the outcome value 10.

The conclusions that we have reached about the mean, median, and mode of our illustrative pdf are true for *any normal* pdf: for a Gaussian probability distribution, these three descriptors have the same outcome value and are thus equal to one another.

We have been considering one particular member of the family of normal pdfs, specifically, the pdf defined by (11.1) with $\mu = 10$ and $\sigma^2 = 4$:

$$y = \frac{1}{\sqrt{(8\pi)}} \times e^{\dfrac{-(x-10)^2}{8}}$$

We shall next examine how different values of these two parameters affect the profile of a normal pdf.

First we will consider the effect of the parameter μ. If we keep σ^2 constant at some value and change only μ, how does that change affect the pdf? Figure 11.2 shows several normal pdfs, all having the same variance, 4, but having different means. We see that these pdfs are identical to one another except for their location along the outcome axis. Thus, a change in μ only shifts the axis of symmetry of a normal curve to the right or left, leaving the basic shape otherwise unmodified.

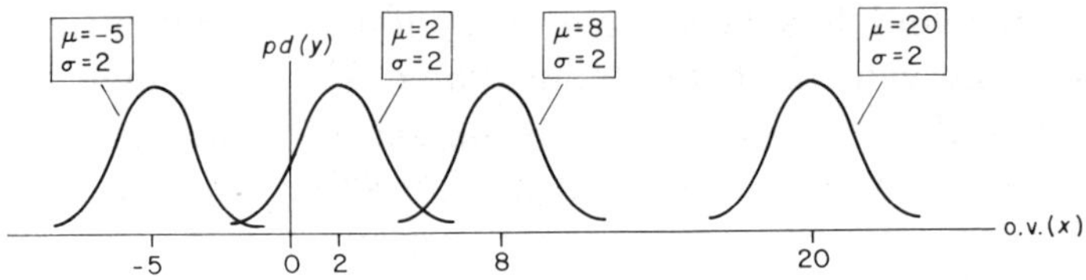

FIGURE 11.2 The effect of varying μ

If, on the other hand, we change only the value of the variance σ^2 keeping the value of μ constant, it will have the effect shown in figure 11.3. Now the axis of symmetry remains unchanged (in our example, at the outcome value 10), but the curve changes in its "spread." The extent of that spread or dispersion about μ will depend on the particular value selected for the variance. The smaller the variance, the more the curve is bunched about the mean, i.e., the more the distribution "peaks" about that value. In contrast, the larger the variance, the more the pdf is spread out, i.e., the flatter or more dispersed it is.

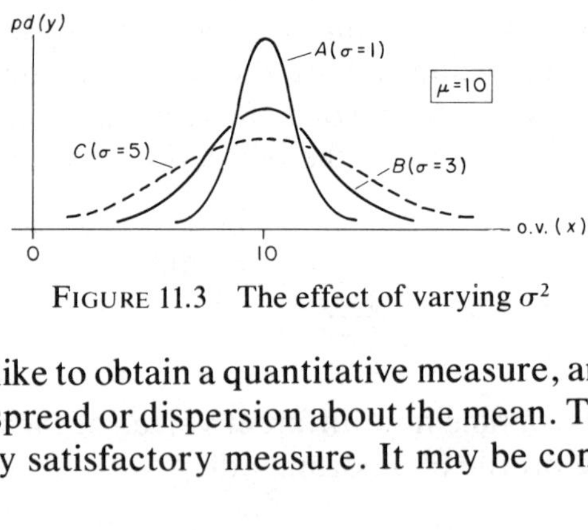

FIGURE 11.3 The effect of varying σ^2

We should like to obtain a quantitative measure, an index, of the extent of the spread or dispersion about the mean. The variance is not an entirely satisfactory measure. It may be considered as an average of squared distances (specifically, a long-term average of squares of deviations about the mean; see chap. 7), and in terms of geometry, squared distances imply measures of an area rather than measures of linear distances. If we wish to obtain some measure of the degree of spread in terms of an outcome axis span, then it would be desirable to transform the variance to some measure that is not an average of squares of distances. The usual approach is simply to take the *positive square root* of the variance as an indicator of the linear extent of the dispersion; taking the square root amounts to "undoing" the squaring operation that generated the variance in the first instance.

We know from chapter 7 that the square root of the variance is called the *standard deviation* and that it is represented by the Greek letter σ. It provides a meaningful index of the dispersion of a normal pdf.

The standard deviation, then, is a magnitude that has significance as a distance, a span along the outcome axis. Furthermore, the term suggests a relationship to a deviation. Indeed, a distance of σ outcome axis units does have a particular significance as a deviation from the mean for a normal pdf: the outcome axis segment from μ to $(\mu + \sigma)$, or, equally, the segment from $(\mu - \sigma)$ to μ, always has one particular probability value associated with that span, a value of approximately 0.3413. For example, the normal pdf in figure 11.1 has a mean of 10 and a standard deviation of 2 ($\sigma^2 = 4$). Consequently, the area under the curve assigned to an outcome axis segment extending from the mean a distance of +2 or −2 will be 0.3413. Thus, the span from 8 to 12 has an associated probability of 0.6826. Since the relationship we have just discussed is true for *any* normal pdf, in figure 11.3 the pdf labeled B ($\mu = 10, \sigma^2 = 9, \sigma = 3$) has an area under the curve in the range from 7 to 10, or from 10 to 13, equal to 0.3413; the two analogous outcome segments for the normal pdf labeled C in figure 11.3 ($\mu = 10, \sigma^2 = 25, \sigma = 5$) would be the segments from 5 to 10, or from 10 to 15, and so on.

Empirical Implications

Let us briefly consider the empirical implications of the characteristics of a normal pdf. The principle of equivalence implies that in a series of repeated trials involving a normal RV, the *relative frequency* of actual outcomes that would fall into an outcome region from μ to $(\mu + \sigma)$, or from $(\mu - \sigma)$ to μ, would also be 0.3413, the same as the value of the probability for that kind of a region. For example, if we had a spinner whose statistical characteristics were defined by the normal pdf in figure 11.1 ($\mu = 10$, $\sigma^2 = 4$) and if we performed 1,000 repeated trials, then we should expect that approximately 0.341 of the 1,000 actual outcome values, or 341 numbers, would lie within the outcome region from 10 to 12 [μ to $(\mu + \sigma)$]; the same number of outcomes, 341, would also be expected to lie within the outcome region from 8 to 10 [$(\mu - \sigma)$ to μ]. If σ^2 had been 25 instead of 4 and if μ had remained equal to 10, the two outcome regions containing 341 actual outcomes among 1,000 trials would then be the regions from 5 to 10 [$(\mu - \sigma)$ to μ] and from 10 to 15 [μ to $(\mu + \sigma)$]. In that case, we should expect that about 682 out of the 1,000 outcomes would have values lying within the span from 5 to 15.

We see, then, that if we perform a number of repeated trials with a normal RV, smaller and larger standard deviations of a pdf imply, correspondingly, smaller and larger degrees of the clustering of outcomes about the mean. In the preceding examples, when $\sigma = 2$, then 68% of outcomes in repeated trials would probably have fallen into the outcome region from 8 to 12, while if σ had been equal to 5 instead, the same percentage of outcomes would probably have fallen into a region from 5 to 15. This relationship between the magnitude of the standard deviation (or the variance, since these two quantities are closely related numerically) and the degree of clustering of outcomes about the mean is an important, frequently used aspect of the empirical meaning of σ and σ^2. Although we have discussed these empirical implications specifically for a normal pdf, they remain true, by and large, for *any kind* of a probability distribution. In general, the standard deviation and mean furnish an index of the expected *degree* of clustering of outcomes from repeated trials and of the *value* about which such outcomes would be likely to cluster, respectively.

The Standard Form

We know from part I that an important feature of a probability distribution is that it defines probabilities associated with outcome regions. Suppose we would want to find the probability of obtaining outcomes falling within some specified outcome region of one particular normal pdf. For example, suppose we wished to know the probability of obtaining an outcome within the region from 9 to 12 for the curve shown in figure 11.1 ($\mu = 10$, $\sigma^2 = 4$, $\sigma = 2$). We know that for any pdf, this probability is equal to the area under the curve in the specified outcome range. Thus, to find the probability of a specified outcome region, we should need only to find the area under the curve in that region. In previous examples this was not too difficult. Simple geometrical approaches could be used. Now, however, we cannot find the stipulated area by using elementary geometry. The shape of the normal curve is too complex; it does not allow us to calculate areas under the curve in a simple fashion, as did, for example, the uniform distribution in figure 5.3, or the triangular distribution in figure 8.1.

In chapter 5 we were introduced to one approach that could be used in these kinds of situations. We learned that one could use straightline approximations, i.e., numerical methods that could provide estimates of areas under complicated curves. We could, therefore, find the desired probability under the normal curve in the designated region from 9 to 12 by using one of these kinds of numerical approaches. While it would work, it would provide only a specific solution to one specific outcome range of one specific member of the normal pdf family. Each time we specified either some other outcome segment, or some other member of the pdf family, or both, we should be back at the beginning—to find the associated probability, we would have to use the numerical approximation methods anew, applying them to our new normal pdf and/or outcome axis segment. Obviously, this approach would be tedious and impractical.

A tool has been developed that obviates the need for this repetitious use of unwieldy approximate numerical methods. It enables one to find the probability for any specified outcome region of any particular member of the normal probability distribution family.

The tool capitalizes on the idea that in a sense, all members of the normal pdf family have "the same shape." Mathematically, they differ from one another only in two ways: in location along the outcome axis (specified by μ), and in the degree of dispersion (specified by σ^2 or σ). These differences are almost like differences in scale. If we could somehow discount these individual differences, we might be able to find one generally applicable method for calculating probabilities in *any* specified region of *any* specified normal pdf.

The approach that allows us to accomplish this objective is based on one particular prototypic normal pdf, the so-called STANDARD normal probability distribution. This is simply a normal curve of the general algebraic form specified by (11.1), with the particular parameter values $\mu = 0$ and $\sigma^2 = 1$ ($\sigma = 1$ as well since $+\sqrt{1} = 1$). This standard normal curve is shown in figure 11.4. There is nothing particularly different about it to distinguish it from any other member of the normal pdf family. The one practical difference is that mathematicians have calculated the values of various areas under the curve for this prototype, and prepared tables that permit one to find the probabilities associated with any specified portion of the outcome axis. Basically, these are tables of the cdf associated with the standard normal pdf. These tables give the cumulative probability for many different outcome values, much as other mathematical tables give the value of a function (for example, a logarithm, or a trigonometric function such as the sine) for various values of the independent variable, x.

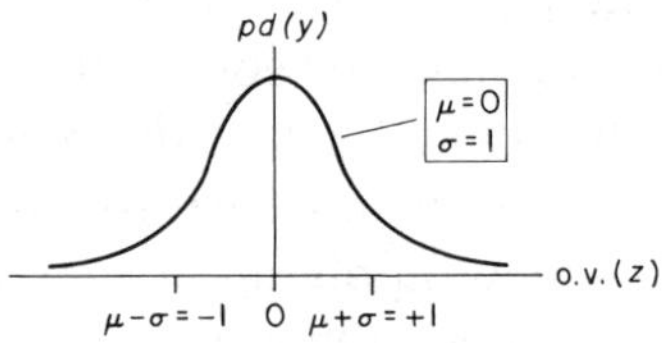

FIGURE 11.4 The standard normal pdf

The specific equation of the standard normal probability density function is obtained by assigning the appropriate parameter values in (11.1). Thus, the standard normal probability curve is defined by the algebraic equation

$$y = \frac{1}{\sqrt{(2\pi)}} \times e^{\frac{-x^2}{2}}.$$

A table of the standard normal cdf provides, for any specified value of x, the corresponding total area under the pdf (i.e., the probability) that lies to the *left* of that x (see chaps. 4 and 5). Since x can assume infinitely many values (the potential outcome is continuous, and not limited in range; see chap. 3), the tables cannot of course really provide cumulative probabilities for "any" value of x; rather, as most other mathematical tables, they provide values for a selected, closely spaced set of values of the independent variable (in our case, the outcome value). If one wished to obtain cumulative probabilities for other than the tabled outcome values, i.e., for values falling between the tabled values, one would follow the usual mathematical procedure and interpolate from the tabled values, just as one would with logarithmic or other tabled functions.

Table 11.1

A portion of the cdf for the standard normal probability distribution (from Appendix A)

Outcome value	Cumulative probability
0.50	0.6915
.51	.6950
.52	.6985
.53	.7091
.54	.7054
.55	.7088
.56	.7123
.57	.7157
.58	.7190
.59	.7224
.60	.7257

Table 11.1 shows a portion of a typical table of the cdf of the standard normal pdf. It specifies the cdf for the outcome range from 0.50 to 0.60 in increments of 0.01. The complete table can be found in Appendix A. The graph of this cdf, called an *ogive* profile, is shown in figure 11.5. We remember that a cdf can be used in a simple fashion to obtain the probability value for any selected portion or segment of the outcome axis. One only needs to subtract two cumulative probabilities, one associated with each of the two end points of the specified outcome segment. One subtracts the smaller from the larger cumulative probability, and that numerical difference is the desired probability value assigned to the outcome segment (see chaps. 4 and 5). For example, from table 11.1 we find directly that for a standard normal pdf, the probability of obtaining an outcome in the region from 0.52 to 0.57 is approximately 0.716 − 0.699, or 0.017.

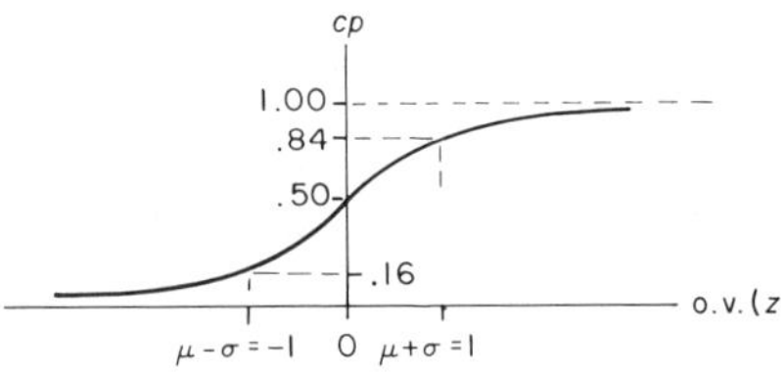

FIGURE 11.5 The standard normal cdf

How does a table of the cdf of a standard normal curve enable us to calculate the probability in a specified region of some other, *nonstandard* member of the normal pdf family, i.e., a normal pdf with $\mu \neq 0$ and/or $\sigma^2 \neq 1$? The step that permits this calculation is a simple mathematical computation that converts any one given outcome value of any particular normal, nonstandard pdf to the corresponding, "equivalent" outcome value of the prototypic, standard normal pdf. The approach can be most simply explained through an actual example.

Consider once more the particular normal pdf shown in figure 11.1. Suppose we wished to find the probability of obtaining an outcome in some specified region, for example, for the region between 6 and 7. We shall see that there is one particular outcome segment of the *standard* normal pdf that "corresponds" to this segment from 6 to 7 of our particular (nonstandard) normal pdf.

The two outcome axis segments "correspond" to one another in the sense that the two corresponding probabilities, one associated with each of these two segments, have *the same value*. All that we need to learn now is how to find the two end points of an outcome axis segment of the *standard* normal pdf that "correspond to" the two end points (6 and 7) of the specified segment. The two standard end point values are found by a simple formula that will be introduced shortly. By using this formula, one finds that the outcome values 6 and 7 of our particular nonstandard pdf correspond, respectively, to the outcome values −2.0 and −1.5 of the standard normal pdf.

These correspondences are indicated in figure 11.6. That figure shows the two normal pdfs, the nonstandard probability distribution of figure 11.1 ($\mu = 10$, $\sigma = 2$) and the standard normal probability distribution ($\mu = 0$, and $\sigma = 1$) of figure 11.4. Figure 11.6 indicates that the outcome region from −2.0 to −1.5 of the standard normal curve corresponds to the outcome region from 6 and 7 of the nonstandard normal curve.

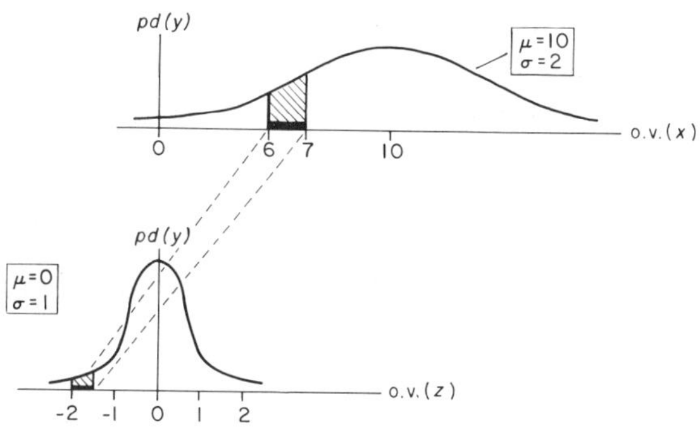

FIGURE 11.6 Corresponding outcome axis segments

We can find the area under the curve of the standard normal pdf between the outcome values −2.0 and −1.5 directly by using the table of the standard normal cdf. From that table, we find that the cumulative probability associated with the outcome value −2.0 is 0.023 and the cumulative probability associated with the outcome value −1.5 is 0.067. Therefore, the probability of finding an outcome in the region between −2.0 and −1.5 of a *standard* normal pdf is the difference between these two cumulative probabilities, 0.067 − 0.023, or 0.044. *That value, 0.044, is also the probability assigned to the "corresponding" outcome region between 6 and 7 of our "nonstandard," original normal curve, the pdf shown in figure 11.1.*

We must fill in the one remaining detail, namely, how one finds the outcome value of the standard normal probability distribution that "corresponds" to a given outcome value of a specified nonstandard normal probability distribution. In terms of our example, the question is: how does one find the two "standard" outcome values that correspond to the two "nonstandard" end point values (6 and 7)? The general approach falls under the heading of "change of variable" techniques, an intricate, fairly advanced mathematical topic. It deals with the general problem of what it means to convert one mathematical function to another, and how one accomplishes and uses such conversions. Much of this topic is quite beyond our scope (see Freeman, chap. 8). We shall, however, encounter several specific, relatively simple applications of this procedure, and in each instance will present techniques for accomplishing certain specific objectives. In the present case, we shall provide a formula that can be used to change an outcome value of a nonstandard normal pdf to its corresponding outcome value of the standard normal pdf (and, as we shall see, vice versa). Although we shall not pursue the point, this formula actually implies a mathematical transformation. It allows us to transform a nonstandard normal pdf into a standard normal probability distribution.

We have a nonstandard normal pdf with a given mean μ and a given standard deviation σ, and we wish to find the standard outcome value that corresponds to a given nonstandard outcome value, x. We obtain the desired "standard" outcome value corresponding to a given outcome value of a nonnormal pdf in two simple arithmetical steps. First, we subtract the specified value of the mean, μ, from the given outcome value x; second, we divide that difference by σ. That procedure will give us the particular outcome value of the standard pdf that is "equivalent" to the given value x. It is the usual practice to call the outcome value of the standard normal probability distribution a z value, rather than an

x value. Thus, in terms of an algebraic formula, to convert an outcome value x of a nonstandard normal pdf into its equivalent "standardized" outcome value z, we use the equation

$$z = \frac{x - \mu}{\sigma} . \tag{11.2}$$

This was the formula that we had used previously to obtain equivalent standard values of the two outcome values 6 and 7. (You may wish to verify the previous results.) To learn more about the implications of (11.2), let us use it to calculate z values corresponding to several other outcome values of the normal pdf shown in figure 11.1 ($\mu = 10$, $\sigma = 2$). Let us calculate the standard outcome value corresponding to outcome value μ (10), $\mu + \sigma$ (12), and $\mu - \sigma$ (8). Using (11.2), we find that the z values corresponding to these outcome values 10, 12, and 8 of the pdf in figure 11.1 are, respectively, 0, +1, and −1. These results are not unique to this particular example. It is true in general that first, when we transform the *mean* of a normal pdf to its corresponding standard outcome value, we obtain the value $z = 0$. Second, when we transform the outcome value lying one standard deviation to the right of the mean, we obtain a standard value of $z = +1$. Finally, when we transform an outcome value lying one standard deviation to the left of the mean, we obtain the standard value $z = -1$. These conclusions are direct consequences of the algebraic form of (11.2) (see problem 11.4).

We should note that there are several alternative but completely equivalent approaches to furnishing the data that specify the cdf of a standard normal probability distribution. These alternative methods capitalize on certain properties that would be true for *any* pdf that is symmetrical about its mean. First, for such a pdf, any two corresponding symmetrical outcome segments have the same assigned probability value (and thus, the same area under the curve). Consider, for example, two outcome segments of the standard normal pdf shown in figure 11.7: the segment lying to the left of the outcome value a, and that lying to the right of b (a and b are equidistant from the mean, 0). These two segments are mirror images of one another. Either is a reflection of the other about the axis of symmetry, the vertical line at the mean, $z = 0$. Therefore, associated areas under the curve and consequently assigned probabilities of these two segments are equal to one another. The same argument would pertain to any other pair of "mirror image" outcome axis segments in figure 11.7, such as the pair "greater than a" and "less than b," or the pair "a to 0" and "0 to b." In each of these kinds of pairs, the two corresponding assigned probabilities are equal to each other.

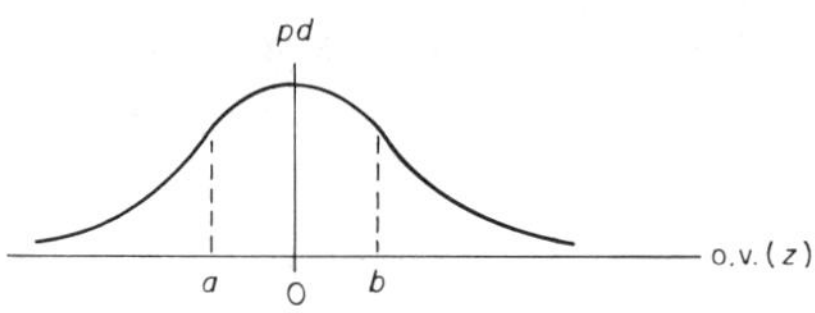

FIGURE 11.7 Symmetrical outcome axis segments

A second and obvious characteristic of a pdf that has this kind of symmetry about the mean is that that outcome value will divide the total area under the curve into two equal parts. That is, as we have already noted previously, the mean is also the median. In figure 11.7, the outcome segment lying to the left of zero as well as the segment lying to the right of zero must each have an assigned probability and associated area under the curve of 0.50.

These two features allow one to furnish the cumulative probability associated with a given outcome value in several different ways. For example, we know almost immediately the value of the cdf at a if we are given the probability assigned to *any one* of these six outcome segments: a to 0, 0 to b, a to b, the whole outcome axis lying to the right of a, the whole outcome axis segment lying to the right of b, or the whole outcome axis segment lying to the left of b (the value of the cdf at b) (see problems 11.7 and 11.8). We can easily and simply calculate the cumulative probability at a given the probability of any one of these six outcome axis segments. We need only to use the two symmetry characteristics just discussed as well as the usual properties that characterize any pdf in general (e.g., the value required for the total area under the curve, or the relationships between the probabilities of complementary pairs of events, and so on; see chaps. 4 and 5).

From these considerations, it follows that the cdf of a standard normal probability distribution could be furnished, for example, by a table that listed only positive values of z. In figure 11.7, b is such an outcome value, and the preceding discussion has demonstrated that if we know the cdf at b, we almost immediately know the corresponding value of the cdf at a (see problems 11.7 and 11.8). It therefore is not really necessary to list the negative outcome values for the standard normal cdf. Presenting only positive outcome values is only one of a number of equivalent representations of the standard normal cdf, then. A different approach is illustrated in the table used by Freeman (p. 417). That table furnishes information about the standard normal cdf by listing for positive standard outcome values such as b the corresponding probability of the segment from a to b in figure 11.7.

These kinds of alternative methods of tabling the cdf of a standard normal probability distribution are all logically equivalent to the more fundamental (as well as more obvious) method illustrated in table 11.1 and used in Appendix A. All these methods furnish the same information, but do so in terms of slightly different procedures. It is therefore necessary to be careful when using any table that presumably lists the cumulative probabilities for a standard normal RV. It may be the kind of tabulation that provides data in a somewhat roundabout fashion and would need to be used accordingly, of course.

We now know how to convert a nonstandard to a standard outcome value, and we thus know how to obtain probabilities for any specified outcome segment of a nonstandard normal pdf. We shall soon see, beginning with chapter 13, how these procedures are used in statistical inference. We shall close this chapter by considering a common application of the normal probability distribution and its limitations.

The Normal Probability Distribution As an Approximation

As previously noted, many real-world situations have statistical properties that closely resemble those of a normally distributed RV. Typically, this means that the envelope of a pf_P that "underlies" some empirical measurement is approximately normal in shape. For instance, let us consider the measurement of a person's height. We shall assume that in some population, the height of the shortest person is 25 cm., and that of the tallest person, 3.00 m. We shall also assume that a person's height will be measured to the nearest 0.001 m. Thus, we are considering a measurement that can be represented by a potential outcome ranging from 0.25 to 3.00 m. in increments of 1 mm. We should recognize this set as limited in range, and discrete (see chap. 2). There are approximately 2,750 possible outcome values in this potential outcome. We now have a potential outcome that corresponds to an empirical measure. What else would we need to represent this measurement situation by an RV_P? That is, if we would wish to consider the measurement of a height in terms of a probabilistic mathematical framework, what other ingredient would we need? Obviously, we would need to have a set of probability values, with one probability being assigned to each of the possible 2,750 outcome values in the potential outcome set (see chap. 4). We know from chapter 10 that the empirical implications of this representation are that the measurement of one person would be conceptualized as one trial of an RV situation, in this case, a roulette wheel. (One height measurement would provide one actual outcome_P or sample value in the context of an RV_P.)

Let us assume that a correct assignment of probability values results in a pf whose envelope approximates the shape of a normal pdf. That situation is shown in the upper portion of figure 11.8. This pf, then, provides the theoretical framework of our height measurement process, and has the usual empirical implications. Let us note carefully that this pf is *not* a normal probability distribution. It cannot be that kind of a distribution, for at least two reasons. First, a normal probability distribution is not limited in range. Our pf, however, *is* limited in range; it is restricted at both ends of the potential outcome segment. Second, a normal probability distribution is a pdf, and the probability distribution in the upper portion of figure 11.8 is a pf; we know that there are always major differences between these two kinds of functions (see chap. 5). The former is continuous and involves probability densities, while the latter is discrete and involves probabilities. We shall discuss some implications of these considerations presently.

Notwithstanding these differences, we wish to approximate the

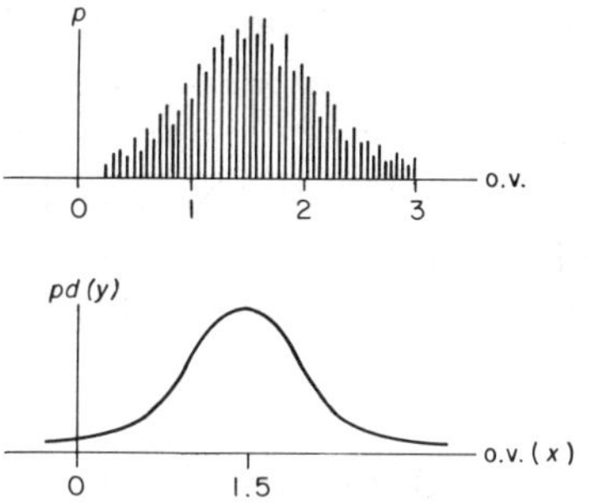

FIGURE 11.8 Approximating a pf by a pdf

pf in figure 11.8 by a "suitable" normal pdf. The motivation is partly theoretical and partly practical. As to the former, it is difficult mathematically to manipulate a pf such as that in figure 11.8 in more advanced theoretical work; a normal pdf lends itself much more readily to mathematical treatment. From a practical, applied point of view, the principal advantage gained by replacing a pf by a pdf is that this substitution greatly facilitates the calculation of probabilities in regions, which is, as we shall see in parts IV and V, a major, recurrent step in statistical work. We can appreciate the advantage of using a pdf instead of a pf for this calculation if we will recall what one must do to find the probability associated with any specified outcome region of a pf. The "direct method" developed in chapter 4 involved the addition of all the probabilities assigned to outcome values that fall within a specified region. Thus, if in our present example we wished to obtain the probability of finding an outcome (height) falling within the range, for instance, 1.20 to 1.40 m., we should need to add together the values of all the probabilities assigned to the outcomes lying within that range; since the discrete outcomes are spaced 1 mm. apart, we would therefore need to add about 200 numbers. This is clumsy and tedious. Obviously, an alternative would be desirable. Perhaps if our pf's profile closely resembles a normal pdf, we shall be able to find some appropriate normal pdf that would provide an adequate estimate for probabilities in any specified outcome region of the pf. If we could find such a normal probability distribution, we know from the earlier work in this chapter that it is a simple matter to find the probability under the curve within any designated segment of the outcome range. We know that if we wished to find the probability of an outcome falling between two specified outcome values, we would only need to (1) convert these two values to standard (z) outcome values, (2) use a table to find the two corresponding cumulative probabilities, and (3) subtract one probability from the other. This would certainly be preferable to adding together 200 probabilities assigned to 200 outcome values of a pf range.

What particular normal pdf would provide an "appropriate" approximation to our pf? As I have mentioned, we intend to use such a normal pdf primarily to compute probabilities over specified outcome regions in the potential outcome range of the pf—0.25 to 3.00 m. Therefore, the normal pdf that we are seeking should be one whose probability in any portion or segment of that outcome region would have aproximately the same value as the corresponding probability specified by the pf. That is, for any designated outcome axis segment within the range of the pf (0.25 to 3.00 m.), the normal pdf we are seeking and the pf of figure 11.8 should specify approximately the same probability value. For example, if the pf in figure 11.8 would specify a probability of 0.34 for the outcome range from 1.000 to 1.500 m., the normal pdf that we are seeking should do likewise. Which normal pdf should we use to provide the desired approximation—i.e., what values should we specify for the mean and variance? One particular choice is intuitively appealing and obvious. The pf that we are seeking to approximate, the pf in figure 11.8, has its own particular mean and variance (and thus, standard deviation), as does any other probability distribution, of course (see part II). A normal pdf having these same two parameter values would be the logical candidate for the desired approximation. Let us assume that the pf in figure 11.8 has a mean of 1.500 m. and a variance of 0.25 (a standard deviation of 0.500 m.). (If we did not know these parameters, we could calculate them from the pf by the methods developed in chap. 7.) The lower portion of figure 11.8 shows the normal pdf that has these two parameter values ($\mu = 1.50$, $\sigma^2 = 0.25$). Although we shall not prove the point, this particular normal curve is a good choice in the sense that the probability value it specifies for any segment selected from the range between 0.25

and 3.00 m. has approximately the same value as the corresponding probability specified by the pf in figure 11.8. That is, for any given outcome axis segment such as that from 0.25 to 0.35 m., or from 2.10 to 2.70 m., etc., these two probability distributions would specify approximately the same assigned probability to such segments. To summarize: if we have a pf whose envelope approximates the shape of a normal pdf, then a normal pdf having the same mean and the same variance as the pf provides a good approximation for the kind of application that we have just been considering.

Errors Introduced by the Approximation

We have replaced a discrete, limited-in-range pf by a continuous, not-limited-in-range pdf (that happens to be a normal probability distribution). This kind of replacement inevitably introduces errors; on a theoretical basis, the approximation cannot be perfect, for two basic reasons.

The first kind of an error is introduced because these two probability distributions differ in range—that is, the error arises because one distribution (the pf) is limited in range, while the other (the pdf) is not. Consequently, while the pf has a probability of zero associated with the outcome regions that lie outside the range of its potential outcome (the regions "less than 0.25 m." and "greater than 3.00 m."), the pdf specifies definite, although small, probabilities over those regions. We know that the pdf specifies probabilities for the region to the left of 0.25 and for the region to the right of 3.00; we see in figure 11.8 that there is an area under the normal curve associated with each of these regions (see chap. 5). In our specific example, while for the pf the probability in the whole region to the left of 0.25 m. is 0, the corresponding probability specified for that region by the normal pdf is approximately 0.006. Similarly, the probability specified by the pf for the whole region to the right of 3.00 m. is exactly 0, while the corresponding probability specified by the pdf is approximately 0.001.

The fact that the pdf assigns probabilities to these two ranges, while the pf does not, has consequences for probability values associated with the range *between* 0.25 and 3.00 m. as well, as the following consideration shows. For the pf, the probability associated with the total region from 0.25 to 3.00 m. must be 1, exactly (why?). For the same region, however, the assigned probability by the normal pdf shown in figure 11.8 must be *less* than 1 (why?). It is approximately 0.993. Therefore, there must be *some* discrepancies between the probability assignments made by these two distributions for some corresponding segments in that outcome region. In general, the pdf will slightly underestimate the actual probabilities specified by the pf for any specified segment in the pf potential outcome (why?).

We have discussed one kind of error inevitably present in the kinds of approximations we are making. The error arises when a limited-in-range probability distribution is approximated by one that is not limited in range. A second kind of theoretically based error arises because of the basic difference in continuity between a pf and a pdf. The former has a *discrete* potential outcome and associated *probabilities*, while the latter has a *continuous* potential outcome and associated *probability densities*. This *must* introduce discrepancies. One kind of discrepancy, for example, concerns the probability assigned to specific outcome values. A pf assigns a definite probability to any outcome value contained in its potential outcome; for example, the pf in figure 11.8 might assign a probability of 0.002 to the particular outcome value of 1.331 m. The pdf, however, would specify that the probability assigned to that or *any other outcome value* would be 0 (see chap. 5). Thus, if we were to ask what probability is associated with a given outcome value, the pf might provide one answer, and the pdf another. Another kind of discrepancy associated with continuity differences arises in certain types of calculations of probabilities over a range. We know that for a pf, the probability in an outcome range lying between two neighboring outcome values is 0 (see chap. 4). For example, for the pf we have been discussing, the probability of obtaining an outcome greater but not including the outcome value 1.001 m. and less than but not including the outcome value 1.002 m. is exactly 0 (why?). The corresponding normal pdf will, however, assign some definite, although very small probability to that region (why?). Thus, were we to ask: what is the probability of obtaining an outcome in the region greater than 1.001 and less than 1.002 m., the pf would specify 0, while the corresponding pdf would specify a definite, although small, value.

These kinds of discrepancies are inherent and inevitable when one uses a normal pdf to approximate a limited-in-range pf. There is also a practical reason why normal pdfs typically introduce errors when they are used as approximations for real-world probabilistic situations. One would not really expect any normal pdf, no matter how carefully selected, to provide an exact fit to the probability values specified by a given pf. Actual situations usually do not follow such ideal mathematical patterns exactly. Such differences between the actual profile of a pf and the ideal profile specified by a normal probability distribution would introduce lesser or greater computational errors, depending on how closely the profile of a given pf followed the shape of a normal curve.

We have been considering approximations based on substituting a pdf for a pf. Conceptually, there are irreducible differences between these two types of functions; practically, these approximations are usually not entirely accurate. As long as we keep these limitations in mind and do not abuse the approach, however, this kind of an approximation can be adequate and highly useful.

We shall next examine some applications of the normal probability distribution to the process of statistical inference.

PROBLEMS

11.1 What is the smallest number of parameters required to specify a normal pdf?

11.2 Are all bell-shaped pdfs normal pdfs? Support your answer.

11.3 A normal pdf is symmetrical about the outcome value 10, and its variance is 144. What are the standard values (z values) corresponding to these outcome values: $-2, 4, 10, 16, 22$, and 34?

11.4 Choose any two numbers for μ and σ^2 (σ^2 must be a positive number). Using your numbers, calculate the z

values corresponding to the following outcome values: μ, $\mu + \sigma$, and $\mu - \sigma$. Generalize your findings: Show algebraically that for any parameter values μ_0 and σ^2_0, the z values that correspond to the outcome values μ_0, $\mu_0 + \sigma_0$, and $\mu_0 - \sigma_0$ are 0, 1, and -1, respectively.

11.5 A normal pdf has the parameters $\mu = 50$ and $\sigma^2 = 64$. Using (11.2) and Appendix A, find the probability of an outcome falling into the following regions: 40 to 60; 43 to 47; less than 34; greater than 60.

11.6 What outcome values of a normal pdf, $\mu = 30$, $\sigma^2 = 49$, correspond to these z values: $-2, -1, -0.5, 0, 0.5, 10, 15$? [Hint: use (11.2) solved for x in terms of z, μ, and σ.]

11.7 The cumulative probability for a standard normal pdf at $z = -1.5$ is approximately 0.067. Using that information, find the probability for the following regions of that standard normal probability distribution: less than -1.5; greater than -1.5; between -1.5 and 0; between 0 and 1.5; greater than 1.5; and less than 1.5.

11.8 Generalize the results of problem 11.7 in the following manner. If the value of the cumulative probability of a standard normal probability distribution at the outcome value $z = -a$ (a is any positive number) is p, what, in terms of p, is the probability assigned to each of the following outcome axis regions: less than $-a$; greater than $-a$; between $-a$ and 0; between 0 and a; greater than a; and less than a.

11.9 In each of the following cases, you are given certain characteristics of a normal pdf. In each case, specify, if you can, both parameters μ and σ^2. In those cases where it is not possible to specify both parameter values, explain why the information provided is insufficient.

(a) The pdf is symmetrical about $x = 22$.

(b) Among the outcome values obtained from repeated trials, 68% fall within the outcome region between -5 and 25, and the median is at $x = 10$.

(c) The magnitude of σ is 10.

(d) An outcome value of $x = 14$ corresponds to the standard value $z = -2$.

(e) An outcome value of $x = 3$ corresponds to the standard value $z = 0$.

(f) The outcome values 10 and 20 correspond to the standard values 1.0 and 2.0, respectively.

(g) The cumulative probability at $x = 30$ is 0.5.

(h) The cumulative probability at $x = 30$ is 0.2.

(i) Among the outcome values obtained from repeated trials, 68% fall within the outcome region between -5 and 25.

11.10 A normal pdf is used to approximate a pdf that has a limited-in-range potential outcome. If we use the normal pdf to calculate the probabilities in various outcome regions of the actual pdf, will our estimate in general be too large, or too small? Explain your answer.

CHAPTER 12

The Normal Probability Distribution and Hypothesis Testing: General Formulations

Null and Alternative Hypotheses

Hypothesis testing is an important, complex topic in inferential statistics. It encompasses a wide range of mathematical as well as scientific issues, and thus requires a good deal of explanation for its comprehension. This chapter is only a first introduction to the principal general notions. Subsequent chapters will explore the particulars of a variety of specific inferential procedures.

Let us return to the hypothetical experiment discussed in chapter 10. In that example, experimenters wished to study the effects of a particular diet on the performance of rats on a learning task. The general question to be answered by the experiment was: "Will rats raised on the special diet perform differently on the test from those raised on a normal diet?" This question is now to be addressed mathematically by applying a so-called statistical *hypothesis test* or *test of significance*.

In order to begin that formal procedure, the original very generally posed question is rephrased, and stated in terms of one or more formal premises or hypotheses—usually, in terms of two logically incompatible (mutually contradictory) alternatives. In our illustrative experiment, one hypothesis might be, for example, "the dietary deficiency makes no difference to test performance," while the opposing assertion might be, "the dietary deficiency does make a difference to test performance." These two kinds of mutually contradictory statements are called a *null* hypothesis (commonly indicated by H_0) and an *alternative* hypothesis (indicated by H_1). From a strictly mathematical point of view, these terms have no particular significance. They serve merely to distinguish between two contrasting hypotheses that might just as well have been labeled H_A and H_B (Hays, 1973, p. 369). From a historical perspective, however, the terms are meaningful. Traditionally, H_0 has been associated with a "no effect" (hence, a "null") premise (Kirk, 1972, pp. 118-140). For example, in many typical drug studies, H_0 would be identified with the premise, "this drug has no demonstrable therapeutic effect."

H_1 would be traditionally associated with the negation of a "no effect" premise. There are two logically different ways in which an opposing premise could be expressed. On the one hand, it could be expressed simply as "H_0 is false." In this version, H_1 would be: "The statement 'dietary deficiency makes no difference' is a false statement." On the other hand, one could state a *specific* alternative premise: one could claim specifically, "*this* H_1 is true." For example, H_1 might be: "Dietary deficiency lengthens rat test performance times by 25%." The former type of a hypothesis ("H_0 is false") is called "inexact," since it does not provide a specific alternative premise but only states a general negation of a contrasting premise. The latter type ("diet degrades performance by 25%") exemplifies hypotheses called, not unexpectedly, "exact," since this type does provide a specific, affirmatively stated premise (Kirk, p. 102; Hays, p. 336).

A First Version of Statistical Hypotheses

So far, we have been considering very general formulations of hypotheses. The formal implementation of a statistical test of significance requires that one restate H_0 and H_1 in mathematically meaningful terms. Let us consider in more detail the "rat test performance" experiment described in chapter 10. To facilitate the introduction of the concepts we are about to present, we shall modify slightly the previous version of that hypothetical study. In that earlier version, we had assumed that the experimenters studied a particular kind of test performance in two groups of 50 animals each, one group receiving a normal, and the other, a deficient, diet. We shall now assume that the test performance of rats raised on a normal diet is so well known that further study would be superfluous, and that therefore the experimenters had elected to study only the test performance of one group of 50 animals raised on the deficient diet. The approach, then, is to measure the performance of these 50 animals, and to compare the results to the previously established, well-known, test norms that characterize the untreated rat population (animals raised on normal diets); the effects of dietary deprivation on learning would be assessed on that comparative basis.

What does it mean to say that the test performance of the general rat population is "well known"? For us in the role as statisticians/experimenters, it would mean that we know "enough" about an RV_P that mathematically represents that attribute. In terms of our specific study, it means that if we view the time taken by a rat to complete its test task as one actual $outcome_P$ (sample value), then the performance of the general, untreated population is represented by a known RV_P (population probability distribution). In general, "knowing" an RV may be a matter of degree. It may be known partially, or it may be fully specified (see part II). In our present experiment, we shall assume that the mathematical pattern of the general population's test performance is fully known. In particular, we shall assume that RV_P is a normal probability distribution with $\mu = 150$ secs. and $\sigma^2 = 100$ ($\sigma = 10$ secs.). That pdf_P is shown in figure 12.1. For the present, this is what we mean, then, when we say we know some attribute of a population "well enough." The empirical implications of this kind of mathematical representation and framework have already been discussed in several contexts (see especially chaps. 3, 4, 5, 10, and 11).

We can now begin to express quantitative hypotheses in statistical terms. We have assumed that H_0 is the premise (exact), "the

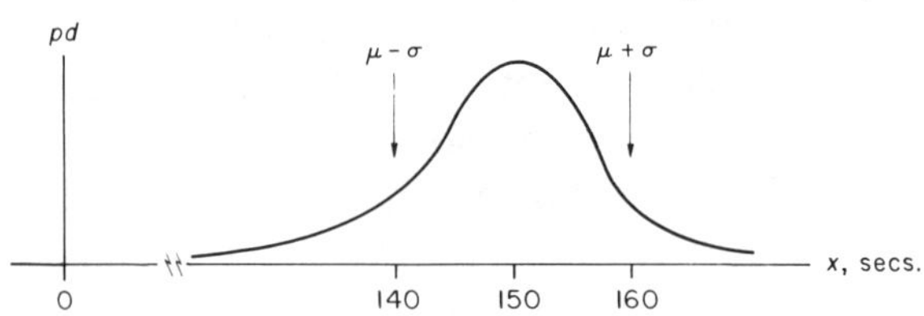

FIGURE 12.1 A population RV

special diet makes no difference to the test performance times," while H_1, the alternative premise (inexact), is, "the diet does make a difference to the test performance." What do these qualitative hypotheses imply in general statistical terms? That is, how would one begin to relate these two qualitatively expressed premises to a quantitative or other formal mathematical framework? The first step should be almost self-evident. H_0 assumes that the performance of our 50 experimentally treated animals is indistinguishable from the performance of the untreated population. The *mathematical* implication is that under the premise H_0, the 50 empirical measures are numbers that have been generated according to the dictates of the "known" RV_P shown in figure 12.1. Let us call that pdf "$RV_{P(0)}$." An initial statistical version of H_0 then is: THE RV_P THAT UNDERLIES THE 50 ACTUAL OUTCOMES$_P$ *IS* THE SAME RV AS THE KNOWN $RV_{P(0)}$ THAT UNDERLIES THE PERFORMANCE OF THE GENERAL POPULATION. This premise, then, expresses in *statistical* terms the qualitative assertion, "the diet makes *no* difference to performance."

We have assumed H_1 to be the inexact alternative hypothesis that the 50 empirical results are *not* those that would be expected from animals representative of the general untreated rat population. In statistical terms, H_1 merely proposes that THE RV_P THAT UNDERLIES OUR 50 ACTUAL OUTCOMES$_P$ *IS NOT* THE SAME AS $RV_{P(0)}$ THAT UNDERLIES THE PERFORMANCE OF THE GENERAL POPULATION. Thus, H_1 asserts mathematically that the diet makes some difference to performance: it states that the 50 actual outcomes did *not* "come from" the $RV_{P(0)}$, the probability distribution depicted in figure 12.1. This pair of hypotheses is represented schematically in figure 12.2.

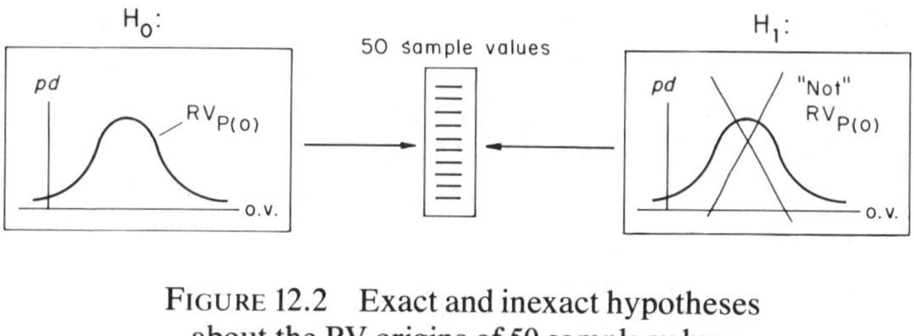

FIGURE 12.2 Exact and inexact hypotheses about the RV origins of 50 sample values

In this illustrative study, H_0, being exact, had specified a definite RV_P ($RV_{P(0)}$) while H_1, being inexact, did not specify a definite probability distribution. In this instance, H_1 had left the alternative pdf vague; the alternative hypothesis merely implied some RV_P other than the pdf specified for H_0. Let us for a moment consider how the situation would have differed had H_1 been an exact hypothesis also. In that case, H_1 would have proposed that the data came from some *other particular* RV_P. Were both H_0 and H_1 exact hypotheses, we would thus be considering two alternative, different, and specific RV_Ps as possible sources of our 50 empirically obtained numbers or actual outcomes$_P$. We might label two such pdfs.specified by H_0 and H_1 as $RV_{P(0)}$ and $RV_{P(1)}$, respectively. In that case, our statistical goal would be to evaluate the 50 outcomes in order to be able to decide between the two alternative conclusions, (1) data came from $RV_{P(0)}$, or (2) data came from $RV_{P(1)}$. This pair of exact hypotheses is exemplified schematically in figure 12.3.

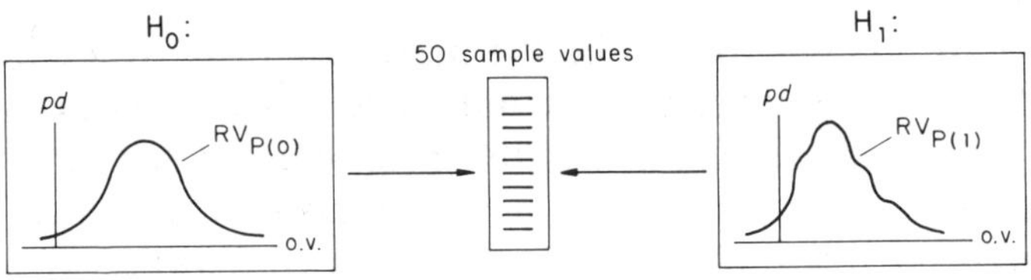

FIGURE 12.3. Two exact hypotheses about the RV origins of 50 sample values

Let us return to our original pair of hypotheses, the exact H_0 and the inexact H_1 (fig. 12.2). We have taken the first step in our statistical procedure. We have translated qualitatively expressed null and alternative hypotheses into two corresponding statistical statements concerning the origins of 50 numbers. How do we decide between H_0 and H_1 on the basis of the experimentally obtained data (the 50 empirically obtained measures of test performance times)? Can we decide by inspection alone, that is, without further mathematical analysis? In other words, is it immediately apparent whether or not a set of 50 empirically obtained measures of time had been "generated," from a mathematical point of view, by $RV_{P(0)}$? It should be obvious that for *any* given set of 50 numbers, we could not decide this issue by inspection alone, for the following reason. The $RV_{P(0)}$ postulated by H_0 as the generator of our data is continuous and not limited in range. In principle, therefore, this kind of a RV could generate *any* actual outcome value; given any set of 50 numbers, all that one could say initially is that these numbers *could* have come from $RV_{P(0)}$. There is no logical basis for excluding such a possibility.

The above reasoning implies that we cannot assess whether H_0 is true or false without further work. We have found that a superficial examination of 50 numbers, the empirical results, cannot provide a well-founded answer. There is no obvious basis for concluding either that our data did come from $RV_{P(0)}$ or that they did not. One must, then, look to other analyses to settle the issue.

A Second Version of Statistical Hypotheses

The general features of the next mathematical step already were introduced (but not explained) in chapter 10. There, we learned that after empirically obtaining a set of actual $outcomes_P$ the statistician would typically reduce these data mathematically to a single number. In any given experimental study, one of a variety of available mathematical techniques would be selected and applied, and an actual $outcome_D$ or a statistic would be obtained. So far, the only explanation offered for taking this step is that this representative number, the statistic, would "somehow" facilitate the analysis of the experimental results. We shall now begin to examine this approach further, although its full import will not start to emerge until various specific quantitative approaches are studied (chaps. 13-18).

We are about to address a vitally important question. Let us for the moment assume that H_0 is true. We know that this hypothesis asserts that the 50 performance measures (actual $outcomes_P$ or sample values) were "really" generated, from the point of view of mathematics, by $RV_{P(0)}$. Let us assume that these 50 numbers have been reduced to a single value (an actual $outcome_D$ or a statistic) by some particular, although as yet unspecified, arithmetical procedure. We know (chap. 10) that this kind of a number can be conceptualized as having been generated by an *underlying derived RV*. The key mathematical question now is: If from a mathematical/formal point of view, one conceptualizes a set of sample values as numbers generated according to a particular underlying RV (in the present example, $RV_{P(0)}$), and if one performs some particular mathematical operation (so far, unspecified) on such a set of numbers to reduce them to a single descriptor (an actual $outcome_D$ or a statistic), then, still speaking from a mathematical perspective, what is the particular RV (the RV_D) that underlies that single number? That is, for a given RV_P and a given mathematical data-reducing procedure, what is the corresponding RV_D?

This important question will be addressed in the remainder of part IV in the context of various specific situations. At this point, only a very general, provisional, answer can be given. The mathematical picture is the following. The characteristics of RV_D will depend on *two* factors. First, RV_D will be determined to some extent by the specific characteristics of the RV_P that underlies the set of sample values. Second, RV_D will be determined in part by the particular mathematical operation that has been selected for a given experiment to be the operation that will reduce a set of sample values to a single actual $outcome_D$, a statistic. Thus, the specifics of any one particular RV_D are determined *jointly* by its two conceptual ancestors: the particular RV_P that generated a set of sample values, and the particular mathematical procedure that has been used to reduce these data to a statistic. We say that *a specific pair, an RV_P and a mathematical operation, will mathematically define or "induce" a specific RV_D*. This idea is shown in figure 12.4.

We should note carefully that this specification of a RV_D jointly by an RV_P and a mathematical data-reducing operation is a *mathematical* specification. It makes no explicit reference to, or use of, a particular set of empirical data. That is, once we have defined a specific underlying RV_P and a specific mathematical data-reducing operation, then the mathematical characteristics of the jointly determined RV_D (that is, the specifics of that probability distribution) are strictly defined as the result of purely mathematical considerations. At present, we shall not consider further the mathematical relationships that exist between RV_P, a mathemat-

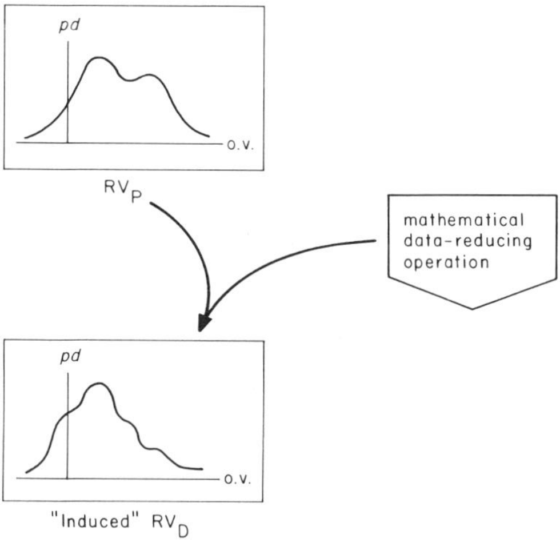

FIGURE 12.4 An RV_D jointly induced by a specified RV_P and a specified data-reducing procedure

ical data-reducing operation, and RV_D. We shall begin to explore these relationships in chapter 13.

Since a particular RV_D is determined in this joint fashion by a particular RV_P and a given mathematical data-reduction method, a change in *either* that RV_P *or* in the mathematical operation (or both) will, in general, produce some corresponding change in the characteristics of RV_D. That is, if some pair of formal entities, let us call them $RV_{P(a)}$ and the mathematical data-reducing operation$_a$, jointly specify some derived probability distribution, let us call it $RV_{D(a)}$, then a *different* RV_P, say, $RV_{P(b)}$ and the *same* mathematical operation$_a$, will "induce" or define a new, different, derived probability distribution, say, $RV_{D(b)}$. Similarly, the *same* RV_P, $RV_{P(a)}$, *and a different data-reducing procedure*, say, the mathematical data-reducing operation$_b$, will define yet another derived probability distribution, say, $RV_{D(c)}$. These conclusions are represented schematically in figures 12.5 and 12.6.

We are now prepared to complete this introduction to hypothesis testing by examining, still in a somewhat general fashion, a second version of H_0 and H_1 (see fig. 12.2). The logic of the procedure will follow directly from the preceding discussions. Consider the following. We have an experiment that has yielded a

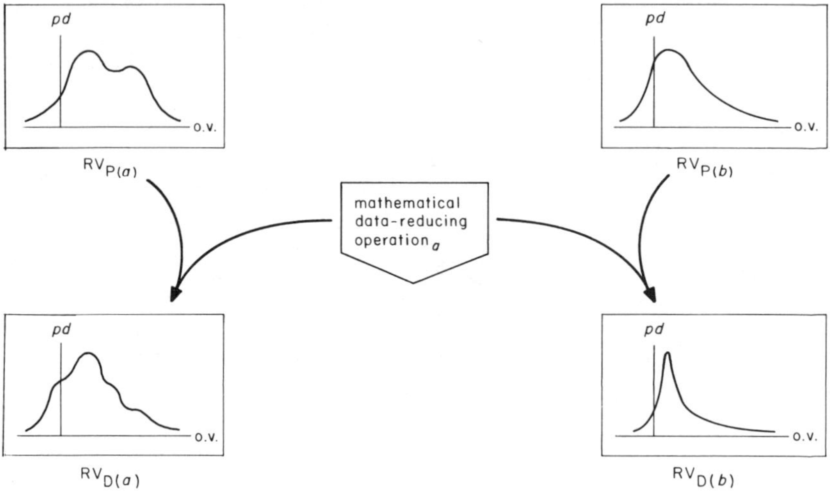

FIGURE 12.5 Different RV_Ps and one data-reducing operation

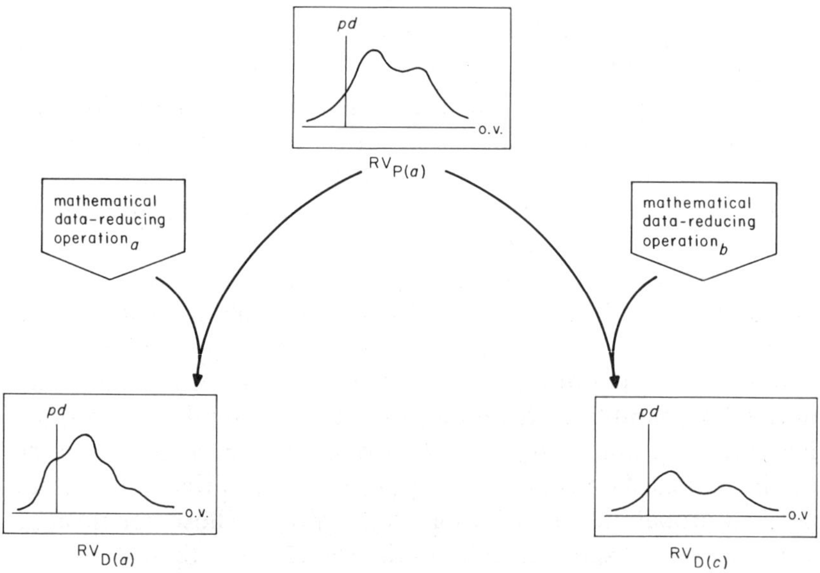

FIGURE 12.6 Different data-reducing operations and one RV_P

set of 50 sample values; and in turn, by means of a particular mathematical data-reduction procedure, these values have yielded one statistic, an actual outcome$_D$. If we postulate a *particular* probability distribution as an underlying RV_P for the 50 sample values, then, since presumably we have used a *particular* data-reducing procedure, we have thereby induced or specified a *particular* underlying derived probability distribution, RV_D (see fig. 12.4). Therefore, if the sample values "came from" a particular RV_P, then the statistic must have "come from" a particular RV_D, namely, the probability distribution that is mathematically defined jointly by RV_P and the specified mathematical data-reducing procedure. This situation is illustrated in figure 12.7.

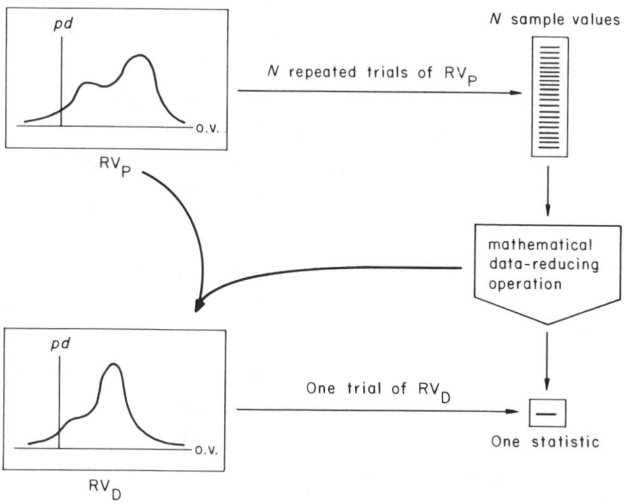

FIGURE 12.7 RV origins of a set of sample values and of a statistic

We can particularize these general considerations as follows. If $RV_{P(0)}$ is the "correct" underlying probability distribution for the set of 50 obtained sample values, then a *particular* RV_D will be the *"correct" underlying probability distribution for the statistic that we have calculated.* Let us call that derived probability distribution $RV_{D(0)}$. In the present discussion, we cannot say exactly what that $RV_{D(0)}$ is, since, although we have specified $RV_{P(0)}$ and said that *some* specific arithmetical data-reduction procedure had been used, we have not yet identified any one particular data-reduction procedure. Therefore, although we know (see figure

12.4) that *some* particular $RV_{D(0)}$ must be induced, we cannot at this point say more than that. Thus, the RV_D shown in figure 12.7 represents some definite, but as yet unspecified pdf. We shall begin to specify particular RV_Ds in chapter 13.

Alternatively, if $RV_{P(0)}$ is *not* the "correct" population probability distribution that underlies the 50 actual outcomes$_P$, then, in turn, $RV_{D(0)}$ will not be the "correct" derived probability distribution that underlies our statistic. This conclusion is based on the previous considerations that were illustrated in figure 12.6. Two *different* RV_Ps and the *same* mathematical data-reducing operation would, in general, lead to two different induced RV_Ds. If, then, in figure 12.7, $RV_{P(0)}$ is *not* the correct underlying pdf, some *other* pdf must be the correct underlying *population* probability distribution. Concomitantly, some pdf *other* than $RV_{D(0)}$ will be the correct underlying *derived* probability distribution. In short, if $RV_{P(0)}$ is correct, then $RV_{D(0)}$ is correct; otherwise, that is, if $RV_{P(0)}$ is incorrect, then, correspondingly, $RV_{D(0)}$ will be incorrect as well.

These considerations imply that we can replace the pair of hypotheses concerning the *RV origins of sample values* (did $RV_{P(0)}$ generate our 50 actual outcomes$_P$, or did it not?) with a pair of hypotheses concerning the *RV origin of a statistic* (did $RV_{D(0)}$ generate the single actual outcome$_D$, or did it not?).

Thus, the pair of hypotheses H_0 and H_1 in figure 12.2 can be transformed to a corresponding pair, H_0' and H_1'. The hypothesis H_0, the 50 sample values were generated by $RV_{P(0)}$, becomes H_0': the statistic was generated by $RV_{D(0)}$. H_1, the hypothesis that the 50 sample values were *not* generated by $RV_{P(0)}$ (i.e., they were generated by some other, unspecified RV_P), becomes H_1': the statistic was *not* generated by $RV_{D(0)}$ (i.e., it was generated by some other, unspecified RV_D). This situation is illustrated in figure 12.8. Basically, that figure combines the ideas illustrated in figures 12.7 for any one hypothesis with the concept illustrated in figure 12.6.

Thus, finally, deciding whether or not the diet affected the test performance treated animals becomes a decision concerning *the RV origin of a derived actual outcome or statistic*. If we were to conclude that H_0' is correct, we should thereby be concluding that

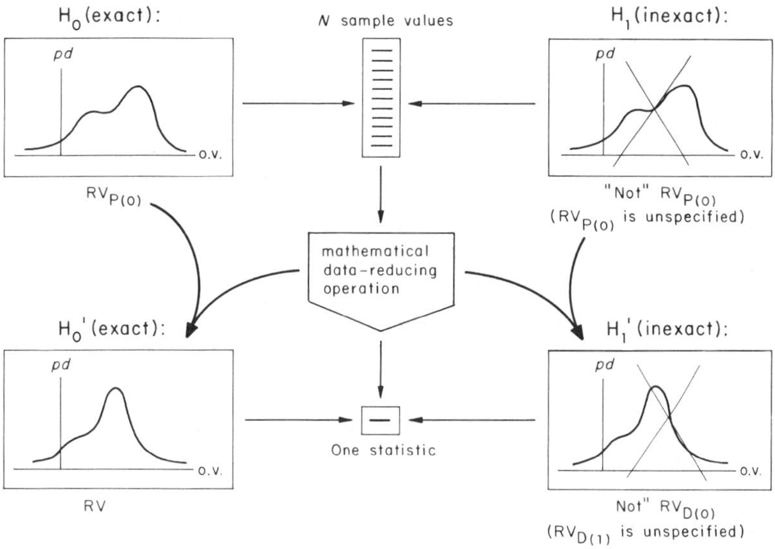

FIGURE 12.8 Two pairs of hypotheses

Ho is correct as well. That is, if we conclude that the statistic came from $RV_{D(0)}$, we would thereby also conclude that the 50 sample values came from $RV_{P(0)}$.[1] In that case, the implication would be that the diet made no difference; the performance of the treated animals had been indistinguishable from the performance that

[1] You may have noticed that now we are reasoning *from* H′ (a hypothesis about a statistic) *to* H (a hypothesis about sample values) and thus are inverting the direction of the original argument. That is, originally we reasoned that if we know RV_P and the data-reducing method, then we can say that there is a specific RV_D, a uniquely determined probability distribution, that underlies the statistic (see figs. 12.4 and 12.7). Our inference moved from RV_P and the data-reducing procedure to RV_D. Now, however, we are arguing that if we know RV_D (and the data-reducing method), we then know the particular RV_P that correspondingly must have generated a set of sample values that led to the statistic in the first instance. Reasoning backward in this fashion is logically justifiable only if our situation has "uniqueness"—i.e., if it is true that there is just *one* RV_P that, for a given data-reducing method, can lead to a given RV_D. That was the reason we needed to introduce the assumption represented in figure 12.6: *Different* RV_Ps and the *same* data-reducing method will lead to *different* RV_Ds. If that were not true, if they could lead to the *same* RV_D, then we could not legitimately invert our line of reasoning. We could *not* conclude that just because a given statistic "came from" a given RV_D, the sample values antecedent to that statistic must have correspondingly "come from" *one* particular, specifiable RV_P. These are complex issues, and are addressed in more advanced courses.

would be expected from untreated animals. If, however, we were to conclude that H_1' had been correct, then we would thereby also conclude that H_1 had been correct as well. That is, if the statistic did not come from $RV_{D(0)}$, then neither did the 50 sample values come from $RV_{P(0)}$. The implication would be that the diet did make a difference; from a statistical point of view, the obtained set of 50 sample values and the statistic calculated from these did not, in a statistical sense, "act like" numbers that one would expect to obtain by trials involving $RV_{P(0)}$ and $RV_{D(0)}$.

We shall begin to see in chapter 13 that the decision between H_0' and H_1', like the decision between H_0 and H_1, cannot be made simply by inspection of the statistic without further analysis. However, as one might expect, deciding between H_0' and H_1' (that is, analyzing and evaluating the RV origin of a single number—an actual $outcome_D$ or statistic) will be considerably more tractable mathematically than deciding directly between H_0 and H_1 (that is, analyzing and evaluating the RV origins of 50 numbers—the actual $outcome_P$ or sample values).

We have pursued this introduction in general terms, and have gone about as far as one can go at this level of generality. The principal conceptual component that has been left unspecified so far is the mathematical data-reducing operation. Accordingly, in the next several chapters, we shall explore specific, frequently used data-processing methods and their implications for statistical inferences.

PROBLEMS

12.1 What is the difference between an exact and an inexact hypothesis? Between a null and an alternative hypothesis?

12.2 What is the difference, conceptually, between H_0 and H_0' (or between H_1 and H_1')?

12.3 What does it mean to say that an RV_D is jointly induced or defined by an RV_P and a mathematical data-reducing operation?

12.4 In principle, how does one decide between two hypotheses concerning the RV origin of a set of N sample values or actual outcomes$_P$?

12.5 A set of N sample values are reduced to a statistic (see chap. 10). If H_0 is the premise that this set originated from N trials of $RV_{P(0)}$, and H_1 the premise that the N sample values originated from N trials of $RV_{P(1)}$, why do these two hypotheses imply two different RV_Ds? Are H_0 and H_1 exact or inexact? Describe H_0' and H_1'.

12.6 One RV_P and mathematical data-reducing operation induce one RV_D, while a second, different RV_P and different data-reducing operation induce another. Are the two RV_Ds necessarily different? Why, or why not?

CHAPTER 13

The Normal Probability Distribution and the Sample Mean

Statisticians and mathematicians use various mathematical procedures or operations to reduce a set of actual outcomes$_P$ or sample values to a single, representative number, an actual outcome$_D$ or statistic. Each method has its own particular applications and characteristics. The mathematical data-reducing method that we shall consider in this chapter consists of a simple, yet basic arithmetical operation: obtaining the average of a set of numbers. We shall transform a set of sample values to a single statistic by computing their average. As this particular statistic is the mean of a set of sample values, it is called the *sample mean*, and commonly is represented by M. We shall discuss some of its principal features and applications in the context of the hypothetical experiment introduced in preceding chapters (the study of the effects of diet on test performance of rats).

Let us assume as before that we had obtained 50 sample values. If we calculate their mean, M, we know from chapters 10 and 12 that in terms of our theoretical mathematical framework, a number such as M (a statistic) is considered to be a number that has been generated from a single trial of an "RV experiment." In the general case, we have called the kind of a probability distribution that is presumed to underlie a statistic a derived probability distribution, or RV_D. In the present particular case, RV_D is the derived probability distribution that underlies the sample mean, M. Accordingly, this RV_D is called *the probability distribution of the sample mean*.

Thus far, we have a set of 50 sample values generated by 50 repeated trials of RV_P, a sample mean M (a statistic) calculated from these sample values, and RV_D, the probability distribution of the sample mean (the probability distribution that underlies M). The obvious question is: how are RV_D and RV_P related? We learned in chapter 12 that in general, the mathematical properties of RV_D will be determined jointly by (1) the mathematical characteristics of RV_P and (2) the particular mathematical operation that is used to reduce a set of sample values to a statistic (see fig. 12.4). We will now examine the first specific case of this general principle.

We need to specify two entities, then, in order to define RV_D. One of these, the data-reducing procedure, has already been selected; it is the arithmetical procedure that reduces a set of sample values to a sample mean M. Let us specify the second entity, the population probability distribution; let us assume that RV_P is a *normal* pdf, with a mean of 150 secs. and a variance of 100. This, of course, is a pdf that we had used in chapter 12 (see fig. 12.1). We now have specified the two ingredients that jointly define RV_D, the probability distribution that underlies the statistic M. In this particular case, what are the mathematical properties of that RV?

The Probability Distribution that Underlies M

It will be useful to address that question in a somewhat more general version. Instead of considering only one specific normal RV_P and a set of specifically 50 experimental subjects, we shall instead consider the more general case of *any normal* RV_P and a general set of N sample values. In this context, N, an integer, represents the number of sample values generated by RV_P in a given experiment. N is called the *sample size*. Let us use a simple subscript notation to represent the general parameters of RV_P. We shall represent its mean by μ_P, its variance by $\sigma^2{}_P$, and its standard deviation by σ_P.

If, then, we generate N sample values from a normal RV_P that has the parameters μ_P and σ_P and obtain a value for the sample mean M, we can specify the characteristics of RV_D, the probability distribution of the sample mean. First, like RV_P, RV_D is a *normal* pdf. Second, its parameters will be related to those of RV_P and to the sample size N in a simple fashion. The *mean* of RV_D will be the *same* as the mean of RV_P, and the *variance* of RV_D will be numerically equal to the *variance* of RV_P *divided* by N. We can state these relationships algebraically. If we represent the mean, variance, and standard deviation of RV_D by μ_D, σ^2_D, and σ_D, respectively, then the following relationships are true in general:

$$\mu_D = \mu_P, \tag{13.1}$$

$$\sigma^2_D = \sigma^2_P/N. \tag{13.2}$$

Furthermore, since $\sigma_D = \sqrt{\sigma^2_D}$ and $\sigma_P = \sqrt{\sigma^2_P}$ by definition,[1]

$$\sigma_D = \sqrt{(\sigma^2_P/N)}, \tag{13.3}$$

or

$$\sigma_D = \frac{\sigma_P}{\sqrt{N}}. \tag{13.4}$$

The last quantity, σ_D, the standard deviation of the probability distribution of the sample mean, is a parameter that assumes a particular importance in many kinds of statistical problems. It has been given the special name *standard error of the mean*.

We can now address our more specific question. If RV_P is a normal pdf, $\mu_P = 150$ secs., $\sigma^2_P = 100$, and if $N = 50$, then RV_D is a normal pdf, $\mu_D = \mu_P = 150$ secs., and $\sigma^2_D = \sigma^2_P/N = 2$. σ_D, the standard error of the mean, is $\sqrt{2}$ or approximately 1.414. This situation is schematically illustrated in figure 13.1. That figure is a particular case of the general situation represented in figure 12.7, and it may be instructive for you to compare these two repre-

[1] It may seem strange that $\sigma = \sqrt{\sigma^2}$ would be true by definition and not because of the obvious algebraic relationship. After all, $x = \sqrt{x^2}$ for reasons of algebra, and not "by definition." The present situation is different, however. We are dealing with two symbols, σ^2 and σ, that represent the variance and the standard deviation, respectively; the latter is *defined* as the square root of the former. σ^2 is *one* symbol; the "²" in that symbol is part of that single whole symbolic unit, and is not an exponent. One therefore cannot treat it as such and "take the square root of σ^2 to obtain σ." One can of course always take the square root of the *numerical quantity* that is symbolized by σ^2.

sentations. Incidentally, this kind of figure will reappear in slightly different versions throughout part IV.

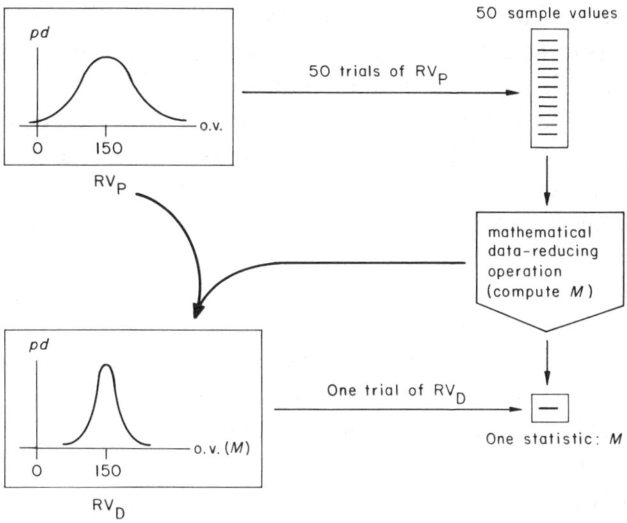

FIGURE 13.1 RV origins of the sample mean *M*

Empirical Considerations

We have considered the mathematical relationships between the parameters of RV_P and RV_D. What are the empirical implications of these relationships? We already have the necessary background to answer that question. First, we had learned in chapter 11 about the empirical meaning that the parameters μ and σ have for *any* normal pdf. We saw that in a set of repeated observations, most of the obtained outcome values would be expected to cluster about μ with a dispersion whose extent was indicated by the magnitude of σ (or σ^2). Second, we have also learned about the empirical meaning of, and distinctions between, repeated observations of RV_P and repeated observations of RV_D (chap. 10). The former concept connotes observations made within a *single* experiment (it connotes a set of sample values), while the latter connotes observations made over *repeated* experiments (it connotes a set of statistics, one for each study). By means of these two groups of concepts we can understand the empirical implications of (13.1) through (13.4). (13.1) implies that both a set of N sample values as well as a set of sample means will tend to cluster about the *same* outcome value (in our case, 150 secs.). The other three equations concern relationships between the dispersions of RV_P and RV_D. Since σ_D is smaller than σ_P by a factor of $1/\sqrt{N}$, one would expect that a set of *sample means* obtained from *several* experiments would show considerably *less* dispersion than a set of *N sample values* acquired in *one* experiment. In other words, sample means would tend to cluster more closely about μ than would sample values.

Let us clarify these conclusions with a numerical example. In our hypothetical experiment, $\sigma_P = 10$, while $\sigma_D = 1.414$, approximately. Therefore, we would expect that in any *one experiment*, about 68% of our set of 50 *sample values* would fall into the outcome range from 140 to 160 secs.; correspondingly, for a set of *sample means* obtained in a series of *repeated experiments*, one would expect about 68% of the values of M to fall into an outcome range roughly between 148.586 to 151.414 secs. (see chap. 11). Obviously, compared to sample values, the sample means tend to fall into a more narrow outcome span.

If we examine equations (13.2) through (13.4) further, we see that the difference in dispersion of RV_P and RV_D is influenced by the magnitude of N. For a given RV_P, the larger N, the smaller σ_D, and vice versa. If, for example, we had used 1,000 instead of 50 subjects in our hypothetical experiment (with RV_P unchanged), then σ_D would have been 0.316 rather than 1.414. In repeated experiments, 68% of the values of M would then probably lie within the outcome range from 149.684 to 150.316 secs., rather than within the previous range (148.586 to 151.414 secs.).

Thus, we have seen that in our first example of a specific RV_D jointly induced by a specific RV_P and a specific data-reducing procedure, the profiles as well as the parameters of the two kinds of probability distributions were related in specific and specifiable ways. Furthermore, we also have seen that the sample size N plays a role. In the present case, it enters as a scale factor that has an effect on the dispersion of RV_D, the probability distribution that underlies our statistic M. Of course, N cannot affect the dispersion of the *population* probability distribution. That dispersion is an attribute of the population. It is determined by the characteristics of the population, and remains the same regardless of how many sample values N we generate during a given experiment.

Before we resume the development of inferential procedures, it might be well to address a question that has so far remained in the background. How does one know about the relationships between RV_P and RV_D? How does one know in the present case, for example, that if RV_P is a normal pdf, then so is RV_D? And how does one know about the relationships between the parameters of the two pdfs?

The latter question frequently is not too difficult to answer. In many situations—for many different types of RV_Ps and mathematical data-reducing operations—one can establish the relationships between corresponding parameters of RV_P and RV_D by relatively elementary mathematical methods. For instance, it is not difficult to show in our present example that the parametric relationships are those expressed in (13.1) through (13.4). For these demonstrations one does need to know, however, how to deal algebraically with certain kinds of mathematical situations. One needs to be able to compute "expected values" algebraically. While this procedure is not difficult, considerable space would be needed to present it adequately and that would take us too far afield. For that reason, and also because expositions are already available (Hays, 1973, pp. 871-875), we shall not pursue these kinds of algebraic analyses here. The point I wish to make is only that mathematical relationships such as those expressed in (13.1) through (13.4) can be readily derived by relatively straightforward mathematical methods (Freeman, 1963, pp. 179-180; Hays, pp. 272-273, 278-279).

The situation becomes quite different, however, when one undertakes to derive the relationships between the *profiles* of RV_P and RV_D. There is usually no simple answer to questions such as, "How does one know that if the population probability distribution is normal, then the probability distribution of the sample mean also is normal?"[2] One usually has to resort to advanced mathematical techniques that involve the use of the family of *moments*. Roughly, one analyzes how the moments of RV_P are transmuted by a mathematical data-reduction method into a corresponding set of moments of RV_D. If one knows this latter set of moments, one can then specify RV_D itself (see, for example, Freeman, p. 202). This is about as far as the matter can be explained without resorting to mathematical procedures that are clearly beyond our scope. Although the explanation necessarily has been quite sketchy, we have at least some idea about the general mathematical approach to the analysis of the relationships between RV_P and RV_D. If these ideas are encountered in more advanced work, they will not be totally unfamiliar and strange.

Acceptance and Rejection Regions

We may now return to the point we had reached in developing a hypothesis-test procedure in chapter 12. We had concluded that in general, the pair of statistical hypotheses H_0 and H_1 would be transformed to a second pair, H_0' and H_1'. The initial statistical issue concerning the RV origins of 50 sample values would be shifted to a second issue concerning the RV origin of a single actual outcome, a statistic. We have now specified a particular data-reducing procedure, and learned what kind of a RV_D is jointly induced by that procedure and a *normal* underlying population probability distribution. We can resume the discussion in specific terms.

We shall first reconsider the two null hypotheses H_0 and H_0', and then the two alternative hypotheses H_1 and H_1'. In each case, the relationships we have just established in general between the population probability distribution and the probability distribution of the sample mean will furnish the link in the logical argu-

[2]We are considering the case of a normal RV_P. If RV_P is not a normal pdf, then in general neither is RV_D (for M) a normal pdf. If RV_P departs only slightly from a normal profile, then the probability distribution of the sample mean M also remains almost a normal pdf. More drastic departures of RV_P from a normal profile would correspondingly tend to induce more drastic departures in the profile of RV_D. At what point, then, would the departure of RV_P from a normal profile be severe enough to invalidate the assumption that RV_D for M is a normal pdf? We shall not address that kind of an issue, but merely note that it is the kind of a practical issue that can become quite important and raise difficulties for statisticians in actual applied work.

ment. First, suppose that H_0 were true, that from a mathematical point of view, the 50 sample values were generated from 50 trials of $RV_{P(0)}$. (That pdf, as we remember from chap. 12, is the normal probability distribution that statistically characterizes the test behavior of the *untreated* animal population. Therefore, saying that 50 sample values obtained from *treated* animals did "come from" $RV_{P(0)}$ implies that the diet made no difference.) The preceding discussion and the relationships expressed in (13.1) through (13.4) imply that if 50 sample values were generated by $RV_{P(0)}$, a normal pdf, $\mu_P = 150$ secs., $\sigma^2_P = 100$, then from a mathematical point of view, the value of M obtained from one performance of an experiment would be a statistic derived from one trial of $RV_{D(0)}$, a normal pdf with $\mu_D = 150$ secs., $\sigma^2_D = 2$. This is the situation we had analyzed previously and exhibited in figure 13.1.

Let us say that we had performed an experiment, obtained 50 sample values, and calculated M. Suppose that we had obtained some specific value such as 152.3 secs. Can we immediately decide whether that value had been generated by $RV_{D(0)}$? We have already encountered a very similar question in conjunction with the origins of the 50 sample values. We concluded in chapter 12 that since the RV_P postulated by H_0 was a normal pdf, a type of pdf that has a continuous, not-limited-in-range potential outcome, we could not *prima facie* reject the possibility that *any* experimentally obtained sample value had, from a mathematical point of view, been generated by that pdf. For the same reasons, we cannot immediately confirm or deny that any particular value of M might or might not have been generated by $RV_{D(0)}$. In principle, that pdf could yield *any* number, and thus any value of M, on a single trial.

How shall we decide about the RV origin of M? The procedure will be based on an examination of alternative RVs. First, if the 50 *sample values* did *not* come from $RV_{P(0)}$, what RV *did* they come from? There would be many possible ways to answer this question; we shall make a particularly simple assumption, and assume that if the 50 sample values did not come from $RV_{P(0)}$, i.e., if H_0 were false and H_1 correct, then these values had been generated by some other RV_P that was just like RV_P in all respects *except* for the value of its *mean*. That is, we are assuming that if H_1 is correct, then, from a mathematical point of view, the 50 sample values have been generated by an RV_P that is a normal pdf, $\sigma^2_P = 100$, and whose mean is unknown. That kind of an RV, we remember from chapter 11, is identical to $RV_{P(0)}$ except that it is shifted in one direction or the other along the outcome axis (see fig. 11.2). The implication is that if the diet did have an effect, then, statistically, it would change the test performance of a group "on average" without changing the dispersion of that treated population's test scores about the (different) mean. Thus, if H_1 is true, then the 50 sample values would have "come from" some normal pdf such as one of those illustrated in figure 13.2.

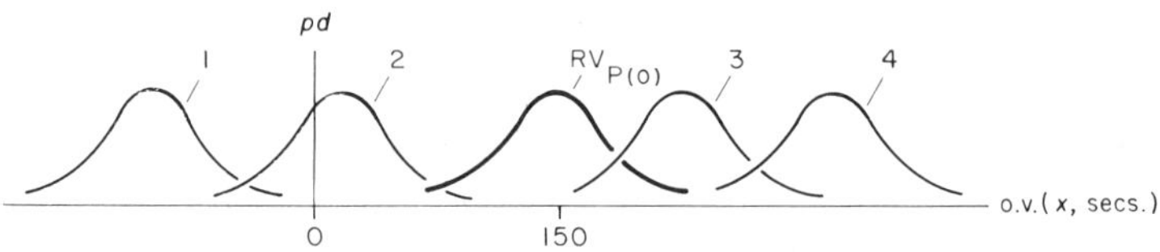

FIGURE 13.2 $RV_{P(0)}$ and four alternative RV_Ps

What does that kind of premise imply about the corresponding RV origin of M? The previously discussed relationships between any population RV and its corresponding probability distribution of the sample mean M continue to apply, of course. Thus, if H_1 is true, then we may infer that for each and every one of the possible alternative RV_Ps such as those shown in figure 13.2 there will be one corresponding RV_D, specified by the parametric relationships expressed in (13.1) through (13.4). This conclusion is illustrated in figure 13.3; for each one of the RV_Ps that could be a possible source of sample values if H_1 were true, there is one corresponding RV_D that could be a source for M if H_1' were true. Thus, finally, deciding between H_0' and H_1' comes to a decision whether $RV_{D(0)}$ or one of the other RV_Ds in figure 13.3 generated M. Since any value of M could have been generated by any of these RV_Ds, the situation requires further analysis.

We base our approach to deciding between H_0' and H_1' on a conclusion that was presented in chapter 11. We remember that in general, if we have a normal RV, then an outcome region that lies relatively close to the mean of that pdf, a region such as that labeled A in figure 13.4, is a region with a relatively *high* associa-

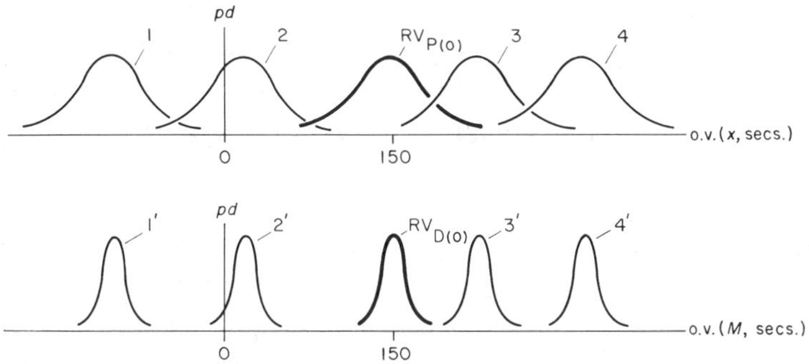

FIGURE 13.3 $RV_{P(0)}$, $RV_{D(0)}$, and four alternative RV_P/RV_D pairs

ted probability. Consequently, if we perform one trial of that RV, it is likely that the outcome would fall into that kind of an "*A*-type" region. If we apply this argument to our present situation, we may conclude that if H_0' were true, then the single outcome value *M* would probably (but not certainly—that's the difficulty) fall into a region fairly close to 150 secs., the mean of its underlying pdf $RV_{D(0)}$. If H_0' were true, and if the pdf in figure 13.4 were $RV_{D(0)}$, then *M* would probably lie in the kind of range labeled *A*.

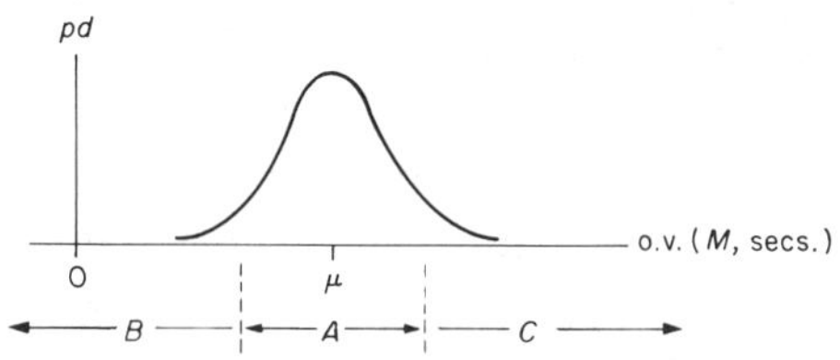

FIGURE 13.4 Likely and unlikely outcome regions

If, however, H_0' were false and H_1' were true, then *M* would be more likely to fall into a region of $RV_{D(0)}$ such as those labeled *B* or *C* in figure 13.4. It would probably fall into a region some distance away from the mean of the "incorrect" underlying RV, $RV_{D(0)}$. And, at the same time, *M* would probably fall into an "*A*-type" region of its correct underlying pdf, i.e., one of the alternatives illustrated in figure 13.3. Either way one looks at it, if H_1' is true, we should expect that the value of *M* obtained from our hypothetical study would lie at some distance from 150 secs. Its value would probably be significantly different from the mean of $RV_{D(0)}$. These informal considerations suggest an approach to deciding between H_0' and H_1'. These two hypotheses correspondingly imply two different types of outcome regions into which *M* would be likely to fall. Accordingly, we shall segment the outcome axis into two such types of regions. One will be a region such as the outcome axis segment *A* in figure 13.4. We have seen that if the value of *M* obtained in an experiment does fall into that kind of a region of $RV_{D(0)}$, a region close to 150 secs., it would seem reasonable to conclude that *M* had been generated by $RV_{D(0)}$. It would thus also seem reasonable to accept H_0'. Therefore, we call an outcome region such as *A* an *acceptance region*[3] (implying acceptance of H_0').

The other logical possibility would be, of course, that *M* could fall outside *A*, and thus into regions such as those labeled *B* and *C* in figure 13.4. If that result were to occur, we should conclude that *M* "did *not* come from" $RV_{D(0)}$, that it came from some other RV_D instead.[4] We shall call regions such as *B* or *C rejection regions* (implying rejection of H_0'). If *M* would fall into such a region, then, we should reject H_0' and thereby tacitly accept H_1'. We would not specify an alternative probability distribution; we would only conclude that it must be *some* alternative RV_D such as one of those shown as graphs 1′, 2′, 3′, and 4′ in figure 13.3.

On the basis of these informal considerations, we have developed a rationale for segmenting the outcome axis into acceptance and rejection regions.[5] An outcome value that demarcates these two kinds of decision regions is called a *critical value*. Two such critical values (*a* and *b*) are shown in figure 13.5.

[3] A distinction is sometimes made between "accepting" a hypothesis and "not rejecting" it (Hays, pp. 350-356; Kirk, pp. 118-126). From a mathematical point of view, these terms refer to the same logical decision, and the label is not important.

[4] We shall ignore the case where *M* has fallen precisely on the boundary between two decision regions. According to the discussion in chapter 5, that case has a zero probability of occurring.

[5] In general, the rationale used to divide the potential outcome into two kinds of regions involves some intricate mathematical questions. There are no ideal, "best" segmentation patterns (Hays, pp. 338-356, 377-378; Freeman, pp. 288-290). Let us agree that the proposed method of segmenting the outcome axis seems to be a reasonable one.

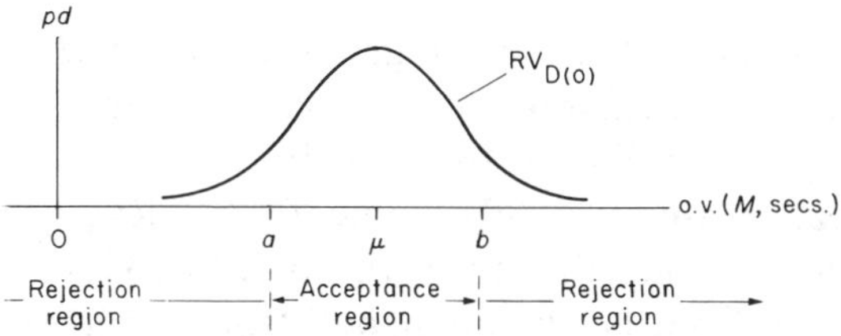

FIGURE 13.5 Decision regions and critical values

The Level of Significance and the Error of the First Kind

The obvious next question is: how does one quantify these qualitative concepts? That is, how large should the acceptance region be—what outcome values should we choose as critical values? The less than ideal answer is that the critical values, and thus the size of the acceptance region, will be selected on the basis of certain subjective decisions. In general, these choices will reflect the kinds of risks that one is willing to take in drawing one or the other conclusion (accepting one or the other of the two hypotheses). This step confronts us with the inescapable fact that inherent in the process of statistical inference is the possibility of making mistakes. Let us see how this situation concerning errors arises.

It will be convenient to discuss the issue in terms of a specific numerical example rather than in terms of the general situation illustrated in figure 13.5. Let us make that figure specific by assigning two arbitrarily selected critical values, 147 and 153 secs. In any one experiment, we should obtain a sample mean M that must necessarily fall into one or the other type of an outcome region. If it were to fall within the region between 147 and 153 secs., we would accept H_0' (or "not reject" it); we would conclude that the correct RV underlying M had indeed been $RV_{D(0)}$. Correspondingly, we would also accept H_0. We would conclude that the correct RV underlying the 50 sample values acquired from *treated* animals had been $RV_{P(0)}$. Now, as we remember, that particular normal pdf ($\mu_P = 150$ secs., $\sigma^2_P = 100$) is not only the RV_P postulated by the null hypothesis H_0. In addition, we have been assuming that it is known from previous studies that this normal pdf is also the population probability distribution that underlies sample values acquired from the general *untreated* population of animals. Therefore, the conclusion that H_0 is true has a second implication. By concluding that the 50 sample values acquired from 50 treated animals did "come from" $RV_{P(0)}$, one would thereby also conclude that from the point of view of statistics, these data could not be distinguished from a corresponding set that one would expect to obtain from 50 untreated animals. These, of course, were the considerations that motivated the initial choice of H_0. The experimenters selected a null hypothesis that proposed an RV origin for sample values acquired from treated animals that is the *same* as the known RV origin of sample values acquired from untreated animals. That selection makes it possible to decide, by deciding in favor of H_0, that the diet did not make any difference to the test performance.

If M would fall into either of the two rejection regions, we would reject H_0' and accept H_1'. We would conclude that $RV_{D(0)}$ is not the correct underlying pdf for M, that the sample mean had "come from" some other normal RV_D—for example, one of those alternatives to $RV_{D(0)}$ illustrated in figure 13.3. Correspondingly, we should also reject H_0 and accept H_1. We would conclude that if $RV_{D(0)}$ did not generate M, then neither did $RV_{P(0)}$ generate the 50 sample values. In other words, we should conclude that from a statistical standpoint, these 50 values were *not* like a set one would expect to obtain from the general untreated population. If M fell into a rejection region, we should decide that the diet did make a difference to the test performance.

Suppose for the sake of argument that this latter case actually did occur in our hypothetical study: M did fall within a rejection region, and we did reject H_0'. Did we make the correct decision? *We cannot ever be certain*. As we know, $RV_{D(0)}$, like any other normal pdf, could in principle generate *any* value of M. All that we can do is to consider how frequently we would make a wrong decision, *rejecting* H_0' *when in fact it had been true*. We shall now address that issue.

If we divide the outcome axis in the manner illustrated in figure 13.6, then, if H_0' is in fact true, how often would we reject that null hypothesis falsely—i.e., how often would M fall into a rejection region? Let us cast this question into a familiar form. If H_0' is true, then, from the point of view of our mathematical framework, M has been generated by one trial of the "correct" underlying pdf, namely, by $RV_{D(0)}$, the probability distribution hypothesized by H_0'. Under these circumstances, if we wish to know how often M would fall into the outcome region we have called the rejection region, we are implicating the probability assigned to that region by $RV_{D(0)}$. That probability will stipulate the relative frequency with which M would be found to lie in those regions *if H_0' is true*.

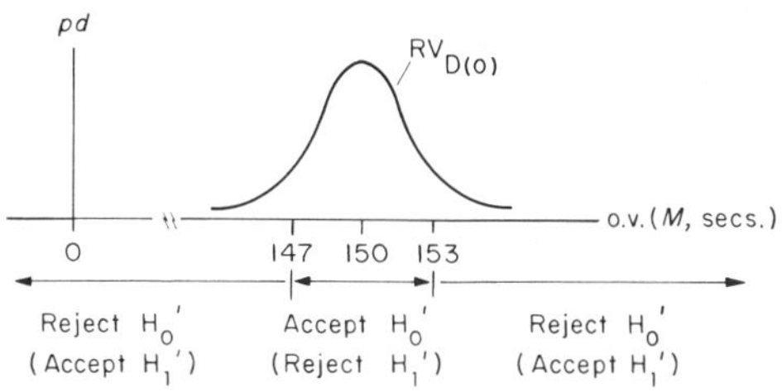

FIGURE 13.6 Specification of critical values

The procedure for finding the probability specified for the rejection regions of the outcome axis by $RV_{D(0)}$ should by now be familiar and obvious. We find the probability assigned to the outcome region lying to the *left* of 147 secs., i.e., the value of the normal cdf at that outcome value, in the usual way. We use (11.2) to calculate the corresponding standard outcome value, and find that z is equal to $(147.0 - 150.0)/\sqrt{2}$, or -2.12. The corresponding cumulative probability is approximately 0.017 (Appendix A). By the arguments in chapter 11 concerning the symmetry of a normal pdf (see fig. 11.7), we conclude that this value is also the probability associated with the outcome range lying to the *right* of the outcome value 153.0. Therefore, the probability associated with the total rejection region (the two tails of $RV_{D(0)}$) is 0.034, approximately.

By the principle of equivalence, 0.034 is also the relative frequency in a number of repeated trials for outcomes lying in those two regions. That is, if one performed, say, 1,000 trials with an RV such as $RV_{D(0)}$, then one would expect to find that in about 3.4% of these trials, or 34 cases, an outcome M had fallen within a region that has been designated as a rejection region. The important inference is that *if* H_0' were actually true, and *if* we were to specify the rejection regions shown in figure 13.6, then we should expect to *erroneously reject* the null hypothesis H_0' 3.4% of the time.

What does it mean to speak about rejecting H_0' a certain percentage of the time? We can answer that from our work in chapter 10. We learned that the empirical connotations of "repeated trials of RV_D" are repeated performances of the complete experiment (each experiment produces one value of *M*). Thus, the meaning of the preceding conclusions is this. If $RV_{D(0)}$ were indeed the *correct* pdf underlying *M*, and if we were to select the outcome values 147 and 153 secs. as critical values, then, if we were to repeat the complete rat experiment a number of times, we should expect that in about 3.4% of those times *M* would fall into a rejection region; consequently, we would expect to falsely reject H_0' that proportion of times.

Let us note the obvious but easily overlooked fact that we can make this kind of a mistake or error *only* if H_0' is in fact true, i.e., only if $RV_{D(0)}$ actually is the probability distribution of the sample mean. If H_0 is not true, we naturally cannot falsely reject it.

We see if the null hypothesis H_0' is true, we must expect that in a repeated series of experiments, we shall reject it falsely a certain number of times. When we perform a single experiment, then, and reject H_0', how can we be sure that this one experiment had not been one of those kinds of experiments in which we would falsely reject H_0'? The answer is, we cannot be sure, ever. If we obtained a sample mean that had fallen into a rejection region, and if, consequently, we had rejected H_0', we could never be completely sure that H_0' had not in fact been true. We could never know with complete assurance that *M* had *not* been generated by $RV_{D(0)}$. If $RV_{D(0)}$ is the *correct* probability distribution for *M*, and if on one trial we do obtain a value for *M* that lies in an outcome region designated as a *rejection* region, then, from a statistical point of view, all that has happened is that a relatively rare event had occurred. *M* had fallen into a relatively "unlikely" region of the potential outcome.

Thus, one must live with the possibility of making this kind of an error and drawing this kind of an erroneous inference from an outcome of an experiment. Since, as we shall soon discover, there is a second, analogous kind of an error that is also possible, the kind of an error that we have been considering is called an *error of the first kind*, or a *type I error*. Its magnitude or level is usually symbolized by the Greek letter α (alpha). As we have noted, it is an error that can occur only when the actual state of affairs is that H_0' is true. Specifically, an error of the first kind can occur *only* if (1) the null hypothesis is in fact true and (2) a statistic nevertheless falls into a rejection region. The magnitude of α provides a measure of how frequently in an imagined number of repetitions of an experiment that error would occur. That is, the size of α indicates how often one may expect to falsely reject the null hypothesis, concluding that there had been an experimental effect when in fact there had been none.

We cannot avoid the possibility of making an error of the first kind, but we can select the level of risk; we are free to specify the magnitude of α at any desired level. If we set α at a certain level, we thereby automatically specify critical values, and vice versa. For example, in our previous discussion we had chosen 147 and 153 secs. as critical values, and found that we had thereby specified the associated probability (as we now see, the value of α) at a level of 0.034. Alternatively, had we specified this level for α, then we should have found that the corresponding critical values that would satisfy the required probability level would again be the two previous outcome values, 147 and 153 secs. We are thus free to specify one or the other factor—either α, or the critical values, but not both. It is similar to being free to specify either the radius or the area of a circle. We may select either one of these two quantities and thus define a particular circle, but we cannot independently assign values to both at the same time. If we specify one, then the other quantity is automatically specified as well.

We have seen in the preceding example that for the critical values of 147 and 153 secs., α was 0.034. In that case, we should expect in a series of repeated experiments to commit an error of the first kind about 3.4% of the time. Suppose we would like to reduce the level of that kind of an error in order to commit it less frequently. In other words, we should like to be more certain that when we do reject H_0', it is indeed false. In order to reduce the probability assigned to the two tails by $RV_{D(0)}$, we should need to move the critical values farther away from the mean of that pdf. We would then have a wider acceptance region. It thus would become less likely that, if H_0' were true, M would fall outside the acceptance region and into a rejection region. For example, we might decide to use 146 and 154 secs. as critical values. By the previous methods we find that α is now only 0.006 instead of its previous value, 0.034. If H_0' were correct, then we should now expect to make a type I error in, for example, only 6 instead of 34 times out of 1,000 experiments. The two situations for the two values of α and two sets of critical values are compared in figure 13.7.

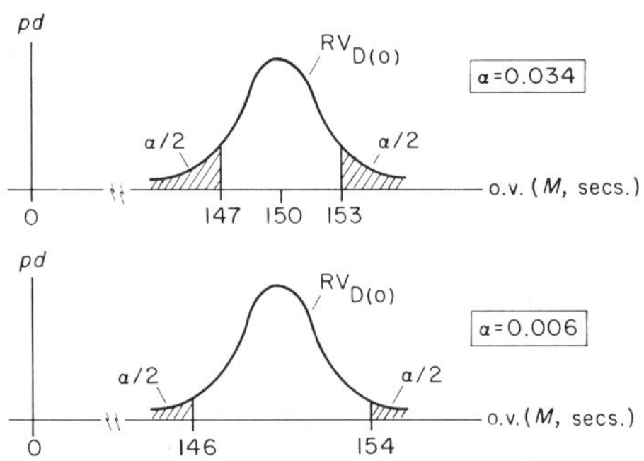

FIGURE 13.7 Two levels of significance

One implication of these conclusions is that if we would wish *never* to commit an error of the first kind, then all we would need to do would be to widen the acceptance region to include the whole outcome axis! Then, no matter what value of M would be obtained in the course of an experiment, it would fall within the acceptance region—because now there would be no rejection region. By dividing the outcome axis in this way, we set the level of α equal to 0. We now can never *falsely* reject H_0', because we shall never reject it at all. The problem with this approach is, of course, that since we would never *reject* the null hypothesis, we would also, equivalently, never *accept* the alternative hypothesis H_1'. We could never conclude from an obtained value of M that H_1' had probably been true. In that case, there would be no need to perform the experiment. We would know our decision in advance:

do not reject H_0'—the diet made no difference. Obviously, there is something wrong with this approach. We can discern qualitatively a fact that we shall soon quantify, namely, that if we decrease our risk of making an error of the first kind, if we set α at a low level, we introduce another effect: we make it less likely (and in the extreme case, impossible) that we shall correctly reject H_0', the null hypothesis. That is, we make it difficult if not impossible to accept the alternative hypothesis H_1' *when that premise is in fact true*.

These considerations have introduced the notion that the smaller the level we set for α, the less likely we shall be to commit an error of the first kind. For example, if we set α at a level of 0.001, then if the null hypothesis is true, we should expect to commit a type I error only once among 1,000 repeated experiments. Accordingly, if in one given experiment that specifies a low level for α we do obtain a value of M that lies in the rejection region, it is highly unlikely that M had "really" been generated by $RV_{D(0)}$. That is, it is highly unlikely that the null hypothesis is in fact true. Consequently, when that result is obtained, when M does fall into a rejection region that according to H_0' has a small probability, that result most probably reflects the fact that M had "really" been generated by some alternative pdf_D, and *not* by $RV_{D(0)}$. Thus, with a relatively small level of α, a result that lies in the rejection region becomes "more significant" to the experimenter. One therefore speaks about *significance* and α. If in a given experiment one sets a particular level of α, one speaks of the decision to reject the null hypothesis in terms of "that particular level of significance." For example, if in an experiment one sets α at 0.05, then one speaks about that particular test being conducted "at the 0.05 level of significance" or, equivalently, that the result is "significant at the 0.05 level." We now see why a hypothesis test is also called a "test of significance."

From a mathematical point of view, the level specified for α represents an arbitrary selection. Mathematically, all that α implies is a specification of a probability level and associated critical values. From a wider experimental perspective, however, the error of the first kind and allied concepts raise various kinds of experimental issues. For example, in a given experiment, what would be the "best" significance level to select? For discussions of these considerations that transcend narrowly statistical issues, see Kirk (pp. 109-112, 118-126, 141-145, 150-159).

Directional or One-Tailed Tests

We shall now consider a variant of the statistical test of significance we have just introduced. In our preceding discussion, we had assumed that the null hypotheses (H_0 and H_0') would be rejected if it appeared that the diet made some significant difference to performance. The direction of the effect, that is, whether the diet speeded or slowed down performance, had not been indicated by the alternative hypotheses. Accordingly, each of the alternatives to H_0 and H_0', namely, H_1 and H_1', implicated RVs (RV_Ps and RV_Ds) whose means were located somewhere else—anywhere else—along the outcome axis other than the outcome value of 150 secs. (see figs. 13.2 and 13.3). Since the means of alternative pdf_Ds such as those labeled 1′, 2′, 3′, and 4′ in figure 13.3 could have been located on either side of the outcome axis region dominated by $RV_{D(0)}$, we correspondingly had two rejection regions, one on either side of the acceptance region (see figs. 13.5 and 13.6). For obvious reasons, this kind of a significance test is called a *nondirectional* or a *two-tailed* test; the alternative hypotheses fail to mention a directionality of the experimental effect, and the rejection region is a double region that covers the two "tails" of $RV_{D(0)}$.

In some studies, however, the experimenters' interests may be somewhat different. Rather than seeking to establish whether or not a particular treatment such as our hypothetical diet made any difference, the experimenters may instead wish to establish whether the treatment had a specific directional effect. For example, they may wish to establish only whether or not the experimental diet had *adverse* effects on the animals' performance. In that case, were the empirical results to imply that perhaps the diet had *improved* performance, this would be considered to be an accidental, scientifically meaningless result; in that kind of a situation, the experimenters' theoretical framework would only admit the possibility that the diet had *degraded* the test performance, that on average the performance times had increased.

This kind of modification in the experimenters' *scientific* alternative hypothesis (note that their null hypothesis has not been changed) will bring corresponding kinds of modifications in the two alternative *statistical* hypotheses, H_1 and H_1'. The alternative scientific hypothesis now postulates test performances that on average are slower in treated than in untreated animals, and therefore H_1 correspondingly postulates that a set of sample values must have been generated by an RV_P that has a mean greater than 150 secs., the mean of $RV_{P(0)}$ (the pdf_P postulated by H_0). In terms of our previous discussion, the mathematical consequence of the change in the scientific hypothesis is that now only pdf_Ps such as those labeled 3 and 4 in figure 13.2 are postulated by H_1 as the kinds of population pdfs that might underlie a set of sample values. Correspondingly, H_1', the hypothesis about the RV origin of M, now postulates that an RV_D admissible under that alternative hypothesis can only be a pdf such as those labeled 3′ or 4′ in figure 13.3.

If H_1' proposes RV_Ds that lie in only one side of $RV_{D(0)}$, the rejection region (i.e., the "acceptance region" for H_1') should likewise cover only one side of the outcome axis. Therefore, the rejection region should be a region such as C in figure 13.4. If an experimentally generated value fell into a region such as C, we should *reject* H_0' and accept H_1'. Otherwise, if M had fallen into regions to the left of C (into regions such as either A or B in fig. 13.4) we should *not reject* H_0'. Of course, either of these decisions will imply a corresponding decision in favor or against H_0.

For obvious reasons, this kind of a test of significance is called a *directional* or a *one-tailed* test. All the concepts developed for nondirectional tests apply virtually without modification to directional tests. We have an acceptance region and a rejection of the outcome axis, a critical value at the boundary of such regions, an error of the first kind, and a level of significance, alpha. The only mathematical difference is that the probability represented by the value of alpha now is assigned *entirely* to *one* tail of $RV_{D(0)}$. We now can commit a type I error, i.e., falsely reject H_0', only in one region of the outcome axis, that lying to the right of the critical value. (The fact that in our example the rejection region lies to the right of the acceptance region is accidental and without significance. In some other experiment, with some other premises, the one-tailed rejection region could equally well lie to the left.)

It may be instructive to compare the critical values and corresponding rejection regions specified by a directional versus a nondirectional test for the same hypothesized underlying $RV_{D(0)}$ (a normal pdf, $\mu_D = 150$ secs., $\sigma^2_D = 2$) and the same level of significance, say, $\alpha = 0.05$. For the nondirectional, two-tailed test, the critical z values that establish a probability of 0.025 for each of the two tails are the values -1.96 and $+1.96$; the corresponding critical outcome values for $RV_{D(0)}$ are 147.23 and 152.77 secs. These are calculated from (11.2), solved for x in terms of z. For the one-tailed or directional test, the critical z or standard value is $+1.65$. That is the standard value that has cumulative probability of 0.95 and, consequently, assigns a probability of 0.05 to the region lying to its right along the outcome axis. The corresponding critical outcome value for $RV_{D(0)}$ is 152.33 secs.

These two situations are compared in figure 13.8. The ways in which one would use the acceptance and rejection regions in the two cases are substantially the same. An experimenter would still accept (or at least, not reject) H_0' if a statistic, in our case the sample mean, M, fell into an acceptance region, and otherwise would reject H_0' and accept H_1'. The risk of making a type I error is at the same level for the two cases, since $\alpha = 0.05$ in each instance. Mathematically, the difference between a one-tailed or directional and a two-tailed or nondirectional test is trivial; it is only a simple modification that reflects a difference in the experimenters' stated interests or perspectives. There are, however,

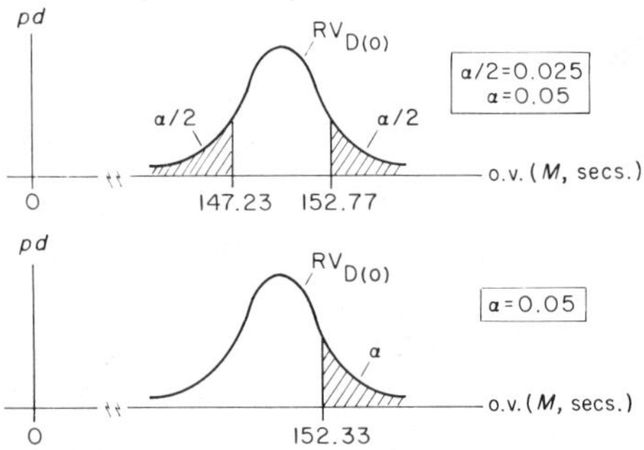

FIGURE 13.8 Directional and nondirectional tests

points of controversy concerning these two types of tests that transcend the narrowly statistical questions we are addressing here (Kirk, pp. 276-290).

Exact Alternative Hypotheses, the Error of the Second Kind, and Power

We have been considering tests of significance that involve an exact null hypothesis (either H_0 or H_0') and an inexact alternative hypothesis (either H_1 or H_1'). We shall conclude this introduction to hypothesis testing and the sample mean by considering the case of an *exact alternative* hypothesis. Conceptually, the situation is not very different from the previous cases. H_0 and H_0' are still the same kinds of null hypotheses—in our example, the hypotheses about the RV origins of 50 sample values and the RV origin of the sample mean *M*, respectively. Now, however, we shall postulate two exact alternatives hypotheses. H_1, the alternative to H_0, will be the premise that the 50 sample values came from one *specific* RV_P other than $RV_{P(0)}$. Correspondingly, H_1', the alternative to H_0', will be the premise that *M* came from a particular RV_D other than $RV_{D(0)}$.

Let us study these matters by means of a numerical example. We shall assume that the experimenters had decided that if the 50 sample values did *not* come from $RV_{P(0)}$ (a normal pdf, $\mu_{P(0)} = 150$ secs., $\sigma^2_{P(0)} = 100$), then these actual outcomes_P came from an RV_P similar to $RV_{P(0)}$ in that it was a normal pdf with a variance of 100, but unlike $RV_{P(0)}$ in that *this* specific alternative RV_P had a mean of 155 instead of 150 secs. Let us call this alternative RV_P hypothesized by H_1, $RV_{P(1)}$. It is a normal pdf, $\mu_{P(1)} = 155$ secs., $\sigma^2_{P(1)} = 100$. H_0 stipulates $RV_{P(0)}$, and H_1 stipulates $RV_{P(1)}$.

If we assume $RV_{P(1)}$ to be the correct pdf that underlies the set of 50 *sample values*, what would be the corresponding $RV_{D(1)}$ stipulated by H_1' as the correct probability distribution that underlies the *sample mean M*? We have already considered the question of the relationships between the parameters of RV_P and RV_D at a general level. The results we obtained defined the parameters of $RV_{D(0)}$ in terms of those of $RV_{P(0)}$ and *N*; see figure 13.1 and (13.1) through (13.4). We now use exactly the same kind of rationale to conclude that if $RV_{P(1)}$ is a normal pdf with $\mu_{P(1)} = 155$ secs. and $\sigma^2_{P(1)} = 100$, then a sample mean M obtained from 50 sample values generated by that RV would have an underlying probability distribution of the sample mean, $RV_{D(1)}$, that would be a normal pdf with the same mean, 155 secs., as $RV_{P(1)}$, and a variance of $\sigma^2_{P(1)}/N$ or 2.

As previously, we will shift the question of deciding between H_0 and H_1 to the parallel question of deciding between H_0' and H_1'. We shall decide whether the 50 sample values obtained from treated animals "came from" $RV_{P(0)}$ or $RV_{P(1)}$ by deciding whether the statistic M "came from" $RV_{D(0)}$ or $RV_{D(1)}$. The logic of the situation is thus a straightforward elaboration of the logic schematically illustrated in figure 13.1. The only difference is that now there is a counterpart to the pair of probability distributions $RV_{P(0)}$ and $RV_{D(0)}$, namely, the pair $RV_{P(1)}$ and $RV_{D(1)}$. This added feature is shown in figure 13.9.

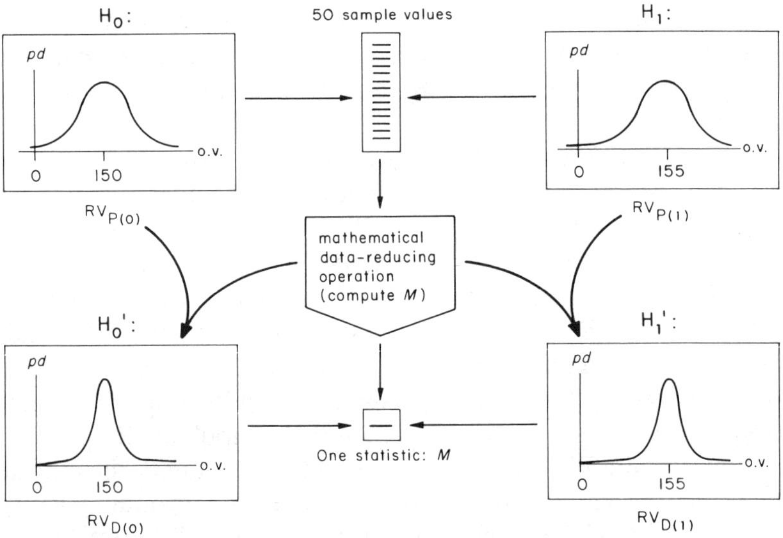

FIGURE 13.9 Two pairs of exact hypotheses

In order to decide in any given experiment whether M came from $RV_{D(0)}$ or $RV_{D(1)}$, we shall follow our familiar basic approach and rationale. We deduce that to begin with, some kind of a directional test must be called for. The alternative hypothesis proposes a specifically directional effect, namely, that the diet on average produced a longer test performance time (155 instead of 150 secs.). We initially follow *exactly* the same steps we had previously used to implement a directional or one-tailed test. We have an RV, $RV_{D(0)}$, proposed by the null hypothesis H_0'. We shall define a rejection region and an acceptance region as usual either by specifying a level for α or by specifying a critical value. Let us suppose that we decide to define the two regions by setting the level of α at 0.05. We shall obtain the same critical value, 152.33 secs., and thus define the *same two decision regions* as in the *directional* test illustrated in figure 13.8. *Thus far, the fact that the alternative hypothesis is exact rather than, as previously, inexact, has not entered the picture at all.* To this point, the situation that we are developing is identical to the situation developed previously for the corresponding directional test with an inexact alternative hypothesis—we have the same $RV_{D(0)}$, level of α, acceptance region, and one-tailed rejection region.

We shall now consider the principal mathematically significant difference between performing a one-tailed test with an inexact alternative hypothesis and performing such a test when the alternative hypothesis specifies a particular RV_D, i.e., when H_1' is exact. Figure 13.10 schematically illustrates the present situation.

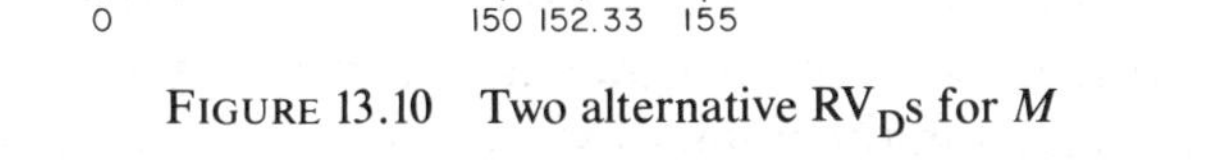

FIGURE 13.10 Two alternative RV_Ds for M

We see the familiar $RV_{D(0)}$ hypothesized by H_0', the critical value, 152.33 secs., that provides the specified level of α (0.05) for a one-tailed test, an acceptance and a rejection region, and the new entity, $RV_{D(1)}$, the alternative pdf specified by H_1' as the probability distribution of the sample mean.

The second pdf, the new entity in the picture, allows us to

discuss and measure another type of error. We have learned that an error of the first kind can be made when H_0' is in fact true; we then may incorrectly reject H_0'. Exactly the same situation exists with respect to the alternative hypothesis H_1' and $RV_{D(1)}$: we may make a kind of "type I" error when H_1' is in fact true. (The reason for the quotation marks will soon become apparent.) In principle, that kind of an error is the same as a type I error, and its magnitude is calculated on the basis of the same rationale also. It is simply a type I error *from the perspective of* $RV_{D(1)}$. The situation, although conceptually straightforward, can be confusing at first and merits careful development.

We have divided the outcome axis into two segments, an acceptance region and a rejection region, separated by the critical value of 152.33 secs. We perform an experiment, obtain 50 sample values, reduce these to a sample mean, and evaluate that statistic. If its value falls into the rejection region, we reject H_0' and accept H_1'. Thus, logically there are two possible decisions that can be made. Correspondingly, logically there are two possible "true states": either H_0' actually is true and H_1' is false, or else H_0' is false and H_1' actually is true. The situation implies four logically possible alternative relationships that can arise between our decision and the true state of affairs: (1) we can accept H_0' when in fact it is true; (2) we can accept H_1' (i.e., reject H_0') when in fact it is true; (3) we can reject H_0' when in fact it is true (this is our familiar type I error); (4) finally, we can accept H_0' (i.e., reject H_1') when in fact it is false. Cases (1) and (2) are those in which a correct decision has been reached, while (3) and (4) are cases in which an error has been committed. These four cases are shown in table 13.1.

The second error, case (4), is from one perspective a familiar type of error, while from another it is a new type. Its familiar meaning is that from the point of view of the alternative hypothesis, it is simply an error of the first kind, a fact that has already been noted. It is an error that we can commit only if H_1' is true. "H_1' is true" means, of course, that from a mathematical standpoint, $RV_{D(1)}$ is actually the pdf that generates M. Therefore, the probability of *incorrectly rejecting* H_1' is the probability that $RV_{D(1)}$ will generate an outcome, a value of M, that will fall into

Table 13.1

Four logically possible cases

Decisions	Actual, true state: H_0' true	Actual, true state: H_1' true
Accept H_0'	(1) correct decision: accept H_0'; H_0' true.	(4) incorrect decision: accept H_0' (reject H_1'); H_0' false (H_1' true). type II error
Reject H_0'	(3) incorrect decision: reject H_0' (accept H_1'); H_0' true (H_1' false). type I error	(2) correct decision: reject H_0' (accept H_1'); H_0' false (H_1' true).

the "rejection region" for H_1'—i.e., into the region identified as the *acceptance region* (for H_0') in figure 13.10. That probability is calculated by the usual method. In our illustrative example, it equals 0.024. If H_1' is true, we should expect that in a set of repeated studies we should *falsely reject the alternative hypothesis* 2.4% of the time. In those cases, we should accept the null hypothesis when in fact it is false.

Although in one sense we are considering a "type I" error, it is in another sense a somewhat different kind of an error; it is committed with respect to an alternative hypothesis, and not, as before, with respect to a null hypothesis. Therefore, it traditionally is given a different name; it is called a *type II* error, or an *error of the second kind*. The magnitude or level of this error is signified by the Greek letter β (beta). That quantity represents, as we have just discussed, the probability that we shall reject H_1', the alternative hypothesis, when it is in fact true (or, what amounts to the same thing, accept H_0' when that null hypothesis is in fact false).

In a sense if we have two exact hypotheses, it is immaterial which we identify as the null and which as the alternative hypothesis. From the standpoint of mathematics, we could have equally well inverted H_0' and H_1' (and H_0 and H_1) in our illustrative study;

we could have said that H_0' stipulates the probability distribution of the sample mean that we had previously called $RV_{D(1)}$ (a normal pdf, $\mu = 155$ secs., $\sigma^2 = 2$), and that H_1' stipulates the normal pdf we had previously called $RV_{D(0)}$ (a normal pdf, $\mu = 150$ secs., $\sigma^2 = 2$). We would simply have *reversed the two RVs* stipulated by these two hypotheses. The meaning of alpha and beta would likewise have been interchanged, *as would their values, provided that we had retained the same critical value*, 152.33 secs. To the mathematician, which of these two underlying pdfs is considered to be stipulated by the null and which stipulated by the alternative hypothesis, and correspondingly, which "type I" error is "really" alpha and which is "really" beta, is a trivial and arbitrary decision. It is simply traditional to call the error of erroneously rejecting a hypothesis a *type I* error if it pertains to the *null* hypothesis, and a *type II* error if it pertains to the *alternative* hypothesis.

There is a second concept that enters the picture when the alternative hypothesis is exact. It is closely associated with the error of the second kind. The concept is the so-called *power of a test*. That term stands for the probability of making a *correct* decision when the *alternative* hypothesis H_1' is in fact *true*.

We have discussed the statistical implications of "H_1' is true" in some detail during the discussion of the error of the second kind and β. We should therefore see quite readily what it means to speak of the probability of making a correct decision when H_1' is true. It connotes the probability assigned by $RV_{D(1)}$ to the outcome region associated with accepting H_1', i.e., the region we have designated as the rejection region (for H_0'). As we can see in figure 13.10, the acceptance and rejection regions are a complementary pair. Therefore, if the probability assigned by $RV_{D(1)}$ to the acceptance region (the "rejection region" for H_1') is β, then the probability assigned by that pdf to the rejection region (the "acceptance region" for H_1') must be $(1 - \beta)$. That is the "power of the test"—the probability of making a correct decision when H_1' is true. It is a probability associated with case (2) in table 13.1.

Thus, both β and the power of a test connote probabilities of events that can occur *only* if H_1' is true, just as α refers to the probability of an event that can occur *only* if H_0' is true. α and β

are probabilities associated with two kinds of *incorrect* decisions, while the power of a test is the probability associated with making one particular kind of a *correct* decision—specifically, it is the probability of the decision to accept H_1' when that alternative hypothesis is in fact true. In other words, if H_1' is true, the probability is β that we shall commit a type II error, and $(1 - \beta)$ that we shall make a correct decision.

These concepts—alpha, beta, and the power of a test—can be confusing at first.[6] Since β is, in a manner of speaking, a kind of α, one way to prevent or clear up confusion is to master α and related concepts thoroughly first in a setting where the second type of error and its related concepts are not even in the picture—in short, in situations that involve *inexact* alternative hypotheses. That is why we began this chapter with those kinds of inferential procedures. If you have difficulties understanding the two types of error and the power of a test, I would urge you to return to the simpler cases presented in the early parts of this chapter and to make sure that you understand the concept of an error of the first kind, and its implications, before you attempt to master the material related to β and the power of a test.

The inferential procedures that we have explored involved a number of entities, namely, α, β, $(1 - \beta)$, N, critical values, and four sets of parameters—the means and variances of $RV_{P(0)}$, $RV_{P(1)}$, $RV_{D(0)}$, and $RV_{D(1)}$. In general, a change in one or more of these quantities will usually bring about allied changes in one or more of the others. For example, if H_1' had proposed an RV different from $RV_{D(1)}$, say, one whose mean had been equal to 160 instead of 155 secs., then, if α had remained unchanged (i.e., if we had retained the critical value of 152.33 secs.), the value of β would have been lower. In terms of figure 13.10, the new $RV_{D(1)}$ would be shifted toward the right, and it would therefore assign a smaller probability to the outcome region lying to the left of the critical value, 152.33 secs. Accordingly, with this new alternative

[6]One reason these concepts may be confusing at first is that each of these probabilities is in one sense not exactly an ordinary probability. These three entities are "conditional" probabilities, a kind of probability we shall not discuss until chapter 20. We are therefore unable to clarify the situation completely at this point.

hypothesis it would become less likely that we would falsely reject H_1'.

These and other similar kinds of interrelationships between the various mathematical entities can be worked out by applying the concepts introduced here in a straightforward manner. In any case, these matters are extensively discussed in the literature (see, for example, Hays, pp. 356-362). We shall not delve into these manifold relationships further, except to note one point that merits particular mention.

In the discussion concerning α, it was suggested that were one to reduce α to a very low level, then another error would tend to become excessive. We can now complete that thought. With reference to figure 13.10 what would happen if, other things being equal, we were to reduce α? In the present example, in order to reduce the level of that error, we must move the *critical value* to the right (in the general case, toward the mean of the other pdf, $RV_{D(1)}$). We can readily see from an inspection of figure 13.10 that this would increase β. Thus, other things being equal, a reduction in the level of one type of error induces a corresponding increase in the level of the other type. In the extreme case, if we make $\alpha = 0$, then $\beta = 1$. The whole outcome axis becomes an acceptance region, and it does not matter what value of M would be obtained in a given experiment. If H_0' is actually true, we shall never commit a type I error; if, however, H_0' is false, we shall *always* commit a type II error. Exactly the opposite situation would arise were one to make $\alpha = 1$ and $\beta = 0$ (see problems 13.13 and 13.14).

The mathematical material that has been presented in this chapter is a straightforward development of previously introduced statistical concepts. There are, however, a number of related, less straightforward issues whose focus is not exclusively on statistical matters. These involve experimental considerations that transcend our limited mathematical scope. Some of these topics have been mentioned in passing. Various brief references have been made to the ongoing and sometimes still controversial discussions in the professional literature concerning such matters as the relationships between scientific and statistical hypotheses, the specification of levels of significance, the choice between directional and nondirectional tests, or the difference between "accepting" and "not rejecting" a hypothesis. These and similar significant experimental issues are usually addressed in a more advanced course such as a course on experimental design.

Although this long chapter has introduced a relatively large amount of new material that may have been difficult to digest on first encounter, we shall see that the benefits from learning this material will extend considerably beyond the present chapter. The material has been presented in the context of significance tests, the sample mean, and a normal RV_P, but, as we shall see in the next chapter, the concepts we have learned will serve us in a large variety of different contexts as well.

PROBLEMS

13.1 In an RV framework, what kind of a number is the sample mean M? What is the RV that underlies it, and how is that RV related to RV_P if that latter probability distribution is a normal pdf?

13.2 Nine sample values were obtained in the course of an experiment. From the point of view of a RV framework, these were generated by a normal RV_P, $\mu = 25$, $\sigma^2 = 121$. What is the RV_D that underlies M?

13.3 What does a *set* of sample means imply? Give both the empirical as well as the mathematical (RV) meaning.

13.4 H_0 stipulates that $RV_{P(0)}$ is a normal pdf, $\mu = 27$, $\sigma^2 = 49$. If that pdf generates 36 sample values, what is the acceptance region (for H_0') of $RV_{D(0)}$? Use a significance level of 0.05, and a two-tailed test.

13.5 In problem 13.4, what is the probability of committing an error of the first kind? Explain what has happened when such an error has been committed.

13.6 In problem 13.4, what would the acceptance region be if $N = 64$ instead of 36? What can you infer generally about the relationship between sample size and acceptance region?

13.7 Verify the critical value shown in figure 13.8 for a one-tailed test of significance, $\alpha = 0.05$.

13.8 What is the difference between a type I and a type II error?

13.9 In one experiment, H_0, the null hypothesis, happens to be true. In terms of the four cases shown in table 13.1, what case occurs when

(a) the value of M falls into the rejection region?

(b) the value of M falls into the acceptance region?

13.10 Repeat problem 13.9, but this time assume that H_0 actually is false.

13.11 H_0 stipulates a normal pdf with a mean of 35 and a variance of 64, while H_1 stipulates a normal pdf with a mean of 28 and a variance of 64; 25 sample values are generated.

(a) Find the critical value if α is set at 0.05.

(b) What is the value of β and of the power of the test?

(c) What do the statistical terms in (b) mean?

(d) Repeat parts (a) and (b) for $\alpha = 0.01$. Compare the results obtained for the two different values of α, and discuss the effects of the size of α on the size of β and on the power of a test.

(e) Repeat parts (a) and (b), but for $N = 64$. Compare the results obtained for the two different values of N, and discuss the effects of the sample size on β and on the power of a test.

13.12 In problem 13.11, one change is made: H_1 now stipulates a normal pdf whose mean is 26 and whose variance is 64.

(a) Does that change affect the critical value? Explain.

(b) Does that change affect β and the power of the test? If so, what is the effect of changing H_1 if the level of significance α remains unchanged?

13.13 In figure 13.10, if α were assigned smaller and smaller values, what would happen to:

(a) the acceptance region?

(b) the rejection region?

(c) the probability of committing an error of the first kind?

(d) the probability of committing an error of the second kind?

(e) the power of the test?

13.14 Repeat problem 13.13 for the case where α is made increasingly larger.

13.15 In general, how does one approach the problem of deciding whether a set of sample values came from one or another RV_P?

13.15 Arguing from the RV origin of M to the RV origin of a set of sample values has provided our basic rationale for significance testing. What is the justification for asserting that one may draw inferences about the origins of sample values from an inference about the RV origin of M? [Hint: review chap. 12.]

13.16 What does the following statement mean: A normal RV_P and the mathematical data-reducing procedure that is used to compute the sample mean M jointly induce a uniquely specified RV_D that underlies that statistic.

13.17 When can a type I error occur? A type II error?

CHAPTER 14

The Normal Probability Distribution and Estimation

So far we have examined one kind of statistical inference, hypothesis testing. We shall now introduce a second kind of inferential procedure, namely, estimation. These two procedures constitute one major branch of statistical methodology (Hays, p. 290; Kirk, p. 113; Freeman, p. 283); they draw on the same logical base, but do so from somewhat different perspectives.

The process of estimation refers to using a statistic to draw inferences about one or more parameters of an underlying RV. This statement implicitly points to the kinship with concepts previously developed in the context of hypothesis testing. It refers to a statistic; hence, it implies a set of antecedent sample values as well as a mathematical data-reducing method, since we could not have a statistic without these two ingredients. The statement also mentions underlying RVs, another concept that had played a large role in the hypothesis-testing methodology. In fact, we shall see that the framework for estimation procedures will require few entirely new conceptual ingredients. We have already developed most of the necessary concepts in the preceding chapters.

There are two different types of estimation: *point estimation*, and *interval estimation*. The former term refers to methodologies that yield a single number as an estimate of a probability distribution parameter, while the latter term refers to those methodologies that estimate a parameter of a probability distribution by specifying a particular numerical range as one that is likely to contain the true value of the parameter. For example, if the parameter we are seeking to estimate is the mean of a probability distribution, a point estimate would lead to a statement such as, "a likely value for the mean is 125.3 secs.," while an interval estimate would be expressed in an assertion such as, "it is estimated that the mean lies between the outcome values 120.4 and 135.7 secs." We shall examine each procedure in turn.

Point Estimation

Suppose we wish to use a set of acquired sample values to yield a single number that will estimate a particular RV parameter. In general, is there an obvious, optimal way to proceed? Freeman (1963) offers a summary of the situation:

> We might hope to find a method or methods which . . . always reveal the true value of the parameter. . . . None exist. Instead, we have a number of methods each with errors of inference peculiar to it. . . . Among these and many other methods we cannot often make an easy choice since we seldom have any firm guide as to the kind of errors of inference we should avoid [p. 228].

We must accept these restrictions as inescapable facts that are rooted in the mathematical properties of statistical inference in general and estimation in particular.

We shall consider estimation principally in terms of specific types of procedures, leaving aside the more esoteric and mathematically difficult questions pertaining to the selection of a particular statistic to perform a given estimation task. Nevertheless, it will be useful as general background information first to survey the principal properties that estimators display.

Suppose that we wish to estimate some parameter of a population probability distribution, for example, one of its moments. We shall proceed as usual by obtaining a set of sample values or actual outcomes$_{\text{P}}$. Next, also as usual, we shall reduce these to a statistic. Presumably, we would select a data-reduction method that would be appropriate for our particular task. The mathematical operation should yield a type of statistic that would be a "good" estimator of the parameter we are seeking. What constitutes a "good" estimator? Ideally, it would be one that performs well in terms of the following four general criteria (Hays, pp. 268-277; Freeman, pp. 229-239).

First, the estimator should be free of *bias*. Roughly, this means that "on average" the estimator, that is, the particular type of statistic we have chosen to generate from the set of sample values, would provide the correct value of the desired parameter. "On average" implies several values of a statistic which, as we already know, in turn implies several repetitions of a complete experiment. If a statistic is unbiased, it has the mathematical property that in principle, were one to repeat an experiment over and over, each time obtaining N sample values and one statistic (our estimator), then the *average* of all the estimators or statistics would ultimately be equal to (or, at least, be very close to) the actual value of the parameter we are attempting to estimate. While we would not necessarily expect our statistic to estimate the parameter exactly in any one given experiment, we would expect that with an unbiased estimator the estimation error would eventually "average out" in a series of repeated experiments.

The second desirable characteristic of an estimator is *consistency*. The precise meaning of this concept lies in a mathematical definition, but the general idea is that a consistent estimator is the kind of statistic that becomes "better," more accurate, the larger the sample size N. That is, if we are using a consistent estimator to estimate an RV parameter, then, if that statistic provides a good estimate from, say, 50 sample values, it will most likely provide a better estimate were one to use more than 50 sample values in a given experiment.

Third, the estimator should be *efficient*. This means, were one to repeat the experiment several times thus obtaining several estimates of a parameter, the values produced by using an efficient estimator would in successive experiments tend to cluster closely about the true, correct parameter value. In other words, if an estimator is efficient, then the several estimates obtained from several repeated experiments should show a relatively small degree of scatter or dispersion about the true parameter value.

Fourth, an estimator should be *sufficient*. Once again this term refers to a rather complex mathematical property, namely, the degree to which a statistic or estimator uses the information that is potentially available from a set of sample values. Briefly, a sufficient estimator is one that does not waste any of the information that is inherent in a set of measures or similar empirical sample values.

We shall encounter several kinds of estimators in subsequent chapters. For the present, we shall explore the use of a familiar statistic, the sample mean M, as an estimator. What is its average? That is, if one were to repeat an experiment many times, each time obtaining one sample mean, and if one were to average these sample means, then what would that average be? We can answer that question easily if we remember that M is not only an arithmetical average of N sample values, but that from an RV perspective M also is one outcome value generated by one trial of its underlying pdf, RV_D. Therefore, like any other RV outcome value, the long-term average of M must be μ_D, the mean of its RV. (See chaps. 7 and 8 for a general discussion of this point, and chap. 11 for a discussion specific to normal pdfs.) Furthermore, we know from (13.1) that μ_D is equal to μ_P, the mean of RV_P.[1] Therefore, if the sample mean M "on average" lies close to μ_D, it will thereby also "on average" lie close to μ_P, the mean of RV_P. This is another way of saying that *the sample mean M is an unbiased estimator of* μ_P, the mean of the population probability distribution that underlies the sample values.

We had learned in chapter 13 that M, one particular kind of a statistic, could be used in a hypothesis test to evaluate whether or not a set of sample values came from a given population probability distribution. Now we see that same statistic used in a different inferential task: it can also be used to estimate the mean of RV_P, if

[1] We had learned this for a particular kind of a population probability distribution, a normal pdf_P. It is true in general, however, regardless of the profile of RV_P: the mean of RV_D, the probability distribution of the sample mean M, always has the same value as the mean of RV_P (see Freeman, pp. 179-180). As a matter of fact, the same is true for (13.2) through (13.4); they hold regardless of the profile of RV_P.

that parameter is unknown. For instance, in the hypothetical experiments that were discussed in chapters 10, 12, and 13, instead of using the 50 sample values and the sample mean M to perform a test of significance, the experimenters could have used these data simply to obtain an estimate of the mean of RV_D and/or RV_P, had those means been unknown.

Although M can be used in this fashion to estimate a specific value of the mean of a probability distribution, such a single number, a point estimate, is less than ideal in some respects. A principal drawback is that since M behaves like an outcome generated by a trial of a normal pfd (RV_D), the value of that statistic may in any one given experiment lie very far from the actual value of μ_D (and μ_P). Because that can always be the case, and because in a given instance we *cannot know* whether we had obtained a typical (fairly close to μ_D) or an atypical (very far from μ_D) value of M, a given experiment may yield a misleading estimate of μ_D and μ_P. There are times when one would like to obtain a less risky estimate. This need has led statisticians to develop a methodology known as interval estimation, our next topic.

Interval Estimation

Point estimation procedures do not provide any measure that indicates how likely it is that an estimate obtained in a given experiment is accurate. We just obtain a number, and there is no concomitant probability that would tell us how risky that estimate is. This lack is remedied to some extent by a methodology that estimates a parameter in terms of an interval and a probability index. The specific interval that is estimated is called a *confidence interval*; the end points of that interval, the two outcome values that define the confidence interval, are called the *confidence limits*; and the probability index is called the *level of confidence* associated with a given interval estimate.

How might one go about obtaining a parameter estimate in terms of a confidence interval and associated level of confidence? Basically, one uses some appropriate statistic and mathematical method of construction to obtain the desired interval estimate of a parameter value. That is, if one wishes to estimate the value of a particular parameter of RV_P, one generates a set of sample values and reduces these to an appropriate statistic; one then uses an appropriate mathematical procedure to construct a pair of confidence limits and thus an interval estimate, from that statistic or outcome $value_D$.

We shall illustrate the general idea by demonstrating how one can estimate an interval for μ_P from the statistic M. Suppose that in the kind of rat study considered earlier we had obtained 50 sample values from 50 treated rats; suppose further that we knew the population probability distribution RV_P to be a normal pdf whose variance σ^2_P was known to be equal to 100, but whose mean μ_P was not known. The goal is to estimate an interval for that unknown parameter from M.

We learned in chapter 13 that if RV_P is a normal pdf with the parameters μ_P and σ^2_P, then the probability distribution RV_D that underlies the sample mean M is also a normal pdf; its parameters μ_D and σ^2_D are related to those of RV_P by (13.1) and (13.2). That means that even though in the present case μ_P and therefore μ_D are unknown, these two parameter values are still equal to one another. Accordingly, were we able to obtain an interval estimate for μ_D from M, we should thereby also obtain an interval estimate for the other mean, μ_P. Our procedure thus becomes that of estimating an interval for μ_D from a given experimentally generated value of M.

We are now assuming that we had performed an experiment, obtained 50 sample values, and reduced these to the sample mean M. How shall we proceed to construct an interval estimate for μ_D (and μ_P) from that value? There are any number of procedures that one might use; we shall choose a simple method suggested by certain considerations pertaining to the way in which outcome values generated by a normal pdf cluster. Specifically, we discussed in chapters 11 and 13 that for *any* normal pdf, it is reasonable to expect that a single trial would produce an outcome value lying within a range such as A in figure 13.4 rather than within ranges such as those labeled B and C in that figure. Of course, we do know that if an underlying RV is a normal pdf, then the actual outcome value obtained from one trial could, in principle, lie anywhere along the outcome axis, including such ranges as B or

C. We are merely saying that if the trial is statistically typical, it will yield an outcome value that lies in an "*A*-type" range.

We can apply these general considerations to *M* and RV_D specifically. If we perform one trial with RV_D (and that is of course the mathematical RV equivalent of computing *M* from a given set of experimentally obtained sample values), then in a typical trial, we should expect the outcome value *M* to lie "fairly close" to μ_D, a short distance to one or the other side of that parameter value. In terms of figure 13.4, we should expect *M* to lie in an "*A*-type" rather than in a "*B*-type" or a "*C*-type" region of RV_D. *That conclusion implies the converse*: if we obtain a value for *M*, the chances are that the parameter μ_D lies in an outcome axis region that is "fairly close" to *M*, within a relatively short distance of the statistic.

That deduction suggests one method of constructing an interval estimate for μ_D. When we have obtained a value of *M* in a given experiment, we could construct the interval estimate for μ_D simply by subtracting and adding some reasonable outcome value to *M*. The simplest procedure would be to subtract and add the same number; that is, when we have acquired *M*, we could designate the estimated interval for μ_D to be the interval from $(M - a)$ to $(M + a)$, where *a* is some suitably chosen positive number. (The matter of that choice will be discussed soon.) Our "mathematical construction" of the interval from an acquired value of *M* is thus elementary. Let us illustrate it by giving a numerical example.

Suppose that in our experiment we had obtained the value $M = 151.2$ secs. from the 50 sample values. Let us say that on the basis of some as yet unknown but reasonable rationale, we decide to let $a = 2.77$ secs. Then our interval estimate for μ_D, and thus for μ_P, would be the interval from $(151.2 - 2.77)$ or 148.43 secs. to $(151.2 + 2.77)$ or 153.97 secs.

If we were to repeat that experiment a number of times, we should expect to obtain different values of *M*, and thus different interval estimates for μ_D. That raises an important question: when will this particular method of interval construction yield a correct interval, i.e., an interval that contains the actual value of μ_D, and when will it not do so? We can deduce the answer easily if we assume that we somehow know the true value of μ_D. Consider the following situation. Suppose we know that the true value of μ_D is 152.0 secs.; for what range of M will our chosen method of interval estimation provide a correct estimate? We can easily find the smallest value that M may have and that still would yield a correct interval estimate: it must be the value (152.0 − 2.77) or 149.23 secs. You can easily demonstrate to yourself that if M has a smaller value than 149.23 secs., the upper confidence limit—i.e., (M + 2.77)—will be too small; the estimated interval will lie below 152.0 secs., the true value of μ_D. Similarly, we can find the largest value that M can assume and that still yields a correct interval estimate: the value is (152.0 + 2.77) or 154.77 secs. When M is larger than that value, the lower confidence limit (M − 2.77) will be too large; μ_D will lie below the estimated interval. To summarize: when M lies in the region between 149.23 and 154.77 secs., the interval-estimation procedure that we are using at present will yield a correct estimate; when M lies outside that region, our estimate will be erroneous.

Let us note very carefully another important feature of this procedure. *Up to this point, probabilities have not entered the picture at all!* So far, we have selected a mathematical rationale for constructing an interval from M, and selected a value for a, the quantity involved in that construction procedure. We have also discovered the range of M that will yield a correct estimate.

Next, we ask ourselves how good our method of construction is. That question *does* raise probabilistic issues. If we perform a series of experiments, obtaining a series of values of M and constructing a series of interval estimates according to our method, how often should we be correct? According to the preceding analysis, if μ_D is 152.0 secs. and a is 2.77 secs., we would be correct each time the value of M lies in the range from 149.23 to 154.77 secs. Therefore, asking "how often are we correct" becomes the question: how often will M lie in the "correct" range? We can answer that question if we know RV_D; we only need to find the probability assigned by that underlying RV to the outcome range of interest. What is RV_D, the probability distribution that underlies the sample mean M? Since in the present case RV_P is a normal pdf, $\sigma^2_P = 100$, and $\mu_P = 152.0$ secs. (by assumption), and since $N = 50$, RV_D is a normal pdf, $\sigma^2_D = 2$, $\mu_D = 152.0$ secs. By using the methods developed in chapter 11, we find that the probability that M will lie in the region $\mu_D \pm 2.77$ secs. (the region from 149.23 to 154.77 secs.) is 0.95. We may now invoke the principle of equivalence to infer that the relative frequency of a correct interval estimate will be 0.95 as well. The final conclusion is that by using the interval-construction method described above, then, if we perform a series of repeated experiments and estimate μ_P and/or μ_D each time, we would on average be correct in 95% of the cases.

Now we must discuss the question of selecting an "appropriate" value for a. We had selected the value $a = 2.77$ secs., and found that with that choice our interval-construction procedure would have a probability of 0.95 that it will yield a correct estimate. Suppose we had selected a different value for a, say, 4.0 secs. By applying the previously developed rationale, we should find that M would now have to lie in the interval from 148.0 to 156.0 secs. in order to generate a correct interval estimate for μ_D. Concomitantly, we should find that the probability of obtaining a correct interval estimate using this new value of a will be 0.994, the probability assigned to the new outcome span by RV_D. If we had selected a value of $a = 2.33$ secs., the probability of obtaining a correct interval estimate would be 0.90, and so on.

We have reached the preceding conclusions concerning the probability of obtaining a correct estimate by assuming that the true value of μ_D was 152.0 secs. The general rationale and results, however, can be applied to *any* actual value of μ_D, and would remain equally valid.

We notice an obvious feature: the *wider* we make our interval estimate, i.e., the *larger* the value that we assign to the quantity a, the *higher* the probability that the interval estimate will include the true value of μ_D; conversely, the *narrower* we make our interval estimate, i.e., the *smaller* we make a, the *lower* the probability of being correct in our estimate. We might say that in the former case, we would be "more confident" of our prediction, and in the latter case, "less confident." It thus seems reasonable to use the probability of the range that yields a correct interval estimate as an index of our "level of confidence." This brings to mind a feature we encountered earlier: we can achieve a higher degree of certainty only at the cost of decreased precision. The larger the predicted interval, the greater is our level of confidence, but also the less precise is our bracketing of μ_D; conversely, the smaller our predicted interval, the lower is our level of confidence, but the more precise is our prediction.

We can carry these thoughts to their logical conclusion. If we make the quantity a very large—indeed, "infinitely" large—then we shall *always* be correct, but never furnish useful information. The predicted interval will be the entire outcome axis, and we could have made that "interval estimate" without performing any experiment; we knew in advance that μ_D lies *somewhere* along that axis. A 1.00 level of confidence is accompanied by a meaningless estimate. Alternatively, if we make the quantity a very small—"infinitely" small—then we shall almost certainly be wrong in our prediction; the probability assigned by a pdf to a zero-length outcome axis span is 0. We shall, however, have achieved the maximum in precision. A 0 confidence level leads to a precise prediction that is almost certain to be wrong. These conclusions reflect a larger statistical truth. Precision and certainty are antithetical. In practical applications of statistics to real-world problems one strives to achieve a balance between these fundamentally incompatible goals.[2]

Our next observation concerns another important matter. We have already encountered the quantity $a = 2.77$ secs. and the pdf RV_D (a normal pdf, $\sigma^2_D = 100$) in another context. In chapter 13, $a = 2.77$ secs. was the quantity that we added to and subtracted from μ_D to obtain the pair of critical values for a two-tailed test of significance performed at the level of $\alpha = 0.05$ (see fig. 13.8 and the related discussion). There thus seems to be a close tie between interval estimation and tests of significance. In a given RV situation, if we use a particular value of a to construct a pair of critical values (the values $\mu \pm a$) for a test of significance at the level α,

[2]The situation is reminiscent of that discussed in chapter 13 with regard to the level of significance and the error of the first kind. We saw that in that context, complete certainty—never making a type I error—implied that an experiment would be superfluous. It could not yield any information; we would never reject the null hypothesis. As in the present case, certainty and information were conflicting goals.

and if we use that same value a to construct a pair of confidence limits (the values $M \pm a$) and thus an interval estimate, apparently the level of significance and the level of confidence are related.[3] The relationship seems to be that the level of confidence is equal to $(1 - \alpha)$. In our previous example, the level of significance $\alpha = 0.05$ was linked to a pair of critical values $\mu \pm 2.77$ secs. (fig. 13.8), while now a level of confidence of 0.95 or $(1 - 0.05)$ is linked to a pair of confidence limits $M \pm 2.77$ secs. Thus, at least in the present examples, the level of confidence is numerically equal to $(1 - \alpha)$. Is this always true? Unfortunately, the answer is: no—unless one alters the natural meaning and definition of the confidence level to accommodate these differences. (See problem 14.5 for an illustration.) On occasion, there may be two different, incompatible definitions of the confidence level. The definition based on the probability assigned to the region over which a correct prediction will be made may lead to a different numerical value for the confidence level than the approach that in the context of significance testing simply defines the confidence level to be $(1 - \alpha)$.[4]

These questions can become quite involved and intricate, for example, when one's method of constructing an interval estimate from a statistic becomes more complex mathematically, or when the probability distributions that underly sample values and statistics depart from the relatively simple form of the normal pdf.

[3]The apparently intimate connections between levels of confidence and levels of significance have led to a good deal of conceptual as well as methodological confusion in the past (see Kirk, pp. 100-101). As our simplified demonstration has suggested, in principle there need not be any such connections between interval-estimation and hypothesis-testing methodologies. Of course, each does have its basis in an RV framework.

[4]The actual situation is carefully analyzed by Freeman (pp. 308-311). Before one introduces any probabilistic considerations at all, one has, by defining a given interval estimation construction, defined a certain outcome region Ω for the statistic. Specifically, Ω is that region within which outcome values of a statistic will yield a correct interval estimate; it is a region defined solely by the "geometrical" (i.e., analytical) features of the situation. Finally, the probability of obtaining an interval estimate that does contain the true value of the parameter is simply the probability that the statistic lies within the region Ω. That probability seems to be the most obvious quantity to use as a definition of the level of confidence.

These issues are beyond our scope, and must be left to be addressed in advanced course work.

Estimation and the Principle of Equivalence

In the first presentation of the principle of equivalence I mentioned that the principle was not entirely correct or complete in its first formulation (chap. 3, fn. 2). I suggested that probabilities and relative frequencies were not quite "equal" to one another but only somehow "equivalent." We are now in a position to elaborate on that remark. To illustrate the issue briefly, let us reconsider the relationship between the sample mean M and the mean μ_D of its underlying RV_D. We saw that usually these two values were equal to one another only in the sense that the "long-term average" of the sample mean, that is, the average of many such values of M, would tend to approach μ_D, the mean of its underlying RV, more and more closely. In any one experiment, however, the value of M might be quite different from the value of μ_D. M is an actual outcome of a trial involving a normal pdf, and we know that such an outcome does not have to be—and rarely is—equal to the mean of the pdf that has generated it.

It is much the same for the relationship between the value of the probability *mathematically* assigned to an outcome value (or outcome axis segment) by a probability distribution and the relative frequency of that outcome value (or outcome axis segment) obtained *empirically* in a particular series of repeated trials. The relative frequency is an *estimator* of the assigned actual probability. Thus, in any one series of repeated trials, an empirically obtained relative frequency of an event may have a quite different value from the probability assigned to that event by a probability distribution. However, in the long run the relative frequency obtained from many trials would tend to approach the true, mathematically assigned probability value more and more closely.[5] Thus, a complete statement of the principle of equivalence in-

[5]Notice the qualifier "tend to." The tendency of the long-term average to approach the actual probability value is a statistical trend, and not an utter certainty. The issue is examined by Hays in his discussion of the law of large numbers (p. 279).

volves mathematical complexities that go considerably beyond those mentioned in the initial, simplified version. In spite of the simplification, that first version did lead us to sound conclusions that could have been reached equally by a more formal but also mathematically complex route.

PROBLEMS

14.1 What is the difference between a point estimate and an interval estimate?

14.2 Since the long-term average of sample values is μ_P, we could use a single sample value rather than M as a point estimate for μ_P. Why is M preferable? [Hint: consider the dispersions of sample values and sample means.]

14.3 Define and discuss the confidence interval and confidence limits.

14.4 Describe and discuss the two ways of conceptualizing the confidence level of an interval estimate.

14.5 In an experiment 100 sample values are obtained. The underlying population probability distribution is a normal pdf whose mean μ_P is unknown, and whose variance $\sigma^2{}_P$ is equal to 144. Suppose we decide to construct an interval estimate for μ_P and/or μ_D by subtracting 2.0 and adding 1.0 to the obtained value of M; i.e., the estimated interval constructed from a given value of M is the interval from $(M - 2.0)$ to $(M + 1.0)$.

(a) What is RV_D?

(b) If the true value of μ_D (and thus, of μ_P) is 45.0, what is the outcome range within which M will produce a correct interval estimate?

(c) What is the probability that M will land in that range? Thus, according to one conception, what is the level of confidence?

(d) If we construct a pair of critical values to test the hypothesis H_0' : $\mu_D = 45.0$ according to an analogous procedure, that is, if we let the two critical values be $(\mu_D - 2.0)$ or 43.0 and $(\mu_D + 1.0)$ or 46.0, what is the significance level of the test?

(e) Compare the confidence level computed in (c) with $(1 - \alpha)$, where α is the significance level computed in (d). Discuss the result of your comparison.

14.6 Suppose we decide to construct an interval estimate for μ_D from M according to the following procedure. From an acquired value of M, we construct the lower confidence limit by multiplying M by 3/4, and the upper confidence limit by multiplying M by 3/2. Let us assume that in a given experiment we obtain the value $M = 110.2$ secs.

(a) What interval would we estimate for μ_D?

(b) If the true value of μ_D is 131.7 secs., for what range of M will the stipulated method of interval construction yield a correct estimate?

(c) Can you compute the confidence level? Why, or why not?

14.7 In a particular experiment, RV_P is discrete (i.e., it is a pf and not a pdf). Therefore, in a series of N repeated trials we can compute a relative frequency for a given outcome value. Is that relative frequency a point estimate or an interval estimate for the actual, true probability assigned by RV_P to that outcome value? Explain your answer.

14.8 Why is an interval estimate made at a 0 level of confidence almost certain to be wrong?

CHAPTER 15

The Chi-Square Probability Distribution

We have completed the initial presentation of two major ways in which an RV framework can be used in statistical inference, namely, hypothesis testing and estimation. For the remainder of part IV, we shall retain that basic framework, examining these kinds of statistical inferential procedures in conjunction with various kinds of nonnormal RVs. In each case, we shall examine the mathematical origins and characteristics of a particular type or class of probability distribution, and then go on to explore one or more of its applications.

Mathematical Origins

The basic statistical definition of the probability distribution we are about to consider makes use of a somewhat artificial mathematical procedure. The procedure is artificial in the sense that it is seldom if ever used in actual applied statistical work. Nevertheless, the type of probability distribution that it leads to *is* one of the mainstays of applied statistics.

By means of that procedure, we shall become familiar with the mathematical origins and characteristics of a new class of probability distributions. In the second portion of this chapter, we shall consider some of the ways in which this kind of probability distribution arises and is used in actual experimental work. As previously mentioned, this general plan will also be followed in the remaining three chapters of part IV.

Let us assume that we have a particular type of RV_P, namely, a standard normal pdf. We once again generate a set of N sample values, say, 15, and reduce these to a single number, a statistic or actual $outcome_D$. The particular mathematical operation used to reduce the sample values is the following. First, we take each one of the 15 sample values and *square* it. Then, we form the *sum* of the 15 squared numbers. *That sum is our new statistic*. From an RV perspective, that kind of a number, as we learned in earlier chapters, is one trial of some underlying RV_D. We obtain one statistic for a given experiment—in our case, an "experiment" consisting of 15 repeated trials with a standard normal pdf_P.

We have learned that if we derive a statistic in the context of a specific RV_P and a specific mathematical data-reducing procedure, then the RV that underlies that statistic must be *some* definite, particular probability distribution. This premise was explained in chapter 12 (see fig. 12.4), and also formed the basis of the discussion concerning the probability distribution of the sample mean M in chapters 13 and 14.

We have also learned, in general terms, that the *same* kind of RV_P used with various *different* kinds of mathematical data-reducing procedures will induce different kinds of RV_Ds (see fig. 12.5). Previously, in chapters 13 and 14, we had a normal RV_P (although not necessarily a standard normal pdf), and the mathematical data-reducing operation used was the process of averaging the set of N sample values generated by RV_P. The resulting statistic was M. We now still have the same kind of an RV_P but are now using a quite different arithmetical procedure to reduce a set of sample values to a single statistic. Accordingly, we should expect that in the present case, RV_D would be quite different from the one kind of RV_D that we have met so far, namely, the probability distribution of the sample mean M. That will indeed be the case.

General Characteristics

We can deduce several of the basic general mathematical characteristics of our new type of RV_D just by applying simple logical arguments. Let us consider the range of RV_D. We can immediately conclude that in the present case, an actual outcome$_D$ can never be negative; the statistic has been constructed by summing squares of numbers, and that kind of a sum must be nonnegative. Accordingly, the potential outcome of RV_D must consist of nonnegative numbers exclusively. The statistic must be equal to or greater than 0.[1] Is there a largest outcome value in the potential outcome of RV_D? We know that any one number in a set of sample values generated by a normal RV_P can, in principle, exceed any specified upper or lower numerical limit. Therefore, since we are forming the statistic from the squares of such sample values, we cannot place an upper limit on the value that this kind of a statistic could assume. If any one term of a sum of positive terms can exceed any proposed limit, so can the sum. Apparently, then, the potential outcome of RV_D is nonnegative, and not limited in range. The potential outcome spans the range from 0 to "plus infinity."

We have considered the range of RV_D; what about its continuity? Is the potential outcome of RV_D continuous or discrete? It should be intuitively obvious that RV_D must be continuous. Its outcome values are arithmetically constructed from actual outcomes of a continuous RV (RV_P, a standard normal pdf). The N sample values can assume any value—they are part of a continuous potential outcome—and therefore one would expect that the sum of their squares would be continuous as well. Apparently, RV_D is continuous, i.e., it is a pdf.

Thus, merely by considering the general characteristics of RV_P and of the mathematical operation that had been used to generate a statistic from a set of N sample values, we were able to draw several conclusions about RV_D: its outcome values must be nonnegative; its potential outcome spans the range from zero to infinity, and thus is classified as not limited in range; and, since an actual outcome can assume any numerical value of zero or

[1]Can the outcome value of our statistic be 0? One could quibble about the answer. Let us note that the only way that one could obtain that outcome value would be if the result of each of the 15 trials of the standard normal RV would be 0—otherwise, our statistic must be greater than 0. While it is possible that all 15 outcomes would be exactly 0, it is highly unlikely; after all, the probability of obtaining exactly 0 on even *one* trial of a normal RV is 0. The issue is neither theoretically nor practically important. We can include 0 in the potential outcome of the statistic or not, as we please.

greater, the potential outcome is continuous. RV_D is a not-limited-in-range pdf. The sketch of our RV_D is shown in figure 15.1. We see that its general characteristics are those that had been predicted from simple logical arguments.

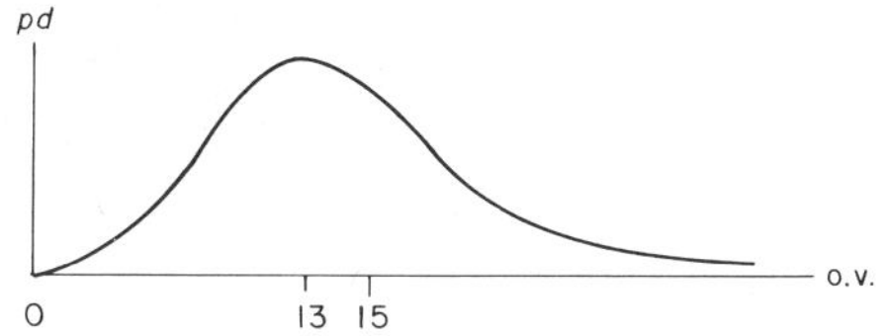

FIGURE 15.1 A nonnormal pdf_D

The outcome values of this particular type of pdf are called *chi-square* values, and this kind of a probability distribution is called a *chi-square* probability distribution. It is *statistically defined* as the particular kind of a pdf that underlies a statistic generated according to our specified data-reducing operation.

We note that the term "chi-square" is being used in a double sense: it is the "name" of an outcome value, and also names a particular type of probability distribution. The term chi-square is usually represented by χ^2, the Greek letter chi, squared. Let us be sure that the apparent complexity or strangeness of this label does not confuse us. When the symbol χ^2 is used to represent an *outcome value*, it is in principle exactly like x, z, or any other symbol that might be used to stand for an outcome value. (We shall meet several others in the chapters that follow immediately.) Thus, even though χ^2 is visually a more complex symbol than, say, z, it represents the same sort of quantity, an outcome value of an RV. When χ^2 is used to represent a type of *probability distribution*, that symbol is in principle just a name of a pdf type, just as the names "normal," "uniform (rectangular)," or similar other labels identify particular types of probability distribution. χ^2, then, is just a symbol used to represent either an outcome value or a pdf. In either case, there is no reason to fear that χ^2 is somehow more difficult or complex conceptually than any other analogous symbols used to represent outcome values or type of probability distributions in statistical work. The sense in which the symbol χ^2 is used in a given instance will be clear from the context.

The chi-square probability distribution belongs to those kinds of pdfs whose profiles can be described by means of an algebraic equation. As we already know from our discussion of the normal probability distribution, an algebraic equation of a pdf specifies for any one value of the independent variable (the outcome value—in this case, χ^2) a corresponding value of the dependent variable, the probability density (see chap. 11). Thus, it is conceivable that the chi-square pdf would be specified by an algebraic equation that had a familiar form, such as

$$y = 3\chi^2 + 5$$

(where y is the value of the probability density corresponding to a given outcome value χ^2). Unfortunately, the algebraic equation for χ^2 is not that simple (see Freeman, p. 204). Its precise form need not concern us, however. We shall be able to study the pdf without using its algebraic specification.

The Parameter

The chi-square, like the normal and many other types of probability distributions, comprises a family of pdfs. Any one of the members is specified by one single parameter, usually represented by the Greek letter ν (nu). That parameter can assume only positive integral values; ν can equal 1, 2, 3, etc. The parameter value has no upper limit, and there are thus an unlimited number of members in the chi-square family of pdfs. Each particular member of that family, then, is specified by that one single index, the parameter ν, and there is one χ^2 pdf corresponding to each of the positive integers. It is common practice to display the parameter value of a particular χ^2 pdf as a subscript in parentheses. Thus, if one is speaking generally of the chi-square pdf with the parameter value ν, one represents it by the symbol $\chi^2_{(\nu)}$; a particular member, say, the chi-square pdf whose parameter value is 10, would be represented by the symbol $\chi^2_{(10)}$.

With respect to the characteristics of the parameters, we can see that there are two principal differences between the χ^2 and the normal RV family. First, two parameters (μ and σ or σ^2) were required to specify a particular member of the normal probability distribution family, whereas a member of χ^2 is specified by a single parameter (ν). Second, μ and σ^2 could be assigned *any* numerical values (although σ^2 has to be nonnegative, of course, being an average of squared numbers; see part II), while ν may only assume one of a restricted although still infinite set of numerical values, the nonnegative integers. In analogy with outcomes, one might say that μ and σ^2 are continuous types of parameters, while ν is discrete. For χ^2, the parameter ν is also the "number of degrees of freedom," a concept we shall discuss shortly. One says that $\chi^2_{(\nu)}$ is "a chi-square distribution with ν degrees of freedom," or, in a specific case, that "$\chi^2_{(10)}$ has 10 degrees of freedom," for example. Figure 15.2 exhibits the graphs of several χ^2 pdfs for different values of ν. Typical members of the χ^2 family are illustrated. We see that in general, as ν becomes larger, the shape of the pdf begins to look more and more like a normal pdf profile. For larger values of ν, perhaps 100 or greater, a χ^2 pdf can be approximated quite well by a suitably selected normal pdf (see Hays, p. 443). We know immediately, however, that this approximation cannot be entirely accurate, since the potential outcome of a normal pdf is different from a potential outcome of a chi-square probability distribution. The former encompasses all of the outcome axis, while the latter includes only nonnegative values.

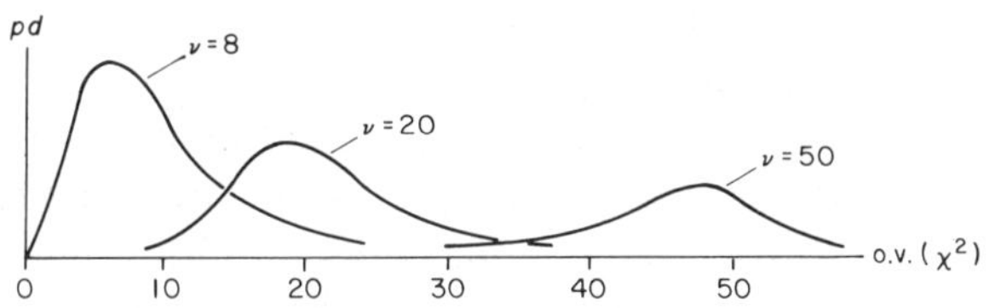

FIGURE 15.2 Typical χ^2 pdfs

For any given member of the chi-square family, certain simple numerical relationships hold between its parameter ν and the probability distribution's mean, variance, and mode. It requires a moderately advanced mathematical analysis based on the algebraic form of the chi-square pdf to demonstrate these relationships between ν and the three special quantities μ, σ^2, and the mode. We shall only state the results. For χ^2 with ν degrees of freedom, the mean, μ, occurs at the outcome value $\chi^2 = \nu$, (15.1)

the variance has the value $\sigma^2 = 2\nu$, and (15.2)

the mode occurs at the outcome value $\chi^2 = (\nu - 2)$ (for $\nu > 3$). (15.3)

These are simple computations, and it is easy to find these values for a given member of the χ^2 family. For instance, for $\chi^2_{(15)}$ (which happens to be the particular pdf illustrated in fig. 15.1), the mean occurs at the outcome value $\chi^2 = 15$, the variance has a value of 30, and the mode occurs at the outcome value $\chi^2 = 13$. We find the standard deviation of our illustrative pdf as usual by taking the positive square root of the variance. For $\chi^2_{(15)}$, $\sigma = \sqrt{30}$ or approximately 5.48.

Degrees of Freedom and Constraints

It is difficult to give an adequate idea of the complex concept of degrees of freedom in a short space. That probably accounts for the remark that it is "A concept of central importance to modern statistical theory which few textbooks have attempted to clarify" (Walker, 1940, p. 253). One difficulty is that it is a concept best explained mathematically, but the required mathematical tools are not elementary. Although we shall introduce the concept briefly, I suggest that you supplement the introduction by at least surveying Walker's or some similar discussion.

The concept has a dual aspect. It has a mathematical basis, and it has close ties to the characteristics of actual physical systems. As far as its mathematical meaning is concerned, the degrees of freedom basically refer to the *number* of quantities that one is free to choose in a given mathematical situation. To illustrate that idea, let us consider the following two situations. First, suppose you were asked simply to choose 15 numbers. How many of these could you choose freely? Obviously, the answer is 15. You have not been restricted in any way in making your selections. One says of this situation that it has "15 degrees of freedom."

Now suppose that instead you are asked to choose 15 numbers that are *deviations from a mean*. As we know from the material in part II, saying that 15 numbers are deviations from a mean has certain implications about their mathematical origin. It implies, first, that there is some antecedent set of 15 numbers; second, that one has computed the mean or average of that set; and, third, that one has formed 15 algebraic differences, the 15 deviations from the mean. In this case, how many of 15 such numbers can you select without restriction? The answer is 14. One particular mathematical requirement is always placed on any set of numbers that is a set of deviations from their mean. It can be shown by simple algebra that the sum of such a set must always be 0, exactly (Hays, p. 222). Therefore, if you have selected any 14 numbers that are considered as part of a set of 15 deviations from the mean, the 15th number is rigidly specified. It must be the one number that, when added to the sum of the other 14 deviations, brings the total sum to 0. For instance, if 14 of 15 deviations from the mean add to, say, 255, then the last deviation *must* equal -255 so that the sum of the 15 terms is 0, as required. We say of this kind of a situation that the requirement that the sum equals 0 has imposed a *constraint* on the freedom of choice. A constraint is a restricting requirement. Previously, one had been free to choose 15 terms—there were 15 degrees of freedom. Now, one mathematical constraint has correspondingly brought about the loss of one degree of freedom, reducing the number of degrees from 15 to 14. There are many other mathematical situations to which this concept applies, but the preceding illustration is typical of the simpler instances.

These mathematical concepts have correspondences in physical situations. We shall only touch on these. Consider a sphere that is free to move in three-dimensional space. How many numbers, "coordinates," must one furnish to fully specify its location and rotational orientation? The answer is 6. Three numbers are required to locate the sphere's center, two numbers to orient its axis in space, and one number to specify the angular orientation of the sphere about that axis—making six numbers in all to be specified. One is free to assign these numbers, and thus one says that a sphere that is completely free to move in three-dimensional space has six degrees of freedom. Suppose that we now insist that the sphere lie on a surface, a billiard table, for example. The center of the sphere now lies in a plane; accordingly, the center can be specified by two numbers, not three as before. The sphere is still free to rotate without restriction, however, and that implies three additional degrees of freedom, as before. Therefore, the total number of degrees of freedom is five. The requirement that the sphere rest on a table has caused the loss of one degree of freedom. The table has acted not only as a physical, actual constraining influence but also as a mathematical constraint that reduces the number of degrees of freedom by one. Further constraints—for example, insisting that the ball roll in a groove—would correspondingly bring about additional reduction in the number of degrees of freedom of the sphere.

Let us return to the hypothetical RV situation that had presumably generated 15 sample values from 15 trials of a standard normal pdf and reduced that set of numbers to a statistic by forming the sum of their squares. We now are in a position to describe the RV that underlies a statistic generated in this fashion: it is $\chi^2_{(15)}$, a chi-square probability distribution with 15 degrees of freedom.

In the present example, it should not be too difficult to see, at least informally, why our mathematical situation has 15 degrees of freedom. We assumed that the 15 sample values had been generated without imposing any of the kinds of mathematical restrictions that would create some confining relationships between these quantities. The sample values were generated in an entirely free way, subject only to the statistical rule imposed by RV_P. In the light of our discussion of the concept of degrees of freedom, one would therefore expect that these 15 numbers, and any quantities derived from these, would have 15 degrees of freedom.

Had we generated a larger or smaller number of sample values, that is, had we used a larger or smaller sample size N, the parameter of RV_D would correspondingly have been larger or smaller. For example, had we used 20 sample values, RV_D would have been $\chi^2_{(20)}$; had we used 10 sample values, RV_D would have been $\chi^2_{(10)}$, and so on. The extension to the general case is obvious. If we generate N outcome values by N repeated trials of a standard normal probability distribution and form a statistic by squaring the sample values and adding the resulting N terms of squares, then the probability distribution that will underlie a statistic generated in this manner is $\chi^2_{(N)}$, a chi-square probability distribution with $\nu = N$.[2] Let us not conclude, however, that the number of degrees of freedom ν of RV_D are always related in this simple fashion to the sample size N. We shall soon explore a chi-square statistic constructed from N sample values whose underlying RV_D does *not* have N degrees of freedom.

Tables

We have learned that there are an infinite number of χ^2 pdfs, one for each value of ν. To use a particular member, say, $\chi^2_{(20)}$, one would in general need to have a table of that probability density function. In principle, that table would have the same basic characteristics as any other table of a continuous RV—for instance, the table of the standard normal probability distribution in Appendix A. The $\chi^2_{(20)}$ RV would be tabulated in terms of either or both of the usual defining mathematical functions, the pdf or cdf. That is, the $\chi^2_{(20)}$ table would show a probability density value and/or a cumulative probability value for each χ^2 value (outcome value) in the tabulated set of outcome values. The table would be used in the usual way, principally to obtain probabilities assigned to specified outcome regions by that RV. For instance, one would be able to obtain the information that the probability assigned by $\chi^2_{(20)}$ to the outcome segment that lies between $\chi^2 = 15$ and $\chi^2 = 28$ is approximately 0.65.

When we studied the normal RV family, we found that although it had infinitely many members, it was unnecessary to have one table for each of those RVs. We saw that in a sense, all normal RVs had "the same shape"—they differed in scale and not in basic configuration. We therefore needed only one table supplemented by a method that would permit us to relate that normal RV to all the others. We chose the standard normal RV as the representative of that family, and used (11.2) as the mathematical bridge that connected the standard to any other member of the normal probability distribution family. Now, unfortunately, this approach is no longer possible. The various members of the χ^2 family do not have the "same shape" in the sense that normal RVs do. Therefore, one

[2]In addition, these N sample values need to be "statistically independent." Roughly, this means that knowing the value of any one of these sample values will provide no new statistical information about the value of any of the others. We shall discuss this topic in chapters 20 and 21.

needs to have one table for any one given member of the χ^2 family. It is important to remember this, because in practice various methods are used to avoid unnecessarily voluminous sets of tables; these methods, although in principle just like our familiar method illustrated in Appendix A, can be confusing on first encounter. Typically, one finds that χ^2 tables provide a coarse cdf for each value of ν in a range such as from 1 to 100; for each degree of freedom, only a few cumulative probability values are listed. We shall return to the question of tabulating RVs in chapter 17.

A Chi-Square Statistic: S^2*, the Sample Variance*

We shall next explore one χ^2 statistic of practical significance. In order to see how it is generated, we shall begin again by specifying an RV_P, a set of sample values, and a mathematical data-reducing operation that transforms the set of sample values to a single statistic. Let us use our familiar RV_P shown in figure 13.1 (a normal pdf, $\mu_P = 150$ secs., $\sigma^2{}_P = 100$) and a set of 15 sample values generated by that RV_P. We shall use the following data-reducing method, one quite similar to that previously discussed in this chapter. The method reduces the set of 15 sample values to *the average of the squares of the deviations from the sample mean.* We have encountered this kind of average in chapters 7 and 8. The calculation is straightforward, and is shown in table 15.1 for a set of 15 hypothetical sample values. First, one finds the mean M of the 15 sample values; next, one forms 15 deviations from that mean; third, each deviation is squared, and one obtains 15 squares of the deviations from the sample mean; fourth and last, these terms are averaged—one adds them, and divides the sum by the number of terms, 15.

The resulting statistic is called the *sample variance* and is usually represented by S^2. Although it is generated by a somewhat more complex arithmetical operation than the operation that generated M from a set of N sample values, from the standpoint of RV theory S^2 is conceptualized in exactly the same way as M. That familiar framework is shown in figure 15.3. If you compare that figure with the corresponding figure 13.1 for M, you will see the obvious parallels. All the conceptual ingredients remain the same:

Table 15.1

Calculating the sample variance S^2

Trial no.	o.v.	Deviation about M: (o.v. − M)	(Deviation)^2
1	148.2	−1.31	1.72
2	157.6	8.09	65.45
3	142.1	−7.41	54.91
4	151.6	2.09	4.37
5	153.3	3.79	14.36
6	137.7	−11.81	139.48
7	152.4	2.89	8.35
8	146.1	−3.41	11.63
9	162.9	13.39	179.29
10	136.0	−13.51	182.52
11	147.8	−1.71	2.92
12	168.5	18.99	360.62
13	157.2	7.69	59.14
14	131.9	−17.61	310.11
15	149.3	−0.21	0.04
Sum:	2,242.6	0	1,394.73
Average:	149.51 ↑ M	0	92.98 ← S^2

RV_P, the set of N sample values, the data-reducing procedure that produces a statistic, and an RV_D (i.e., a pdf that underlies the statistic) jointly specified by RV_P and the data-reducing method. The difference between figures 13.1 and 15.3 is primarily one of detail, not principle. The framework expressed in these two sketches is fundamental to statistical inference. We shall encounter it again, unmodified in its basic characteristics, in each one of the remaining chapters of part IV.

We have obtained a value for S^2 in the stated manner. What might its underlying RV be? It should come as no surprise that in this case RV_D is χ^2, essentially. In the present example, that pdf

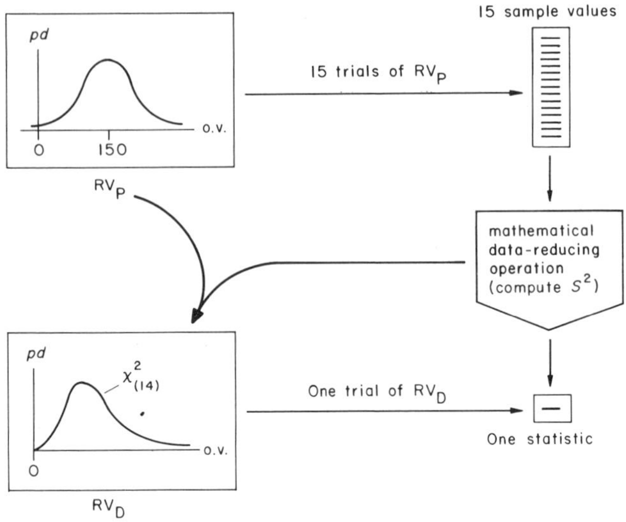

FIGURE 15.3 RV origins of the sample variance S^2

has 14 (*not* 15) degrees of freedom. That should not be surprising either. In our introduction to the concept of degrees of freedom we saw that a set of deviations from the mean would have one degree of freedom less than the number of sample values; squaring 15 deviations from the mean does not change the fact that they have 14 degrees of freedom. Essentially, the RV that underlies S^2 is $\chi^2_{(14)}$. The qualifier "essentially" is needed because it is not S^2 itself that has $\chi^2_{(14)}$ as the underlying RV, but S^2 times a constant. In the present case, the value of that constant is 15—the number of sample values—divided by 100—the value of the variance of the population distribution. It is the quantity ($0.15 \times S^2$) that is distributed as $\chi^2_{(14)}$. That is, the outcome values for that pdf represent $0.15 \times S^2$, rather than S^2 alone.

Although it might appear complicated at first, the present situation really is very simple: RV$_D$, the probability distribution that underlies S^2, is a $\chi^2_{(14)}$ pdf whose χ^2 outcome values must be relabeled—i.e., altered by a simple scale factor—in order to represent S^2 itself. It is as though we had a pdf whose outcome values were expressed in one set of units—say, pounds—and we had to convert the axis labels by a scale factor so that the numbers on that axis would represent some other set of units, say, ounces. The procedure used to change χ^2 to equivalent S^2 values (or vice versa) is a simple arithmetical step. If it is the quantity $0.15 \times S^2$ rather than S^2 itself that is equal to a χ^2 outcome value—that is, if

$$0.15 \times S^2 = \chi^2, \tag{15.4}$$

then to change a χ^2 outcome value to the associated S^2 value we only need to divide:

$$S^2 = \frac{\chi^2}{0.15}$$

or:

$$S^2 = 6.66 \times \chi^2. \tag{15.5}$$

The situation is represented in figure 15.4 in the following manner. First of all, $\chi^2_{(14)}$ is shown as any other pdf would be—χ^2 outcome values are shown on a horizontal axis, and the corresponding probability density values assigned by the pdf are shown on a vertical axis, as usual. In addition, since in the present case there is one particular S^2 value corresponding to each χ^2 outcome value and vice versa—see (15.4) and (15.5)—we may relabel the outcome axis to show that relationship. We can think of the pdf $\chi^2_{(14)}$ also in terms of outcome values that have been converted to equivalent S^2 values, in this particular case by applying (15.5). This equivalence is shown in figure 15.4 by a double set of outcome axis labels. The upper set represents the straightforward χ^2 outcome values, and the lower set represents the corresponding S^2 values. This double system of labels represents by means of a graph the relationship expressed algebraically in (15.5).

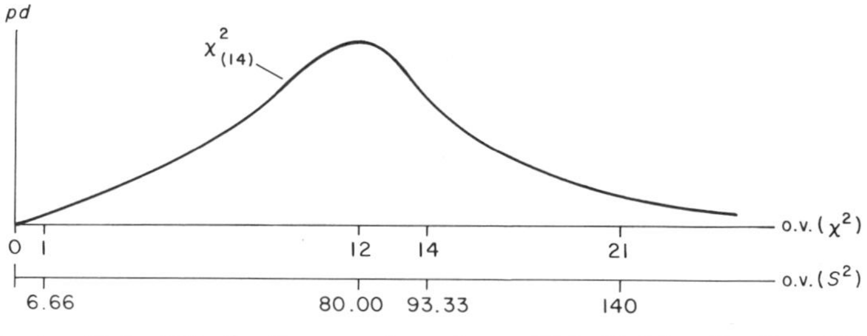

FIGURE 15.4 RV_D for the sample variance S^2 (with $N = 15$, $\sigma^2_P = 100$)

The relationships between the S^2 and χ^2 outcome values are used in a straightforward fashion. Let us see how they might be used to find the probability for a specified range of S^2. Suppose, for example, we would need to find the probability that in any one experiment, our statistic S^2, the sample variance, will lie in a range between 65 and 140. What are the corresponding χ^2 outcome values? From (15.4) we find that the χ^2 outcome values corresponding to the specified range of S^2 values lie in the outcome range from $\chi^2 = 10$ to $\chi^2 = 21$. We consult a table of the $\chi^2_{(14)}$ pdf, and find that the cumulative probabilities of the two end points 10 and 21 are 0.25 and 0.90, approximately. Accordingly, the probability that a χ^2 outcome value will lie between 10 and 21, or, *equivalently*, the probability that the value of the statistic S^2 will lie between 65 and 140, is 0.90 − 0.25, or 0.65. Incidentally, we know from chapter 5 that 0.65 also is the area under the $\chi^2_{(14)}$ curve in figure 15.4 between $S^2 = 65$ and $S^2 = 140$ (or between $\chi^2 = 10$ and $\chi^2 = 21$).

We had constructed our S^2 statistic from 15 sample values ($N = 15$) generated by a normal RV_P that has a variance of 100 ($\sigma^2_P = 100$). The correct scale factor in this specific example is 0.15. If, however, our sample values had been generated by a normal population RV that had some other variance than 100, and/or if we had generated a sample size other than $N = 15$, the scale factor that multiplies S^2 would be altered accordingly. Let us see what that scale factor would be in the general case, that is, the case where a normal RV_P with a variance represented by the general symbol σ^2_P generates a set of sample values whose size is represented by the general symbol N. For this general case, the scale factor is (N/σ^2_P). Thus, (15.4) and (15.5), the equations that were specific to our example ($\sigma^2_P = 100$, $N = 15$), are special cases of the general equations that relate χ^2 outcome values and the associated S^2:

$$\frac{N \times S^2}{\sigma^2_P} = \chi^2, \tag{15.6}$$

and

$$S^2 = \frac{\sigma^2_P}{N} \times \chi^2. \tag{15.7}$$

(In any given instance, σ^2_P and N are two specific numbers, of course.) In our previous example, N had been 15, and σ^2_P had been 100. If we substitute these values in (15.6) and (15.7), we shall obtain the "special case" (15.4) and (15.5), respectively.

What about the degrees of freedom of the associated RV_D, the pdf that underlies S^2 (suitably modified by a scale factor)? In the general case, it is $\chi^2_{(N-1)}$, the chi-square pdf with $(N - 1)$ degrees of freedom, that is the correct RV_D. Note carefully that $\nu = (N - 1)$ and *not* N. In the previous example, with $N = 15$, $\nu = (N - 1)$ or 14.

Why is it that it is $(N \times S^2)/\sigma^2_P$ rather than S^2 alone that has $\chi^2_{(N-1)}$ as the underlying probability distribution, and why is $\nu = (N - 1)$ rather than some other value—say, N? A meaningful explanation of these matters must invoke the use of moments and other more advanced mathematical procedures (see Freeman, pp. 206-207, for example). Intuitive explanations are sometimes offered in introductory expositions, but I feel that they usually only mystify the reader; these kinds of pseudoexplanations obscure the fact that there is a solid but somewhat complex mathematical basis for the preceding conclusions. There seems to be no simple way in which the correct mathematical procedures can be presented intuitively.

The Sample Variance and Point Estimation

We have been considering a normal RV_P, a set of N sample values generated by that probability distribution, a data-reducing operation that yields S^2, and the RV_D that underlies that statistic. To apply this framework to statistical inference, we use concepts and approaches that are basically the same as those developed in the context of the sample mean M in chapters 13 and 14. For example, to perform a test of significance, one would, as usual, specify a level of significance α, find the corresponding critical value or values (depending on whether the alternative hypothesis called for a one- or two-tailed test of significance), and examine the experimentally obtained value of the statistic to see whether it fell into an acceptance or a rejection region.

There are, however, certain differences between inferential procedures involving M and those involving S^2. One of these concern difficulties that arise in defining critical values or confidence limits in procedures involving S^2; the difficulties arise because the underlying distribution associated with S^2 is asymmetrical, a feature that was not true for the RV that underlies M. The lack of symmetry of χ^2 does raise certain methodological difficulties, but these are beyond the scope of our work (see, for example, Freeman, pp. 325-326; or Hays, p. 442). Another difference, more immediately relevant to our discussion, is that whereas M typically is involved in hypotheses or estimation procedures concerning *means* of a population probability distribution, S^2 typically is involved in hypothesis tests or estimates concerning *variances* of population probability distributions. Let us examine a simple illustrative example.

Let us assume that we know a population probability distribution RV_P is normal, but that we do *not* know the value of its variance σ^2_P. We can obtain a point estimate of that parameter value in the following fashion. We generate a set of N sample values by N trials of RV_P, and construct the statistic S^2. We have seen that in this kind of a situation, the probability distribution that underlies the quantity $(N \times S^2)/\sigma^2_P$ is $\chi^2_{(N-1)}$, the chi-square probability distribution with $(N - 1)$ degrees of freedom. From the perspective of an RV framework, what outcome value might one expect to obtain from a "typical" trial of $\chi^2_{(N-1)}$? From various previous discussions (chaps. 7, 8, and 11-14) we know in general that although an outcome value obtained on one trial may lie anywhere in the potential outcome range of its underlying RV, a "typical," usual trial will yield an outcome value near μ, the mean of that underlying RV. RV_D—in the present case, $\chi^2_{(N-1)}$—is just one particular RV. Therefore, if we perform one trial with RV_D (i.e., obtain the statistic S^2 from an experiment) and if we have no information about the *population* probability distribution (other than that it is a normal pdf), then it would not be unreasonable to assume that the value obtained from one trial of RV_D represents a value close to the mean of RV_D—indeed, to assume that the obtained outcome value is equal to that mean. If RV_D is $\chi^2_{(N-1)}$, then what is the mean of that pdf? (15.1) tells us that for *any* $\chi^2_{(\nu)}$, $\mu = \nu$, in general. In our case, since $\nu = (N - 1)$, $\mu = (N - 1)$.

Thus, on the basis of the preceding considerations, we can finally draw the following conclusion. If we perform one trial with $\chi^2_{(N-1)}$ and obtain one value for our statistic S^2, it is reasonable to expect that *the value of* S^2 *and the value of* σ^2_P *will be such that*

$$\frac{N \times S^2}{\sigma^2_P} = \mu \text{ of } \chi^2_{(N-1)} = (N-1). \qquad (15.8)$$

We may then conclude that if we perform an experiment and construct S^2 from N sample values generated by a normal RV_P, it is reasonable to suppose that *the value of* σ^2_P*, the variance of the normal population distribution* RV_P*, is a value that will make (15.8) true*. In other words, we should expect that σ^2_P is such that

$$\frac{N \times S^2}{\sigma^2_P} = (N-1),$$

or

$$\sigma^2_P = \frac{N}{(N-1)} \times S^2. \qquad (15.9)$$

In terms of a numerical example, if we had used a sample size N of 50, and if we had experimentally obtained a value of 110.4 for S^2, then a reasonable point estimate for σ^2_P would be $(50/49) \times S^2$, or 112.65.

Equation (15.9) invites an interesting interpretation. It can be interpreted to mean that a good guess for a population variance σ^2_P is obtained by using the value experimentally obtained for the sample variance, *slightly modified* by the factor $[(N)/(N-1)]$. That means that S^2 is a slightly *biased* estimator of σ^2_P. It slightly underestimates that parameter and therefore must be corrected by a simple numerical adjustment. Previously, in the case of M, we had a statistic that was an unbiased estimator of the mean of the population distribution (see chap. 14). Now we have encountered a biased estimator. We see that in the present instance, this kind of a statistic is just as useful as an unbiased statistic. One simply corrects for the known bias. The correction factor involves N, the sample size. We see from (15.9) that as the sample size increases, the correction factor (and thus, the degree of bias) decreases and approaches unity. For large N, S^2 provides an estimate that is almost unbiased (see problem 15.8).

Although at this time we shall not consider any other inferential uses of the χ^2 probability distribution in detail, we note that there are numerous other such uses. One important particular application concerns the evaluation of the so-called goodness of fit of data. Briefly, that term refers to the following kind of situation. Let us assume that we have some theoretical tool that is presumed to predict certain kinds of data. For instance, let us assume that we have developed an equation that we believe will adequately predict the amount of daily rainfall. We make a set of predictions, and later compare these to actual data. Is our formula correct? We would conclude that it is, if our predictions had matched the measured data exactly. Unfortunately, such accuracy can almost never be achieved in dealing with complex phenomena. Therefore, we should expect that various imponderables would prevent the formula from making absolutely correct prediction. We would expect some discrepancy between the two sets of values, and we probably should not be disappointed. We would have a set of errors associated with our predicted and actual data. The question is: is that error excessive, is our formula useless, or does it give useful even though inexact information? The errors can be analyzed within a chi-square RV framework to help answer this question; a meaningful χ^2 statistic can be derived from the sum of the squares of these errors (Hays, pp. 719-723). You are not expected to know the details of that procedure at present, of course. The discussion is only intended as a qualitative illustration of the kinds of applications that involve the use of a χ^2 pdf.

We now have become familiar with two different types of probability distributions, the normal, and the chi-square. We shall next investigate a third family, the t distribution, whose mathematical origin is rooted in both these pdfs.

PROBLEMS

15.1 How many parameters are needed to uniquely specify one member of the chi-square probability distribution family?

15.2 If a chi-square outcome value is generated according to the procedure first discussed—the procedure pertaining to (15.1)—why cannot that outcome value be negative?

15.3 Describe and discuss the number of degrees of freedom that are associated with the following situations:

(a) The position of a train along a track.

(b) The exact position of an automobile on a road.

(c) The position of a balloon.

(d) The selection of any 35 numbers.

(e) The shape of a lump of clay.

15.4 For $\chi^2_{(100)}$, what is μ? σ^2?

15.5 A standard normal pdf_P generates 10 sample values. We square each number, and compute the sum of these squares. We have reduced the sample values to a statistic. What is RV_D?

15.6 We may form another statistic, the sample variance S^2, from the 10 sample values described in problem 15.5.

(a) How does this mathematical data-reducing operation differ from the corresponding operation in problem 15.5?

(b) What is RV_D now? How and why does it differ from RV_D in problem 15.5?

(c) In the present example, how are the χ^2 outcome values related to S^2?

15.7 A set of 20 sample values is generated from a normal RV_P, $\sigma^2_\text{P} = 25$. The sample values are reduced to the statistic S^2.

(a) If you wanted to know the probability the S^2 lies in some specified range, what pdf table would you need?

(b) How would you use that table to find the probability that S^2 will lie in the range from $S^2 = 20$ to $S^2 = 45$?

15.8 S^2 is computed from 30 sample values generated by a normal RV_P.

(a) On average, by what percentage will S^2 differ from the parameter σ^2_P?

(b) On average, does S^2 yield too large or too small an estimate for σ^2_P? Justify your answer.

(c) How large must the sample size N be before the error committed by estimating σ^2_P with S^2 (uncorrected) is 1% or less?

CHAPTER 16

Student's *t* Probability Distribution

Once again, we shall present the statistical specification of a probability distribution in terms of a procedure that one would rarely encounter in actual experimental work. The development will parallel that used in chapter 15. We shall construct a statistic by means of a somewhat artificial mathematical procedure, and will find that it has led to the definition of a kind of probability distribution that has considerable experimental significance and utility.

Mathematical Origins

Let us assume that we have an RV_P that is a *standard* normal probability distribution—a situation that by now should be thoroughly familiar. We shall construct a statistic in several steps. First, we will generate *one* sample value; let us represent that actual outcome value by z. Next, we will generate N more sample values. Third, we shall square each of these N values and form a sum from the N squared quantities; let us represent this sum by y. Finally, we form the following ratio involving z, y, and N:

$$\frac{z}{\sqrt{\frac{y}{N}}}. \tag{16.1}$$

This ratio is our new statistic; it is an outcome value that usually is symbolized by the letter t.

We know from our previous discussions that since the statistic (16.1) has been obtained by using a *specific* mathematical data-reducing operation on a set of sample values generated by a *specific* RV_P, it must have some *specific* underlying RV_D. We shall examine that probability distribution shortly. First, let us examine the ratio (16.1) further. The quantity under the square root sign should not be altogether new to us. The sum represented by y has been formed from the squares of N outcome values generated by trials involving a standard normal pdf; we ought to recognize that therefore y is an outcome value whose underlying pdf is $\chi^2_{(N)}$, a chi-square pdf that has N degrees of freedom. From a statistical point of view, then, the quantity under the radical (square root sign) is an outcome value generated by one trial of $\chi^2_{(N)}$ divided by the number of degrees of freedom of that underlying pdf. What about the quantity z in the numerator? It is simply an outcome value generated by one trial of a standard normal pdf; that had been our initial assumption. We see that the ratio (16.1) implicates both a normal as well as a chi-square pdf.

The probability distribution that underlies a statistic generated according to the procedure just presented is a pdf known as the t probability distribution, or Student's t (named after the pseudonym used by its originator; see Freeman, pp. 208-209; Kirk, p. 96). Since the denominator of (16.1) involves a chi-square pdf with N degrees of freedom, one might expect that there would be one particular t distribution corresponding to each possible value of N. This is the case. The t probability distribution is once again a family of pdfs, and each member is characterized by a single parameter value. The parameter of t has the same conceptual origins and numerical properties as the corresponding parameter for chi-square; indeed, it, like the parameter of χ^2, is also referred to as "the number of degrees of freedom" and represented by the Greek letter ν. For a given member of the family of the t probability distribution, the number of degrees of freedom is the same as the number of degrees of freedom of the chi-square statistic in the denominator of (16.1). Thus, one would say, for example, that the pdf that underlies the t outcome value or t ratio specified by (16.1) is "Student's t probability distribution with N degrees of freedom." In a specific situation, N would of course be some positive integer.

Once again, each member of the t family is a pdf that in principle is like any other probability density function. It is a mathematical function that assigns probability density values to a potential outcome set, that set is continuous, etc. Incidentally, we should notice that like the symbol χ^2, t serves a dual function. It can stand for an outcome value such as (16.1), and it can also stand for the "name" of a particular kind of pdf or pdf family.

The profile of a t probability distribution can be described by means of an algebraic equation that is quite complicated. We shall not need to use this algebraic description which can be found in most intermediate statistics textbooks (see, for example, Freeman, pp. 208-209; Hays, pp. 392-398).

Each member of the family is a pdf whose graph is a symmetrical bell-shaped curve. Its mean and center of symmetry is the outcome value $t = 0$. There is a simple algebraic relationship between ν and the variance of a given member of the t family, provided ν is equal to 3 or more. It is the relationship $\sigma^2 = [\nu/(\nu - 2)]$.

Although t is a bell-shaped pdf, it is *not* a normal pdf; its algebraic equation is quite different from (11.1), and its mathematical origin is of course quite different as well. For larger values of ν, however, the shape of the t probability distribution does approach a standard normal profile. This is reflected in the formula that describes the relationship between the variance of a particular member of the t pdf family and its number of degrees of freedom. If we examine that previously cited formula, we can see that as ν becomes greater, the variance comes closer and closer to 1, the value of the variance of a standard normal pdf.[1] Indeed, for larger values of ν, a standard normal pdf provides a quite good approximation to a t pdf. How large must ν be before it is legitimate to use this kind of an approximation? That depends on the degree of error that one is willing to tolerate in a given application. Usually, if the number of degrees of freedom is at least 30 to 100 or so, the standard normal pdf will furnish a quite satisfactory approximation (see Hays, pp. 395-396). t distributions for several values of ν are shown in figure 16.1; for comparison, a standard normal pdf is also shown in that figure.

[1]This is of course only supporting evidence, not proof, that the t probability distribution approaches a standard normal profile as ν becomes large.

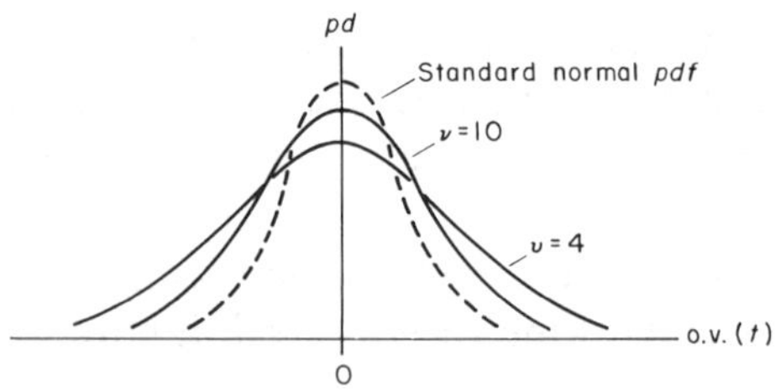

FIGURE 16.1 Typical t pdfs

Tables of the t distribution typically are presented in exactly the same way as tables of the chi-square family (see Hays, p. 885; Freeman, p. 425). The discussion in chapter 15 about the problems and procedures entailed in the tabulation of χ^2 applies equally well here, and therefore will not be repeated.

A Statistic

The t distribution arises in a number of experimentally important contexts and is used in a variety of inferential procedures. It is a probability distribution that "shows a remarkable range and diversity of application" (Freeman, p. 210). At present we shall explore only one particular way in which this kind of pdf arises in actual experimental work. Many other applications are reported and discussed in the literature (for example, see Hays, pp. 399-412, 593-594; Freeman, pp. 318-319).

Typically, the t probability distribution is involved in inferential procedures about *means* of RVs. We had already developed one kind of statistic, M, for these kinds of applications. Why, then, should we need another? We shall see. Let us first specify one particular mathematical data-reducing method that yields a statistic whose underlying RV is a t pdf. It is a mathematical operation that is frequently used in actual experiments.

Let us say that we have generated a set of N sample values by N repeated trials with an underlying normal population probability distribution whose mean is some known value μ_P, but whose variance σ^2_P is unknown or unspecified. We shall reduce that set of sample values to a statistic by the following steps. We (1) compute M, (2) compute S^2, and, for reasons to be discussed later, (3) form the ratio

$$\frac{(M - \mu_P)}{\sqrt{\dfrac{S^2}{(N - 1)}}} \,. \tag{16.2}$$

We have arrived at a familiar stage of our usual procedure. We have specified an RV_P, a set of sample values generated by repeated trials of that pdf_P, and a particular mathematical operation that is to be used to reduce that set of N values to a single statistic. Accordingly, we know from a number of previous discussions and specific cases that we have specified one particular RV_D as well. In the present case, the statistic calculated according to (16.2) is a t ratio or t statistic, and its underlying pdf is a t probability distribution with $(N - 1)$—and *not* N—degrees of freedom. The situation is shown schematically in figure 16.2.

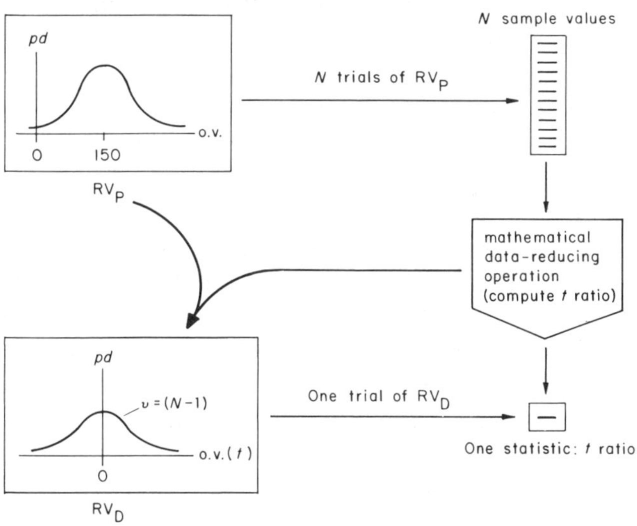

FIGURE 16.2 RV origins of a t ratio

We had previously defined an underlying t pdf in terms of a statistic that is the ratio between z, an outcome value generated by a standard normal pdf, and the square root of (y/N), a chi-square outcome value divided by its number of degrees of freedom—(16.1). We now are claiming that the statistic (16.2) also has a t probability distribution as its underlying RV_D. Why should that be the case? The ratio (16.2) does not at first glance appear to have the characteristics required by the defining ratio (16.1). The numerator of (16.2) does not appear to be a quantity like z, nor does the term under the radical sign of the denominator of (16.2) appear to be a quantity like y/N, yet it can be shown algebraically that the statistic (16.2) stems from a ratio such as (16.1).[2] That demonstration is presented in Appendix B.

It should by now be apparent that we have repeatedly been following a chain of reasoning whose principal logical constituents remain essentially the same from one case to the next. It is the rationale whose general features are represented in figure 12.7; figures 13.1, 15.3, and 16.2 are specific forms of that general case. Although each of these three latter situations has its own distinguishing characteristics, the three cases embody the same logical structure. We now may begin to see how an RV framework conceptually unifies apparently disparate statistical and experimental situations.

The principal differences between the three above-mentioned cases reflect specific differences in the mathematical operations used to reduce a set of N sample values to a statistic; RV_P remains a normal pdf. In the first case, the reduction method that is used is one that generates M, the sample mean; the RV_D that underlies that statistic is a normal pdf (chaps. 13 and 14). In the second case, the data-reduction method that is used is one that generates S^2, the sample variance; the RV_D that underlies that statistic is a chi-square pdf (chap. 15). In the present case, the data-reduction method that is used is the operation that generates the t ratio in

[2]Strictly speaking, it is not sufficient to demonstrate that algebraic equivalence. In order to prove that the ratio (16.2) is mathematically equivalent to the ratio (16.1) that defines a t outcome value, one must also show that the numerator and denominator of (16.2) are "statistically independent" (a concept we shall study in part V). While it is relatively easy to show the algebraic equivalence between (16.1) and (16.2) (see Appendix B), it is considerably more difficult to analyze the question of statistical independence in this instance (see Freeman, pp. 206-207).

(16.2); the RV_D that underlies that statistic is a t pdf.[3] The discussion in chapter 12 may now take on added meaning. We learned in general that *different* data-reducing methods in conjunction with the *same* type of RV_P will "induce" *different* RV_Ds that underlie statistics (fig. 12.6). We now see specific cases of that general proposition.

A Significance Test

In (16.2) we have a statistic that involves μ_P, the mean of the population RV, and we can use that statistic in various inferential procedures pertaining to that parameter. The procedures are in principle like those investigated in preceding chapters; they are either tests of significance or estimation procedures. The details may be different from those in the earlier examples, but the general conceptual framework remains the same in all essentials. We shall briefly consider how the t ratio statistic in (16.2) may be used in a simple test of significance.

Let us once more use the general framework of our familiar rat-diet study, with a few minor modifications. Let us assume that the experimenters know that sample values obtained from treated animals have an underlying RV_P that is a normal pdf; both its parameters are unknown. In a particular experiment, 25 sample values are generated. The experimenters wish to test the null hypothesis H_0: The 25 sample values "came from" a normal $RV_{P(0)}$ whose mean $\mu_{P(0)}$ is 150.0 secs., against the alternative hypothesis H_1: H_0 is false (i.e., $RV_{P(0)}$ did *not* generate the 25 sample values). Notice that neither H_0 nor H_1 makes any assumptions concerning the variance of the population probability distribution.

Superficially, this is the kind of a problem we addressed in the early part of chapter 13. The null hypothesis postulates that the RV origin of a set of sample values is a particular normal pdf, the probability distribution we had earlier called "$RV_{P(0)}$," while H_1 postulates that H_0 is false without specifying an alternative RV_P. An analysis of the present situation shows, however, that if we

[3]If RV_P is not a normal pdf, then in each of these three cases RV_D will depart from the probability distribution profiles that we have been considering (see chap. 13, n.2).

attempt to implement the hypothesis-test procedure used in chapter 13, we cannot carry it out. The main difference and difficulty is that now we neither know nor postulate a variance $\sigma^2{}_{P(0)}$ for $RV_{P(0)}$. Consequently, we should find that when we stipulate a significance level α, we are unable to compute the corresponding critical values that define acceptance and rejection regions for $RV_{D(0)}$ and H_0' by the procedures presented in chapter 13 (see problem 16.3).

This is the kind of situation where the t statistic methodology becomes pertinent. The reason that we may proceed without knowing the variance $\sigma^2{}_P$ is that the t ratio (16.2) substitutes and incorporates an estimate, the sample variance S^2, for the parameter value. We do, however, pay a slight penalty for using an estimator rather than an actual parameter value. The probability distribution that underlies our statistic—a t pdf—has a somewhat larger dispersion about the mean than the corresponding standard normal pdf. Therefore, for a given significance level, the acceptance region for a t pdf will be greater, and our test will correspondingly be slightly less informative. (See n. 2 in chap. 14 and the related discussion concerning the antithetical goals of precision and certainty.)

Let us examine the way one might use a t ratio statistic in a two-tailed test of significance. Let us return to the hypothetical experiment that generated 25 sample values from a normal RV_P; we had assumed that the experimenters wished to determine whether or not the mean μ_P of RV_P is equal to 150.0 secs. To initiate the test, we reduce the 25 sample values to a t ratio according to the formula in (16.2). We simply compute M and S^2 from the 25 sample values, and "plug" these two values into (16.2); for the remaining quantities in (16.2), we use the value $\mu_P = 150.0$ secs. (our hypothesized value), and the sample size $N = 25$. We obtain some number, the t ratio statistic.

If H_0 is actually true, i.e., if μ_P does equal 150.0 secs., then the statistic (16.2) will have "come from" one particular underlying RV_D. As we know from our earlier discussion, that probability distribution is the t pdf with $(N - 1)$ degrees of freedom.

The remaining steps should be familiar from chapter 13. We select the significance level α, and find the two corresponding critical values. (We are now able to do so, since we can specify RV_D completely). Finally, we examine the value of our statistic (16.2) to see whether it lies in an "A-type" region (in terms of fig. 13.4) of $RV_{D(0)}$. If it does, we cannot reject H_0'; we cannot reject the premise that $RV_{D(0)}$ actually did generate the statistic obtained in the given experiment. Concomitantly, we cannot reject H_0: the 25 sample values were generated by a normal RV_P whose mean is 150.0 secs. (i.e., $RV_{P(0)}$). If, however, the statistic (16.2) falls into a rejection region of $RV_{D(0)}$, we come to the opposite conclusion. We reject H_0' and H_0, and/or accept H_1' and H_1. We conclude that probably $RV_{D(0)}$ did not generate the statistic, and therefore $RV_{P(0)}$ did not generate the sample values. The diet probably did make a difference.

Let us consider a numerical example. Let us say we decide to perform the two-tailed significance test at a level of $\alpha = 0.05$. From a table of $RV_{D(0)}$—in this case, the *t* probability distribution with 24 degrees of freedom—we find that the two critical values are $t = \pm 2.06$. Suppose our 25 sample values yielded the values $M = 145.7$ secs. and $S^2 = 110.4$. The value of (16.2) would be -2.00. That *t* outcome value would thus lie within the acceptance region for the null hypothesis, the region from $t = -2.06$ to $t = +2.06$; we would not reject H_0', and thus would not reject H_0.

Alternatively, if in a similar experiment we were to obtain the values $M = 156.3$ secs. and $S^2 = 108.4$, then (16.2) would have the value $t = +2.97$. The statistic would lie in one of the two rejection regions for the null hypothesis, and we would reject H_0' (and H_0). We thereby would accept the alternative hypothesis H_1': $RV_{D(0)}$ did not generate (16.2), as well as the alternative hypothesis H_1: $RV_{P(0)}$ did not generate the 25 sample values.

Nonnormal Population Probability Distributions

Finally, there is a general issue that we have thus far only mentioned in passing. In each of the preceding discussions of hypothetical experiments, we had assumed that the population probability distribution has been a normal pdf. This assumption is, of course, frequently not quite correct in actual experimental situations (see chap. 11). If RV_P is not exactly a normal pdf, what are the consequences for our statistical methodology? For instance, in the present case, if RV_P is not precisely a normal pdf, is the RV that underlies our statistic t still a t probability distribution, more or less? In general, these are difficult questions that raise important practical problems in experimental studies. Each case needs to be examined individually. Some kinds of statistics are quite vulnerable to the failure of assumptions concerning the characteristics of RV_P. In those cases, if the assumptions are not almost exactly correct, the profile of RV_D is significantly affected and considerable experimental errors may be introduced. Other kinds of statistics are "more robust"; in those cases, one may safely depart significantly from basic assumptions concerning RV_P and still be able to use the same kind of statistical test with satisfactory results. The t statistic falls into this latter category. Apparently, the t pdf still provides a good estimate of the RV that underlies the statistic (16.2) even if RV_P is significantly different from a normal pdf (Hays, p. 410).

PROBLEMS

16.1 In general, what kinds of RV situations necessitate the use of a t ratio statistic?

16.2 Suppose that the following six sample values had been generated by a normal RV_P: 8.3, 5.7, 7.0, 3.6, 5.1, and −6.5.

(a) Form a t ratio statistic to test the hypothesis $\mu_P = 3.5$.

(b) What RV_D underlies that statistic?

(c) If the critical values corresponding to a significance level $\alpha = 0.10$ are the outcome values $t = \pm 2.02$, would you accept or reject the hypothesis proposed in (a)?

(d) Suppose you were to use the standard normal pdf to approximate the true RV_D. What would be the two critical values for $\alpha = 0.10$?

(e) By using this approximation, would you increase or decrease your chance of committing an error of the first kind, or would that chance remain the same? Explain your answer.

16.3 Suppose you know that RV_P is a normal pdf, $\mu_P = 140.0$ secs. In a given experiment, RV_P generates 25 sample values.

(a) What is RV_D for M? [Hint: examine (13.1) and (13.2).]

(b) What is the length of an "*A*-type" region (with reference to fig. 13.4) that has a probability of 0.99 assigned by RV_D?

(c) If you cannot answer (b), explain the nature of the difficulty.

(d) On the basis of your examination of this problem, can one find a pair of critical values for RV_D for M in the kind of situation we have been considering here?

16.4 How many parameters are required to define a particular member of the *t* pdf family?

16.5 In what way is a *t* pdf different from a normal pdf? What is the principal mathematical difference?

16.6 What does it mean to say that $t_{(N-1)}$ underlies the statistic (16.2)?

16.7 One can form a number of different kinds of statistics from a set of N sample values generated by a normal RV_P. So far, we have considered the statistics M, S^2, and the *t* ratio (16.2). For these three, why are the three underlying RV_Ds different from each other? [Hint: see chap. 12.]

16.8 In the significance test illustrated in this chapter, suppose we had obtained the values $M = 144.2$ secs. and $S^2 = 95.1$. For $\alpha = 0.05$ and $N = 25$, would these results lead you to reject the null hypothesis H_0: $\mu_P = 138.0$ secs.?

16.9 If RV_P is not a normal pdf, why is the RV_D that underlies (16.2) not a *t* probability distribution?

CHAPTER 17

The *F* Probability Distribution and the Analysis of Variance

Mathematical Origins

The probability distribution to be introduced in this chapter underlies a statistic generated according to a mathematical data-reducing procedure that once again begins with a standard normal RV. We shall first generate two sets of sample values. One series of repeated trials will generate N_1 sample values, and the other, N_2 sample values. (In a given instance, N_1 and N_2 may be two different numbers, or they may be the same.) We next square each of the N_1 sample values in the first set, and add the squared terms; let us represent the resulting sum by x. We follow the identical procedure with the N_2 numbers in the second set; let us represent the resulting sum of those N_2 squared terms by y.

This procedure should be familiar. You should recognize that x and y are actual outcome values whose underlying probability distributions are $\chi^2_{(N_1)}$ and $\chi^2_{(N_2)}$, respectively. Therefore, an alternative but mathematically fully equivalent procedure for generating these two outcome values would be to imagine that one has *two* RVs, $\chi^2_{(N_1)}$ and $\chi^2_{(N_2)}$, and that one trial of each will yield the outcome values x and y, respectively.

We have obtained two quantities, x and y. The last step in deriving a statistic from the N_1 and N_2 sample values is to form the ratio

$$\frac{\frac{x}{N_1}}{\frac{y}{N_2}}. \tag{17.1}$$

This quantity is our new statistic. It is called an F value or an F ratio. Correspondingly, its underlying pdf is called an F probability distribution or Fisher's F (after Sir Ronald Fisher, a prominent early contributor to its development).

Once more, as in the case of χ^2 and t, a symbol is being used in two different ways. In the present case, the same symbol F stands for either (1) a statistic or outcome value$_D$ or (2) a type of probability distribution. In a given instance, the meaning of the symbol should be clear from the context.

The F pdf comprises a family of probability distributions whose members are distinguished from one another by parameters. Since the statistic (17.1) is constructed from two χ^2 outcome values and thus brings two χ^2 pdfs into the picture, it should not be surprising to find that the specification of any one particular member of the F pdf family requires specification of two parameter values. These correspond to the two degrees of freedom, $\nu_1 = N_1$ and $\nu_2 = N_2$, associated with x and y, respectively. The F pdf thus is a two-parameter family, in contradistinction to single-parameter families such as χ^2 and t. One speaks of the F probability distribution that underlies the ratio (17.1) as "The F probability distribution with N_1 and N_2 degrees of freedom." The usual notation for this RV is $F_{(\nu_1,\, \nu_2)}$; a particular member would be described by two particular positive integers—for example, $F_{(28,\, 13)}$.

The general properties of the F probability distribution reflect the family's mathematical ancestry. The potential outcome set of a member of the F pdf family is identical to that of a chi-square pdf; it is a continuous, not-limited-in-range potential outcome comprising nonnegative outcome values only. Each $F_{(\nu_1,\, \nu_2)}$ pdf can be described by a complicated algebraic formula that defines a probability density value in terms of the two values ν_1 and ν_2 and the corresponding F outcome value (see Hays, p. 445; Freeman, p. 210). From this algebraic formula, it can be shown that for a given F probability distribution with ν_1 and ν_2 degrees of freedom, the mean μ occurs at the outcome value $F = \nu_2/(\nu_2 - 2)$, for $\nu_2 > 2$, and the mode at $F = (1 - 2/\nu_1)/(1 + 2/\nu_2)$, for $\nu_1 > 2$ (Lewis, 1960, p. 313). The variance may also be specified in terms of ν_1 and ν_2, but the formula is more elaborate (see Hays, p. 445). If we examine these formulae, we find that for larger values of the two parameters, both the mean and the mode tend to lie near the outcome value $F = 1$; the mode always lies to the left, and the mean to the right, of that outcome value.

The profile of a graph of an F pdf depends on the specific values of ν_1 and ν_2, but the typical profile is quite similar to that of a typical χ^2 pdf; it is quasi-bell-shaped, with a tail extending to the right. Several characteristic profiles are shown in figure 17.1.

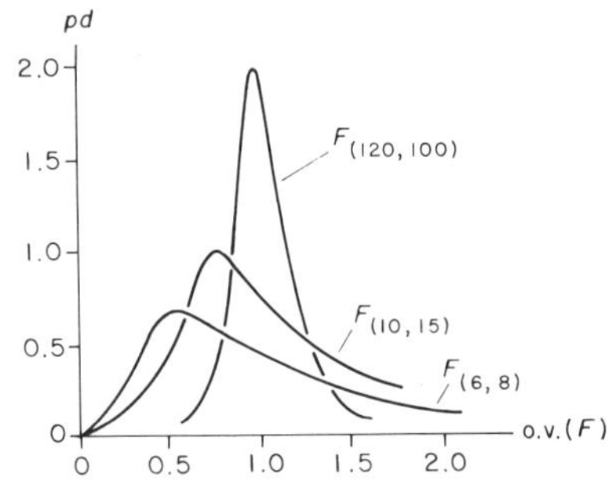

FIGURE 17.1 Typical F pdfs

Tables

We had previously established that one of the principal ways of specifying a function for an RV is to present a basic table that would list a selected set of outcome values, and a corresponding set of probability densities (or, for discrete RVs, probabilities) and/or cumulative probability values (see Appendix A). As we learned in part I, a pdf (or pf) and a cdf are equivalent specifications, because given any one particular pdf, we can construct one, and only one, corresponding cdf, and vice versa. Nevertheless, it sometimes is convenient to present both types of functions in one table. For example, this has been done in Appendix A; both the pdf and the cdf of a standard normal probability distribution have been tabulated.

Let us review the issues pertaining to the tabulation of different families of RVs. We know that there are an infinite number of members in the normal RV family, but that in a sense they all have "the same mathematical shape." Therefore, one needs to have a table of only one specific member of that family; one can then derive the relevant data for any of the other members by suitable arithmetical manipulations. The usual practice is to tabulate the so-called standard normal RV ($\mu = 0$, $\sigma^2 = 1$), and to use (11.2) as the link between outcome values of the standard and those of other normal probability distributions. Then, if we wish to obtain pdf or cdf data for a given nonstandard normal pdf, we can use (11.2) to find the z outcome value of the standard normal probability distribution that corresponds to a given x outcome value of the nonstandard probability distribution.

We have learned that this economical procedure could not be followed in the case of the chi-square and t RV families. In both of these families, the mathematical shape of any one of its members is basically different from that of every other member; therefore, in principle each probability distribution requires its own separate tabulation. Suppose one would wish to furnish tables for the first 100 members of such a one-parameter family (that is, for the parameter values 1, 2, . . ., 100). Obviously, in most instances it would be impractical to provide 100 tables, one cdf or pdf table for each RV. I mentioned in chapters 15 and 16 that the usual procedure is to construct one table that is essentially a condensation of 100 separate RV tables. This approach is illustrated schematically in table 17.1. That kind of a table lists, for each one of the first 100 members of a hypothetical single-parameter family, outcome values corresponding to a few selected cumulative probability values. The particular probability values that are usually found in that kind of table reflect the kinds of significance levels that are conventionally used in typical hypothesis tests. That is, the probability values in the top row of table 17.1 include those values most frequently assigned in actual practice to the tails of RVs in tests of significance.

At first glance, the format of a table such as 17.1 seems to be the reverse of the basic format used in Appendix A. In table 17.1, *outcome values* are listed for specified *cumulative probability values*, while the basic format of a cdf table lists *cumulative probability values* for specified *outcome values*. On closer examination, however, it becomes apparent that even though the formats of the two tables seem to be different, the two kinds of

Table 17.1

A hypothetical one-parameter RV family

Value of parameter	Cumulative probability					
	0.01	0.02	0.05	0.10	0.95	0.99
1						
2						
3						
35	3.7	4.2	6.7	7.3	18.9	22.4
100						

outcome values for $\nu = 35$

tabulation provide essentially the same kind of information.[1] In order to demonstrate that equivalence, table 17.2 has been constructed from hypothetical data presented in table 17.1 for the particular probability distribution whose parameter value is 35. Table 17.2 is a basic table that shows cumulative probabilities for a set of selected outcome values, as usual. In essence, it has been possible to prepare a conventional although coarse, limited table of the cdf of that particular probability distribution from some of the data in table 17.1. We can construct a similar cdf table for any one of 99 other RVs from a table such as 17.1. Thus, that kind of a summary table lists a few cdf data points for many different RVs (in our illustration, for 100).

The approach to tabulation illustrated in table 17.1 becomes

[1]This is the case because in the kinds of continuous RVs that we have been considering there exists an unambiguous pairing between any given cumulative probability value (other than 0 or 1) and a corresponding outcome value. Given either one will uniquely specify the other. (We say that in this case, the cdf has a "unique inverse.")

Table 17.2

A cdf for $\nu = 35$
(from table 17.1)

o.v.	*cp*
3.7	0.01
4.2	.02
6.7	.05
7.3	.10
18.9	.95
22.4	.99

impractical when the specification of an RV requires more than one parameter value, as the following considerations show. Suppose we would wish to use the format of table 17.1 to present a table of the *F* pdf family for the first 100 values of *each* of the two parameters. This means we would wish to present data for 100 × 100, or 10,000, probability distributions. Combinations of 100 values of each of two parameters will define 10,000 parameter pairs such as (1, 1), (1, 2), (1, 3), . . ., (1, 100); (2, 1), (2, 2), (2, 3), . . ., (2, 100); . . . ; (100, 1), (100, 2), (100, 3), . . .,(100, 100). Each of these 10,000 paired values of parameters would specify one $F_{(\nu_1,\ \nu_2)}$ probability distribution. If we wished to present data for all these RVs by means of a table such as 17.1, the table would have to have 10,000 horizontal lines, one for each probability distribution. This cumbersome method can usually be avoided because, as we shall see presently, the predominant application of the *F* distribution is in a one-tailed test of significance that uses only the *right-hand tail* of the pdf. Therefore, the only information that is usually needed for a given member of the *F* family is *one critical value* for a *specified level of significance* α. Accordingly, the usual procedure for tabulating the *F* or similar two-parameter probability distribution families is to prepare *one* table for *each one* of several commonly and conventionally used levels of significance (such as 0.01, 0.02, 0.05, or 0.10). Each table provides *one* critical value for each *one* of many RVs. The general idea is illustrated in table 17.3. That table schematically represents data for 100 × 100 or 10,000 F probability distributions. For each of these RVs, the table provides one critical value for a one-tailed (right-hand tail) test of significance—in this particular example, at a 0.01 level. The information provided is very simple. For example, the table tells us that the critical value for $F_{(40, 60)}$ for a directional test of significance at a 0.01 level is the outcome value $F = 1.94$. In other words, a table such as 17.3 tells us that for $F_{(40, 60)}$, the value of the cdf at $F = 1.94$ is 0.99 (Why?); the table thus specifies *one pair of values*, an *outcome value* and an *associated cumulative probability*, for each one of 10,000 RVs.

Table 17.3

Format for tabulating critical values for 10,000 members of a two-parameter RV family
($\alpha = 0.01$, right-hand tail)

ν_2 \ ν_1	1	2	3	4	40	99	100
1							
2							
3							
4							
60					1.94		
99							
100							

for $F_{(40, 60)}$, the cumulative probability at $F = 1.94$ is 0.99

If we wish to specify critical values associated with a different level of significance α, we shall need a second table. Suppose we had such a table—for $\alpha = 0.05$, for example. We would find that the critical value for $F_{(40,\ 60)}$ to be the outcome value $F = 1.59$. We now would know that the two cumulative probability values associated with the outcome values $F = 1.59$ and $F = 1.94$ are, respectively, 0.95 and 0.99. In effect, we would now have two data points of the cdf of $F_{(40,\ 60)}$. We can see that from a *set* of tables such as table 17.3, one can reconstruct a coarse set of cdf data for any one of many (in our case, 10,000) *F* probability distributions. Each table would provide *one* data point for the cdf of any one of these probability distributions.

Although tables such as 17.1 and 17.3 may at first glance seem quite unlike the basic kind of pdf or cdf table (such as the table in Appendix A), these tables provide essentially the same kind of data. If we understand the fundamental ideas behind the tabulation of a probability distribution, then in any given instance we should also be able to uncover and understand the particular rationale that underlies even an unusual or idiosyncratic method of tabulation.

Introduction to the Analysis of Variance

The mathematical genesis of the *F* pdf family has been presented in terms of a procedure that one would not be likely to find used in an actual experiment; in practice, one does not usually obtain an *F* ratio by generating two sets of sample values from an underlying standard normal pdf, squaring these, etc. Instead, an *F* value statistic typically arises in one of several other ways.[2] Probably the most prominent of these is a process known as the *analysis of variance* (commonly abbreviated as ANOVA), "one of the most widely used statistical procedures in the behavioral sciences" (Kirk, p. 225). In fact, most of the quantities that were used in chapter 2 to illustrate the concept of a single outcome value mathematically derived from experimental data were statistics that derived from ANOVA procedures.

[2] We had encountered analogous situations in chapters 13, 15, and 16. In each of these, a new type of statistic and associated RV_D were introduced in terms of an idealized mathematical procedure, and subsequently, "practical" versions of that statistic and their applications were presented—for M, S^2, and the t ratio (16.2). We are still following that sequence.

In previous chapters, the quantities that illustrated the kinds of statistics used in actual practice—the sample mean M, the sample variance S^2, and the t ratio (16.2)—were statistics generated by means of quite simple arithmetical procedures. The data-reducing methods used in ANOVA experiments, however, are more complex; the algebraic formulae that specify these procedures, and the corresponding arithmetical manipulations that transform a set of sample values into a statistic, are relatively elaborate. One could present these methods at this point, of course, but that approach tends to raise difficulties in an introductory exposition. The complexities of the manipulations tend at first to obscure the underlying rationale of the ANOVA process. Furthermore, while it is possible to present mathematically superficial arguments to rationalize the mechanics of the manipulations, these kinds of explanations usually tend to be unconvincing and more confusing than helpful. Therefore, our usual method of exposition will not be followed exactly in this introduction to ANOVA. Previously, when a particular illustrative "practical" inferential procedure had been presented, specific computational details for obtaining the appropriate statistic were given and discussed. In this chapter, in order to present the concepts in as clear and uncluttered a manner as possible, we shall not enter into a discussion or examination of the mechanics used in ANOVA procedures. We shall merely present a general overview of the underlying logical framework, leaving the particulars of computational procedures to subsequent, more advanced course work.

We were considering hypothetical experiments that involved only one group of experimental subjects and one "experimental treatment" (the special diet in the rat study, for example). We shall now consider more elaborate kinds of experiments. We shall first consider a situation where several "levels" of a particular kind of experimental treatment are investigated. Experiments that evaluate the effectiveness of several different methods of academic instruction, or assess the therapeutic effectiveness of different dosage levels of medication, would be studies that used several "levels of an experimental treatment." The terminology will be used in a very general sense, with "treatment" representing just about any kind of experimentally administered procedure, and "level" representing different qualitative or quantitative aspects of such treatments. We shall introduce some of the fundamental conceptual elements of ANOVA procedures in terms of a hypothetical study that uses several qualitative levels of treatment.

Let us assume that one wishes to investigate 8 different methods of instruction used in some subject area. The experimental plan is to teach each one of 8 different groups of 50 students by a different method. The efficacy of the 8 instructional methods will be compared and assessed in terms of some suitable academic test that yields one numerical measure for each of the 400 students. The data that result from this kind of an experiment can be organized in the manner indicated schematically in table

Table 17.4

Format for ANOVA data

Student no.	Method of instruction							
	A	B	C	D	E	F	G	H
1								
2								
3								
				400 outcome values$_P$				
4								
|								
|								
|								
49								
50								
Group means M_i:	M_1	M_2	M_3	M_4	M_5	M_6	M_7	M_8
Within group variances S^2_i:	S^2_1	S^2_2	S^2_3	S^2_4	S^2_5	S^2_6	S^2_7	S^2_8

Grand mean M: average of all 400 outcome values$_P$

Between-groups variance $S^2_M = \dfrac{(M_1 - M)^2 + (M_2 - M)^2 + \ldots + (M_8 - M)^2}{8}$

17.4. There would be 8 columns, one for each method of instruction, and there would be 50 test scores or numerical measures in each one of these columns. The *scientific* question is: are there any differences in the scores of the 8 groups? It should not be too difficult to recognize the basic similarity between this study and those investigated in the previous chapters.

It should be almost self-evident what must be done in order to place the situation within a statistical framework. We consider the data in any *one* of the 8 columns to be a set of 50 sample values generated by repeated trials of some *one* particular population RV that characterizes the performance *of that group*. In other words, for the purpose of statistical analysis we shall imagine that there is some *one* RV_P that underlies *each* of the 8 groups of 50 sample values. The scientific question, "Are the 8 instructional methods different?" now becomes the statistical question, "Do the data provide any statistical evidence that there are differences among the 8 RV_Ps that underlie these 8 groups of 50 sample values?"

In order to make that statistical question more specific, we shall make a simplifying assumption. We shall assume that somehow we know that each one of the 8 underlying RV_Ps (they may or may not be the same—we do not yet know that) are *normal* pdfs that all have the *same variance*. The question, "Are the 8 RV_Ps different from one another?" thus becomes the specific question, "Do the 8 normal pdfs have the same *mean*?" We are proposing that the mathematical equivalent of a difference in effectiveness between the instructional methods is a difference between the means of the 8 RV_Ps. Thus, we have implied two initial statistical hypotheses. H_0, the null hypothesis, is: all 8 RV_Ps have the same mean. H_1, the alternative hypothesis, is: one or more of these means are different from the rest.

The ANOVA methodology then is principally a procedure that allows one to decide whether or not a set of sample values "came from" RV_Ps that all have the same mean, say, μ_P. We shall examine that question by a statistical procedure that reduces data arranged according to the plan in table 17.4 to a statistic that is an F ratio or F value. As we shall see, *if* there are no significant experimental differences, if all RV_Ps have the *same mean*, then we would expect the value of that statistic to lie close to the outcome value $F = 1$. If, however, there are significant experimental effects, if all 8 RV_{PS} apparently do *not* have the same mean, then we should expect the F ratio to be significantly *larger* than 1. Perhaps you can see a one-tailed test of significance looming on the horizon. As you may remember, during the discussion of the tabulation of the F probability distribution family, I mentioned that this kind of RV is usually used in a one-tailed test of significance that utilizes only the right-hand tail. We now begin to see why this might be the case.

We shall need to develop several mathematical concepts and the applicable terminology. One set of concepts concerns the *means* of the *data*. One can now identify *two* different types of sample means in a data matrix such as that shown schematically in table 17.4. First, there is the familiar sample mean that can be calculated for each group: we have 8 groups (containing 50 sample values each), and therefore can compute 8 means called *group sample means*. These are represented as M_1, M_2, . . ., and M_8 in table 17.4. We will use the symbol M_i to indicate a general member of that set of group sample means. Next, we can also calculate the mean of all 400 sample values; that average is called the *grand sample mean*, and will be represented by M, without subscript.

A second issue concerns sample *variances*. One can identify *three* different kinds within the data structure. The first is the familiar kind of sample variance that can be calculated by the usual method for any *one* of the 8 groups of sample values (see chap. 15 and table 15.1). Since we have 8 groups, we may compute 8 sample variances. These will be represented by $S^2{}_1$, $S^2{}_2$, . . ., and $S^2{}_8$. We shall call any one of these kinds of variances a *within-group sample variance*; each one is calculated from the sample values contained in only one group. The second type of sample variance, while somewhat different in detail, is basically still just a particular kind of sample variance. It arises in the following manner. We had computed 8 group sample means, the set M_i. Therefore, one can form 8 deviations of a group sample mean from the grand sample mean, $(M_i - M)$, one deviation from each group sample mean M_i. We now have 8 numbers and can compute a *sample variance* of that set of 8 "samplelike" values by our usual method. The procedure is indicated in table 17.4. We call the resulting average the *between-groups sample variance*, and represent it by the symbol S^2_M. Finally, we can also compute a sample variance from all 400 sample values, according to our usual procedures. We form 400 deviations from M, square these, etc. We shall call the resulting average simply the *sample variance* (or sometimes, the grand sample variance), and represent it by S^2, without subscript.

To summarize: from a set of data in a table such as 17.4, we can obtain *two* types of sample means (8 of the first type, M_i; one of the second, M). We can also obtain *three* types of sample variances (8 of the first type, S^2_i; one each of the second and third type, S^2_M and S^2).

We now are ready to generate the statistic that reduces all 400 sample values to a single number. As I have stated, we shall not explain the computational details, but only indicate the principles of the process.

The procedure focuses on the variances S^2_i and S^2_M (hence the name, analysis of variance). In essense, what we shall do is to use sample variances as estimators of one population variance. This procedure should not be altogether unfamiliar; we have already met a simple version of the present situation when we used an ordinary sample variance S^2 to calculate a point estimate of a variance of a population RV—see equation (15.9). ANOVA procedures apply this general idea in a mathematically more complex fashion. First, it can be shown by purely algebraic means that certain general mathematical relationships always exist between the three types of sample variances that we have developed—S^2_i, S^2_M, and S^2 (see chap. 21 and Freeman, p. 212). Furthermore, and this is the crux of the matter, one can demonstrate that *if H_0 is true*, if in effect all the sample values had been generated from the same *one* single underlying RV_P, then by suitable mathematical manipulations one can obtain two quantities, one from the set of S^2_i, and the other from S^2_M, that each independently provide a point estimate of the same variance, namely, the variance of that single RV_P. If, however, *H_1 is true*, if the means of one or more of the RV_Ps are *significantly different* from the rest, then the variance estimate obtained by using S^2_M will tend to be significantly *greater* than the variance estimate obtained by using the 8 S^2_i.

(These conclusions rest on mathematical proofs, and will become more meaningful when we return to these issues in part V.) At any rate, *two quantities*, one constructed from the between-groups sample variance, and the other from the set of within-group sample variances, *will estimate the same parameter* (an RV_P variance) *if* H_0 *is true; otherwise* the between-groups sample variance will estimate a *larger* value. *These facts provide the basic rationale for all ANOVA procedures.*

Let us restate these conclusions in terms of our hypothetical experiment. If H_0 is true and all 400 sample values had been generated by one RV_P—if the 8 RV_Ps that underlie the 8 groups of 50 sample values are in fact the same RV_P—then two separate estimates of the variance of RV_P will tend to estimate the same value. If, however, there are some differences between the means of the 8 RV_Ps, if H_1 is true, then the two estimates will tend to be different from one another. The estimate *A* based on the between-groups sample variance S^2_M will tend to provide a *larger* value than the estimate *B* based on the 8 within-group sample variances, S^2_i. For the present, we shall have to be satisfied with a statement of these bare facts. Specifically, we obtain one estimator—let us call it *A*—by a suitable mathematical manipulation of S^2_M, the between-groups sample variance; we obtain a second estimator—let us call it *B*—by suitable mathematical manipulations of the 8 values S^2_i, the within-group sample variances. If H_0 is true, then in any one experiment, *A* and *B* will tend to assume the same numerical value.

The next task in the ANOVA procedure, then, is to compare two quantities that, if H_0 were true, would tend toward the same numerical estimate. How might one compare two such quantities mathematically? We can consider that question quite generally. If *a* and *b* are any two quantities that each tend to assume the same value, then the ratio a/b tends to lie near the value 1. Therefore, we can compare two separate estimates of μ_P derived from the two types of sample variances by forming a ratio between the two estimates *A* and *B*. Then, if H_0 is *true*, the ratio A/B will tend to fall close to the value 1. If, however, H_0 is *false*, then, as we have said, *A* will tend to estimate a larger quantity than *B*; therefore, the ratio A/B will in that case tend to be greater than 1.

We have finally arrived at our usual stage of a hypothesis-testing procedure. We have generated a statistic, the ratio A/B, and have discovered that if H_0 is true, we should expect that statistic to fall near a particular outcome value—in this case, 1. If H_1 is true, we should expect that statistic to fall into a numerical range "significantly" above 1. Obviously, to evaluate the statistic obtained in the course of a specific experiment, we would need to examine that value as usual to see whether or not it had fallen into an outcome range that would be "likely" if H_0 is true. The question thus poses the familiar problem that we had first encountered in chapter 13 (see, for example, fig. 13.4). We must establish decision regions for our statistic, and that of course implies that we must consider the pdf that underlies our particular statistic, the ratio A/B.

If H_0 is true, then the pdf that underlies our ratio A/B is an F probability distribution, as you might have anticipated. In other words, if all 8 population RVs are the same, then that ratio is an F ratio or F value. Although a formal proof of this assertion is beyond our scope, the following considerations show that the contention is at least plausible. The denominator B has been formed from a set of 8 within-group sample variances. We learned in chapter 15 that the sample variance of a group of sample values is closely related to a chi-square statistic. Therefore, it seems reasonable that B itself should be closely related to a chi-square statistic. The numerator A has been formed from the between-groups sample variance. While it is not quite so apparent that it, too, might be like a chi-square statistic, it can be shown that if H_0 is true, then A is indeed closely related to a particular kind of chi-square outcome value (see Freeman, p. 212). Thus, it should at least not seem implausible that if H_0 is true, our statistic A/B is a ratio that is exactly the kind of statistic we had specified as an F outcome value in (17.1). We finally infer that if the null hypothesis H_0 is true, then our statistic A/B is an F ratio or F value that has an underlying F probability distribution. Figure 17.2 represents this situation schematically. We see the familiar logical structure that reflects the joint specification of an underlying RV_D by (1) a given RV_P and (2) a particular data-reducing operation that generates a statistic from a set of sample values.

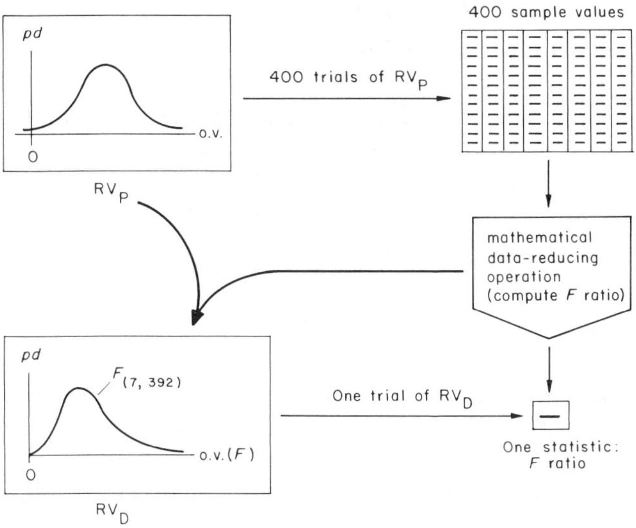

FIGURE 17.2 RV origins of an *F* ratio

Since we now know these relationships for our specific case, we are able to recast H_0 and H_1, the original pair of statistical hypotheses concerning the RV origins of sample values, into H_0' and H_1', a corresponding pair concerning the RV origin of a statistic. If H_0 is true, if all 400 sample values did come from the same RV_P, then H_0' is true: our statistic, the *F* ratio A/B, "came from" one particular, identifiable *F* probability distribution.

We will implement the usual last steps of any significance test, but first, in order to proceed, we must complete our specification of RV_D. We know that RV_D is *some* specifiable *F* probability distribution (see fig. 17.2), but we have not yet said *which* particular member of that family it is. We have not given the values of the two parameters for the present hypothetical experiment. It can be shown that for the kind of experimental situation we are considering, the correct pdf that underlies our statistic if H_0 is true is $F_{(7, 392)}$. We shall not consider the details that enable one to formally demonstrate that the values 7 and 392 are the two correct parameter values. That is one of those facets of ANOVA that are beyond our scope; a sound demonstration is based on advanced mathematics (see Freeman, pp. 211-217). We shall restrict ourselves to a few general remarks. The first parameter concerns the number of degrees of freedom associated with the numerator A of our F ratio statistic. As we know, that numerator is a quantity that is intimately related to the between-groups sample variance S^2_M. In turn, we know that that quantity has been formed from 8 "samplelike" values, the 8 deviations of the group sample means from the grand sample mean. As we had learned in chapter 15, a sample variance formed from N sample values is associated with $(N - 1)$ degrees of freedom. Therefore, it should seem plausible that A, a quantity that is like a sample variance formed from 8 sample values, should have 7 degrees of freedom. In general, the numerator of a statistic such as the one we are considering now has a number of degrees of freedom that are *one less* than the number of levels of treatment (the number of columns in a table such as table 17.4). A similar but more elaborate argument can be used to demonstrate that the number of degrees of freedom associated with B, the quantity in the denominator of our F value statistic, is in general a number equal to the number of sample values (in our case, 400) *less* the number of levels of treatment (in our case, 8). If we have a ratio whose numerator involves a quantity that is a chi-square outcome value with 7 degrees of freedom, and whose denominator involves a chi-square outcome value with 392 degrees of freedom, then, according to (17.1) and the related discussion, we are dealing with an F value whose underlying pdf is an F probability distribution with $\nu_1 = 7$ and $\nu_2 = 392$. $F_{(7, 392)}$, the RV_D that underlies our statistic *if* H_0 *is true*, is sketched in figure 17.2. We see the characteristic F pdf profile that has a mode at an outcome value slightly less than $F = 1$.[3]

We now know the specific RV_D that is proposed by H_0' to be the pdf that "originates" our F ratio statistic A/B, and we can complete the process of hypothesis testing. If H_0 is true, then according to our previous discussion we would expect A/B to lie near $F = 1$; if H_0 is false, then the statistic will not have been generated by RV_D (H_0' will be false), and we would expect the value of the ratio to be significantly larger than 1. Obviously, a directional test is indicated. We take the usual steps—we specify α, find the

[3] According to the previously cited formula for the mode, that outcome value for $F_{(7, 392)}$ is $F = [1 - (2/7)] / [1 + (2/392)]$, or approximately $F = 0.71$.

corresponding critical value, and, in a given experiment, evaluate the value obtained for our *F* ratio statistic accordingly.

Suppose the experimenters had specified a level of significance $\alpha = 0.05$. From a table such as 17.3, we would find that the corresponding critical value for $F_{(7, 392)}$ is approximately $F = 2.0$. Thus, in a given experiment, the value of the *F* ratio statistic would have to exceed $F = 2.0$ before H_0' (and concomitantly, H_0) would be rejected at a 0.05 level of significance. If *F* were less than 2.0, the experimenters would conclude that there had *not* been sufficient evidence to warrant the conclusion that *F* did not "come from" $F_{(7, 392)}$—the RV_D postulated by H_0'; in turn, that conclusion would imply that there had *not* been sufficient evidence to conclude that the mean of one or more of the 8 RV_Ps was significantly different from the rest. Finally, one would infer that the 8 different methods of instruction did *not* seem to make any significant difference for the performance of the academic test that had been used as the experimental measure.

Had we selected a significance level of 0.01, the corresponding critical value would have been approximately $F = 2.7$. The statistic would have had to depart even further from its expected value of 1 before one would be willing to reject the null hypothesis. Accordingly, a rejection of H_0' at the 0.01 level would be "more significant" than a rejection at the 0.05 level (see chap. 13).

Additional Considerations

We have surveyed the main ingredients that are common to ANOVA procedures. In one sense, one might say that this is almost "all there is to ANOVA"; the mathematical essentials can be stated in only a few pages (see, for example, Freeman, pp. 211-217). In another sense, however, there is a great deal more to be said about ANOVA, as shown by the very extensive professional literature concerning that procedure. Truly, the analysis ANOVA "can be extended, on an elaborate scale" (*ibid.*, p. 345). These extensions concern various experimentally significant issues, and we shall conclude this introduction by mentioning some of the more prominent of these.

In our hypothetical experiment, we had investigated only one kind of treatment—one "dimension"—namely, method of instruction. Obviously, other dimensions also could affect student test performance. Some kinds of ANOVA experiments are designed to study two or more dimensions of treatments simultaneously. For example, in our illustrative experiment the investigators might have chosen also to investigate the effects of the amount of study time as a second dimension, as a second type of "experimental treatment." There are several ways in which that might be accomplished. One of the simpler procedures would be the following.

Suppose the investigators would wish to investigate the effects of different amounts of study time on test performance by "applying 5 different levels of treatment," by using 5 different study schedules. Let us suppose further that again 400 students will be involved, and that the effects of different study schedules will be assessed by the same academic test used to assess the differential effects of different methods of instruction. The experimenters must decide on a plan for allocating these two dimensions of treatment at 8 and 5 levels, respectively, to the group of subjects. The general field that deals with these kinds of issues is "the design of experiments." It is a large subject area that is usually examined in more advanced courses; accordingly, we shall say little about it, and refer you to the pertinent literature (see Collateral Reading, at end of part IV). There are any number of plans that could be followed in designing our hypothetical study. We shall use a simple design. We shall divide the 400 subjects in two overlapping ways. The first will be the previously used scheme that divides the group into 8 groups of 50 subjects each; one level of instructional method would be administered to each of these 8 groups. The second way divides the 400 subjects into 5 groups of 80 subjects each according to the following plan. The first group of 80 subjects will be formed by taking the first 10 in each of the 8 groups of 50 subjects; the second group of 80 will be formed by taking the second 10 subjects from each of the 8 groups of 50, and so on. The arrangement results in a set of students and thus in a set of scores, which can be represented by a table such as 17.5. We see that this table is really very much like the previous table 17.4. Indeed, from the perspective of the first dimension, methods of instruction, it is unchanged. The second dimension, study schedules, merely has created a second type of division in the table. The 8 levels of the first dimension are still represented by 8 groups of 50 test scores in 8 *columns*, while the corresponding 5 levels of the second dimension are represented by 5 groups of 80 test scores in 5 *rows*. If we wished to analyze the effects of the two dimensions separately, we could do so. We could conduct an ANOVA of the 8 columns of data exactly as before, and assess the effects of methods of instruction; we could also conduct a similar analysis of the 5 rows of data, and assess the effects of different study schedules. So far, little that is conceptually new has been introduced.

Table 17.5

ANOVA format for two treatment dimensions

Study schedule	Method of instruction							
	A	B	C	D	E	F	G	H
I								
II								
III			10 scores in each of the 40 cells					
IV								
V								

The new element in this kind of a situation arises because in addition to the 8 sets of scores in the columns and the 5 sets of scores in the rows, we can identify another, different set of subgroups; these are the 40 groups of 10 scores each that are in each "window" or *cell* of the 40 cells in table 17.5. Each of these 40 groups has been subjected to one particular combination of method of instruction and study schedule that is different from any of the other 39. In that sense, each one of these 40 groups of 10 scores represents scores from a group that has been subjected to a unique treatment. This situation suggests that one can analyze the data in yet another way. They can be analyzed not only in the usual way to evaluate the differences between column group means, or between row group means. The data can also be analyzed to evaluate whether any significant differences exist between the *means of the 40 subgroups* of 10 scores each. Thus, it is possible that independently of the outcome of the first kind of assessment—even if neither the method of instruction nor the study schedules affect test scores—the data might reveal the presence of certain kinds of idiosyncratic effects; they might show that there are significant effects on the test performance that appear to result from and be specific to certain particular *combinations* of method of instruction and amount of class time. A simple numerical example will illustrate the general idea.

Suppose we have investigated two levels of instructional methods and two levels of study schedules, and obtained the results shown in table 17.6. The number in each of the four cells represents the total of the test scores of 10 subjects in that subgroup. We see that the total test scores from subjects instructed by method *A* are the same as the scores obtained from students instructed by method *B*. The column totals of these two sets of test scores are the same; therefore, so are the two column group means. We see that the same considerations hold for the two study schedules I and II; data in the two rows imply that test score totals were unaffected by the type of study schedule used. We would thus conclude that in general, neither method of instruction nor study schedule significantly affected test performance. Certain combinations of method of instruction and study schedule, however, do seem to yield scores that are considerably different from those of other combinations. Instructional method *A* combined

Table 17.6

Interaction effects

	A	*B*	Sum
I	80	40	120
II	40	80	120
Sum	120	120	

with study schedule I, and method *B* combined with schedule II, bring about considerably higher score totals from 10 subjects than do the other two combinations of treatment, *A*/II and *B*/I. We would infer that although neither of the two dimensions brought about significant differences in performance, there were certain *combinations of levels* of the two dimensions that did seem to make a difference to test performance.

This kind of phenomenon is an example of an *interaction effect*. It is an effect that can arise when particular levels of two or more treatment dimensions produce special, uncharacteristic results. The techniques of ANOVA can be extended to permit an analysis of this facet of a set of data.

One set of considerations arises, then, when the design of ANOVA is more complex than the simple example that we had used to introduce the methodology. A second important set of considerations arises because the conclusions from ANOVA are limited in one particular respect. Let us suppose that an experiment analyzed by ANOVA techniques has led to the rejection of the null hypothesis; we conclude that apparently there are significant differences between the means of the various RV_{P}s that have generated our data. Which levels of treatment were different, was there more than one different mean, how different might the means of the different RV_{P}s be? That is, in terms of our first hypothetical experiment of this chapter, which of the 8 methods of instruction were different? Was more than one method significantly different from the rest? Was a different method better, or worse, than the other methods? How large were the differences? These and similar kinds of questions are not addressed by ANOVA. All that those kinds of procedures can tell us is whether or not there seem to be some significant differences in a *whole set of data*. If we wish to have more detailed information than that, we must analyze the data further by other techniques.

This kind of investigation falls under the general heading of "comparisons among means." The investigations can be carried out by a number of different statistical tests (Kirk, pp. 311-325; Hays, pp. 581-612), and these raise a set of new questions and considerations. We cannot pursue that topic further here; I will only indicate one kind of issue by a simple illustrative example.

Suppose that in our previous experiment (table 17.4) we had rejected the null hypothesis and concluded that there were differences between the means of the eight RV_Ps. Suppose also that we wish to investigate this apparent difference further by comparing the 8 group sample means in pairs. That is, we shall use some statistical test to determine whether a pair of group sample means suggests that there is a difference between the means of the corresponding pair of RV_P means.[4] How many tests shall we need to perform—how many pairs of group sample means can we form from the 8 M_i? We can form 28 pairs; thus, if we wish to examine each pair in a statistical test, we shall need to perform 28 different tests of significance. So far, so good. One kind of difficulty arises, however, because each one of the 28 tests is subject to a type I error. Consider the following. If we assume that we perform the 28 tests each at a level of significance $\alpha = 0.05$, then, if in fact all 28 null hypotheses are true, how often shall we incorrectly reject such a hypothesis? From previous discussions, we had learned that the level of α specifies the frequency with which one would expect to commit a type I error in a series of experiments (see chap. 13). This is now exactly our situation. We should expect to commit a type I error once every 20 experiments; we are conducting 28 experiments, so it becomes likely that we shall commit that kind of an error at least once. If we had more than 8 levels of treatment, the possibility of committing a type I error would escalate. For example, with 20 levels of treatment (and thus 20 group sample means), we can form 190 pairs of group sample means. At a significance level of 0.05, the probability that we will commit a type I error if we compare all these means pairwise is 0.999941; in other words, even if there are in fact no differences between the means RV_P, we are almost certain to erroneously decide that *some* of these parameters are different from the rest.[5] As Hays notes, "Given enough significance tests, you are almost bound to get at least one significant result, even though the experiment is the purest nonsense" (p. 611). Nor can one avoid that kind of difficulty by simple strategies. For example, if we attempt to reduce the number of tests by selecting for testing only those sets of data that seem to be meaningful, we are in danger of using data twice, once to select "significant" pairs of columns, and once to "prove" that this pair contains significant information. That kind of procedure is redundant and based on fallacious reasoning.

The principal purpose of discussing these illustrative topics was to provide a sense of the kinds of complexities that ANOVA procedures involve in actual experimental applications. There is thus considerable additional material that needs to be studied before one can be said to have mastered ANOVA procedures.

PROBLEMS

17.1 The sample value *a* is obtained from a single trial of $\chi^2_{(17)}$, and the sample value *b*, from a single trial of $\chi^2_{(10)}$. These two outcome values are reduced to a single statistic according to the formula $(a/17) \div (b/10)$.

(a) What RV_D underlies that statistic?

(b) What does it mean to say that a certain RV underlies that statistic?

17.2 Explain the two different ways in which the symbol *F* is used.

17.3 How many parameters are required to define one member of the *F* pdf family?

17.4 For $F_{(42,\ 13)}$,

(a) what is the mean?

(b) what is the mode?

17.5 What information does a data matrix such as table 17.1 provide?

[4]For instance, there is a statistical test that uses the kind of *t* ratio defined in (16.2) to evaluate whether a difference between a pair of within-group sample means is significant at a stipulated level α.

[5]If we perform *G* pairwise tests at a level of significance α, where *G* is the number of pairs that can be formed from *N* within-group sample means (i.e., the number of combinations of *N* objects taken two at a time), then, if all the RV_P means are in fact the same, the probability that one will *not* commit a type I error is given by $[1 - (1 - \alpha)^G]$ (Hays, p. 611).

17.6 If you wanted to construct a table of one particular member of the F pdf family, say, $F_{(10, 20)}$, how many tables like table 17.1 would you need? How would you use these, and what kind of a table would you obtain? What two kinds of numbers would that table contain? [Hint: see chaps. 4 and 5.]

17.7 For one particular F probability distribution, the critical F outcome values for a directional test of significance performed at a level of significance $\alpha = 0.02$ (right-hand tail) is $F = 4.7$. What is the value of the cdf of that RV at $F = 4.7$?

17.8 What does the term "levels of treatment" mean?

17.9 In one particular ANOVA study involving 600 subjects, 20 levels of treatment were investigated. An F ratio was formed from the 600 acquired sample values.

(a) How many $RV_{P}s$ are implicated?

(b) What is the name of the statistic obtained by reducing the 600 sample values?

(c) What would H_0 be?

(d) What would H_0' be?

(e) If there are no treatment effects, what would you expect the value of the statistic to be, *on average*? Explain your answer.

17.10 In problem 17.9, the RV_D underlying the F ratio is $F_{(19, 580)}$.

(a) If you were to perform a test of significance at the level $\alpha = 0.10$, what information would you need about RV_D?

(b) How would you use that information to decide whether or not H_0' should be rejected?

17.11 Consider an ANOVA data matrix such as table 17.1.

(a) Name the two kinds of sample means that are computed; describe the computational approach.

(b) Name the three kinds of sample variances that are computed; describe the computational approach.

17.12 In ANOVA, what is the statistical formulation that corresponds to the scientific statement, "different levels of treatment produce different experimental effects"? In a given experiment, what is the fundamental statistical rationale that is used to decide whether that kind of an experimental effect is present?

17.13 We know that in ANOVA experiments, the statistic is an *F* ratio.

(a) What two quantities are the principal ingredients in the numerator and denominator, respectively, of that statistic?

(b) If there actually is *no* treatment effect, what parameter does the numerator and the denominator estimate?

(c) How is that characteristic used in ANOVA procedures?

17.14 If there are T_1 levels of one kind of treatment and T_2 levels of another, how many different combinations of the two kinds of treatments are there?

17.15 In general, if we perform a test of significance at a level of $\alpha = 0.01$, and if H_0 is in fact true, we know that we must expect to commit an error of the first kind once out of every 100 repeated experiments, on average. Why are pairwise comparisons of group sample means particularly vulnerable to that kind of an error?

CHAPTER 18

The Binomial Probability Distribution

Mathematical Origins

The kind of probability distribution that we shall explore in this chapter can arise in a variety of statistical situations. One way to conceptualize its mathematical genesis is as the RV_D that underlies a statistic generated in the following fashion. Let us suppose that we have a population probability distribution that can be represented by a roulette wheel with two slots marked 0 and 1. This is our first example of an RV_P that is discrete and thus defined by a probability function rather than by a probability density function.

RV_P has two outcome values in its potential outcome set, the numbers 0 and 1. Thus, the pf that defines RV_P assigns two probability values, one to each of the two outcomes. Let us call these two probabilities a and b. In terms of the notation introduced in chapter 3, we write

$$p(0) = a, p(1) = b. \tag{18.1}$$

Since we have only two simple outcomes in the potential set, these must form a complementary pair (see problem 18.1). Therefore, $a + b = 1$, exactly; if we specify either one of these two probability values, we thereby indirectly specify the other as well.

We shall now generate a set of N sample values, as usual, by N repeated trials of RV_P. This set of values will contain only 0s and 1s. Next, we shall form a statistic from this set by a particularly simple arithmetical procedure: we just add all the values, or, equivalently, we count the number of 1s in the set of N numbers.

Either way, we obtain one of the $(N + 1)$ nonnegative integers 0, 1, 2, . . ., N as a result. That integer is our statistic.

We have defined an RV_P, and a mathematical procedure that reduces a set of N sample values generated by that probability distribution to a single number, a statistic. Accordingly, we have implicitly defined an RV_D that underlies our statistic. This is the familiar premise that we have employed in chapter 12 and all the succeeding chapters. What can we say about that RV_D in the present case? One thing should be obvious: that probability distribution$_D$ *must* be discrete. We arrive at that conclusion by considering the potential outcome of RV_D. What values can the statistic generated according to our specified procedure assume? We already know that the values are the $(N + 1)$ nonnegative integers from 0 to N, inclusive. The potential outcome set of RV_D is thus discrete and limited in range, and therefore also listable, as we learned in chapter 2.

We conclude that RV_D is a *probability function* whose potential outcome set includes all the nonnegative integers from 0 through N. Figure 18.1 illustrates the usual logical structure for our particular kind of situation. We see that an RV_D has been defined jointly by RV_P and a mathematical data-reducing operation. In

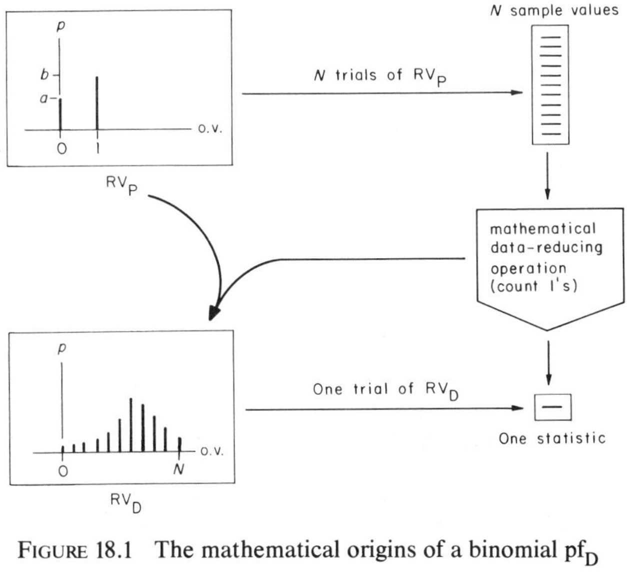

FIGURE 18.1 The mathematical origins of a binomial pf_D

order to complete the specification of that pf, it only remains for us to specify the *probability values* that RV_D assigns to this potential outcome. The actual values will depend on *two* quantities, the sample size N, and the probability b, assigned to the outcome value 1 by RV_P. RV_D is a member of a family of pfs whose members are specified by the two parameters N and b (or a, since $a = 1 - b$). If we specify these two numbers, then in a given instance one can specify RV_D. One can by suitable mathematical techniques compute the probabilities that are assigned by RV_D. The two parameters have different formal properties from those we had encountered previously; one of these, N, is a parameter that can assume any integral value from 0 to N, while the other, b, is a "continuous" parameter, a probability, that can assume any value between 0 and 1, inclusive.

An RV_D that arises in the above manner is a member of a family of probability functions called the *binomial* probability distribution.[1] We shall explore the mathematical characteristics of members of that pf family by examining one particular probability distribution. Let us arbitrarily choose the RV_D that is generated if $N = 10$ and $p(1) = 0.60$. The graph of that probability distribution is shown in figure 18.2; the corresponding specification of the pf is given in table 18.1. The envelope of the graph is quasi-bell-shaped, with a peak at the outcome value 6; that outcome value also happens to be the mean of our particular RV_D. The variance equals 2.4. We shall soon provide formulae that give these values

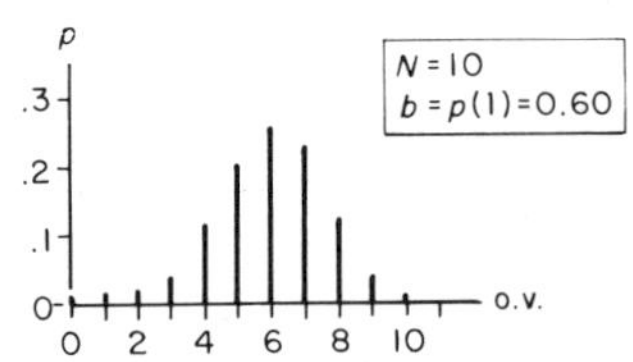

FIGURE 18.2 A binomial RV_D

[1]The term reflects the kinship between this class of pfs and the binomial expression $(a + b)$. Specifically, there are close formal similarities between probability values assigned by a binomial pf to $(N + 1)$ outcome values and the $(N + 1)$ coefficients in the algebraic expansion of the binomial expression $(a + b)^N$.

for a general member of the binomial family (i.e., the formulae for the mean and the variance of RV_D in terms of N and b).

Table 18.1

The pf for RV_D in figure 18.2

O.V.	p
0	0.000+
1	.002 . . .
2	.011
3	.043
4	.112
5	.201
6	.251
7	.215
8	.121
9	.040
10	.006

Let us next examine the effects of different values of the parameters. The parameter N obviously directly affects the potential outcome set of RV_D, since that set comprises the integers 0, 1, . . ., N. If we retain the same value, 0.60, for $p(1)$, and use different values of N, we obtain pf_Ds that have the characteristics shown in figure 18.3; we see that the potential outcomes are different from one another, as anticipated; the peak of the curve, however, remains at the same relative position in that outcome set.

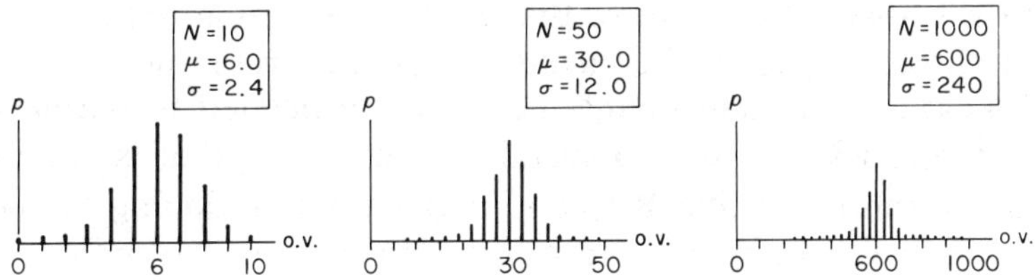

FIGURE 18.3 RV_D for different sample sizes N; $b = 0.60$

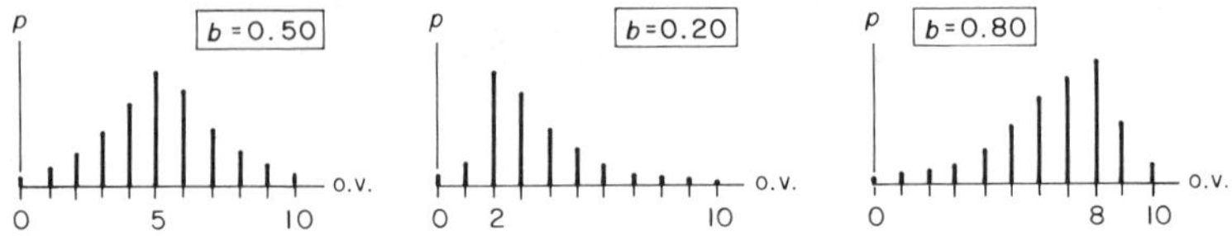

FIGURE 18.4 RV_D for different values of b; $N = 10$

The effect of varying $p(1)$ is shown in figure 18.4. Evidently, the value of that probability determines the relative location of the peak of the probability distribution.

In the general case, the value of the *mean* of a binomial probability function is given by

$$\mu = N \times b. \tag{18.2}$$

The general expression for the variance is

$$\sigma^2 = N \times b \times (1 - b), \tag{18.3}$$

or, equivalently, $N \times a \times (1 - a)$. As N becomes large, the envelope of the binomial pf becomes quite similar in shape to a graph of a normal pdf. Therefore, for large N, it is possible to use a suitably chosen pdf as an approximation to a binomial pf; that kind of an approximation, however, is subject to the basic limitations discussed in chapter 11.

Nonparametric and Distribution-Free Tests

As has been our practice in chapters 13 to 17, we shall illustrate the use of our new family of probability distributions by applying it in a statistical procedure that is used in actual experiments. First, however, we shall consider a more general issue.

Previously, we had maintained that we needed to define the *population* RV in order to specify the one RV_D that is uniquely defined jointly by that RV_P and a given data-reducing method. This had been the premise introduced in chapter 12 (see figs. 12.4 or 12.7) and used repeatedly since. Even though in principle it is always true—given (1) a specific population RV and (2) a specific data-reducing method that provides a statistic from sample values generated by an RV_P, a specific RV_D is uniquely defined—in practice it may be difficult to specify RV_D. For example, RV_P may not be sufficiently well specified; its form may be largely or totally undefined. In other instances, the profile of RV_P may be known but mathematically intractable; that is, there might not be known theoretical methods that would allow one to deduce the form for RV_D from a highly irregular kind of RV_P.

At any rate, there are times when experimenters must resort to statistical procedures that make few, if any, assumptions about RV_P. One does, however, pay a price for using these kinds of procedures. Because they do make fewer assumptions (or, equivalently, use less information about RV_P), they do not produce quite as specific inferential results as methods based on more fully specified RV_Ps. It is often said of these kinds of procedures that they are "weaker" than those we previously explored. In other words, because one uses less information about the mathematical origin of sample values, one's conclusions about those data are correspondingly weaker. Mathematics cannot compensate for impoverished information.

The kinds of tests we are discussing are called *nonparametric* or *distribution-free* tests. Although those two terms are occasionally used interchangeably, they actually refer to two different types of procedures. Strictly speaking, distribution-free tests are those that make *no* assumptions whatsoever about the probability distribution that underlies a set of sample values. Nonparametric tests are those that make only a *few*, usually very general, assumptions about RV_P; for example, they may assume that RV_P is unimodal—i.e., that it has a single peak—or perhaps that RV_P is symmetrical about some unspecified outcome value. Let us carefully note one critical feature of these kinds of tests. While they make few if any assumptions about the characteristics of RV_P, the probability distribution that underlies a set of *sample values*, they most definitely *do* specify the parameters or general characteristics of RV_D, the probability distribution that underlies the *statistic*. "Nonparametric" or "distribution-free" refers to RV_P, and *not* to RV_D. We shall soon illustrate that statement in terms of a specific example.

Most of these kinds of statistical tests reduce a set of sample values to a statistic by a mathematical data-reducing procedure that employs counting or some similar mathematically simple manipulation. Consequently, the RV_Ds that are used in most of these kinds of procedures characteristically are discrete pfs; their potential outcome set comprises a set of nonnegative integers. It should be apparent that the binomial pf family suits these specifications; we shall conclude this chapter and part IV by presenting an example of a simple nonparametric test, the sign test.

A Sign Test

The class of inferential procedures called "sign tests" are so named because these tests compare pairs of sample values and indicate the numerical difference between a given pair in terms of a plus or a minus sign. To illustrate the procedures, let us imagine that we have generated two sets of 10 sample values from some unspecified RV_Ps. The question is: did the two sets come from the same, or from two different, RV_Ps? If we knew more about RV_P, we could use a parametric test similar to one of those explored in the previous chapters. However, we shall make no assumptions about the population probability distributions, and therefore must use a mathematically more primitive procedure.

The hypothetical results of the "empirical experiment" are the 10 pairs of data in table 18.2. In order to reduce this set of sample values to a statistic, we shall examine these pairs one at a time. If in a given pair the sample value from column A is larger than that from column B, we record +, a plus sign; otherwise, we record −, a minus sign. (We shall assume that there are no tied scores among these 10 pairs.) Next, we simply count the number of plus signs. The resulting nonnegative integer is our statistic.

The remainder of the test is simple as well. If the RV_P that generated the data in column A is the same as the RV_P that generated the data in column B, then it is equally probable that in a given pair, the first number will be larger than the second, or vice versa.[2] The underlying RV_D is a binomial pf, $N = 10$, $p(1) = 0.50$

[2]Actually, this is not quite correct, but the inaccuracy will not affect the general features we are illustrating with the present example (see Lindgren, 1968, p. 413).

Table 18.2

Hypothetical data for a sign test

Pair no.	O.V. A	B	Sign
1	14	11	+
2	13	17	−
3	9	42	−
4	6	20	−
5	11	5	+
6	19	3	+
7	22	14	+
8	17	16	+
9	41	3	+
10	47	12	+

(see Lindgren, 1968, pp. 411-416; Hays, pp. 193-197; Kirk, pp. 339-345).

We are again at our usual stage in a hypothesis test. If the null hypothesis is true, if both sets of data come from the same RV_P, then our statistic will have been generated by a particular RV_D. The specific situation is illustrated in figure 18.5; table 18.3 presents the pf for RV_D.

All that needs to be done to complete the test is to set a level of significance α and then to evaluate the statistic. If we select $\alpha = 0.05$, we can discover from table 18.3 that a two-tailed test at a 0.05 level of significance implies that we would *not* reject H_0 if our statistic fell between the critical values of 2 and 8, inclusive (see problem 18.5). In other words, if we compare the ten pairs of data and find that there were *fewer* than 2, or *more* than 8, plus signs, we should infer that the two sets of data had probably been generated by two different (although quite unknown) RV_Ps. We would reject the null hypothesis.

We must admit that our procedure appears to slightly bend the logical structure we had invoked in all the previous inferential

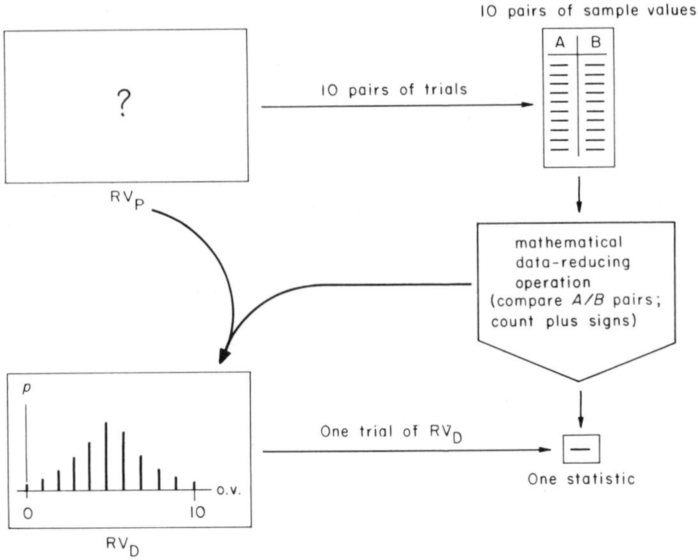

FIGURE 18.5 RV origins of a sign test statistic

Table 18.3

Binomial pf_D underlying a sign test statistic

o.v.	p	
0	0.001 . . .	$p(\text{o.v.} < 2) = 0.011$
1	.010	
2	.044	
3	.117	
4	.205	
5	.246	
6	.205	
7	.117	
8	.044	
9	.010	$p(\text{o.v.} > 8) = 0.011$
10	.001	

tests. Up to this point, we maintained that one must be able to specify both an RV_P and a data-reducing procedure before one could specify RV_D, the probability distribution that underlies a particular type of statistic. We now see that one is able to specify RV_D with less data about RV_P; however, the general principle really is correct, as a deeper analysis of the present situation would reveal.

PROBLEMS

18.1 In (18.1), the associated RV_P had only two possible outcome values, the values 0 and 1.

(a) What kind of a probability distribution is RV_P?

(b) Why must $p(0) + p(1) = 1.00$, exactly?

18.2 Demonstrate that for the two values represented by a and b in (18.1), $a \times (1 - a) = b \times (1 - b)$. [Hint: use the requirement that $(a + b)$ must equal 1, exactly.] Can you find a third way of expressing (18.3)?

18.3 If we generate N sample values from the RV_P illustrated in figure 18.1, why does the potential outcome of RV_D have $(N + 1)$ values?

18.4 Discuss the differences between parametric and nonparametric procedures.

18.5 In the hypothetical experiment that illustrates a sign test in this chapter,

(a) What are the probabilities of the regions "less than 2" and "greater than 8"?

(b) Consequently, what is the actual level of significance α in this test?

(c) What are the two probabilities for the regions "less than 1.5" and "greater than 8.8"?

(d) Compare your answers to (a) and (c). That comparison should be suggestive: What can you say generally about the specification of critical values if RV_D is a pf rather than a pdf?

18.6 Suppose $p(1)$ for RV_P is the value $b = 0.40$.
   (a) Compute σ_D for $N = 10$, 100, and 1000.
   (b) In each of those cases, what percentage of the total potential outcome range of RV_D is the span from $(\mu - \sigma)$ to $(\mu + \sigma)$?
   (c) Therefore, what can you deduce about the general relationship between the sample size N and the dispersion of RV_D?

COLLATERAL READING IN EXPERIMENTAL DESIGN AND INFERENTIAL PROCEDURES

Campbell, J. C. & Stanley, D. D. (1963), *Experimental and Quasi-Experimental Designs for Research*. Chicago: Rand McNally.

Cox, D. R. (1958), *Planning of Experiments*. New York: Wiley.

Edwards, A. L. (1972), *Experimental Design in Psychological Research*, 4th ed. New York: Holt, Rinehart & Winston.

Kirk, R. E. (1968), *Experimental Design*. Belmont, Calif.: Brooks/Cole.

Lee, W. (1975), *Experimental Design and Analysis*. San Francisco: Freeman.

Lindquist, E. F. (1953), *Design and Analysis of Experiments in Psychology and Education*. Boston: Houghton Mifflin.

Rosenthal, R. (1976), *Experimenter Effects in Behavioral Research*, 2nd enlarged ed. New York: Halsted.

Siegel, S. (1956), *Nonparametric Statistics*. New York: McGraw-Hill.

Slonim, M. (1960), *Sampling in a Nut Shell*. New York: Simon & Schuster.

Winer, B. J. (1971), *Statistical Principles in Experimental Design*, 2nd ed. New York: McGraw-Hill.

PART V

Two Random Variables

CHAPTER 19

Extension of the Framework

In the previous sections, all the actual and all the potential outcomes we had been considering shared certain common formal features. In every instance, whether we were considering an outcome generated by a spinner, by a roulette wheel, by a population probability distribution (RV_P), or by a derived probability distribution (RV_D), an actual outcome was always a single number, a member of a potential outcome set that could be represented in terms of a single outcome axis. Furthermore, concomitantly with this formal property of the outcomes, in each instance we postulated that there is some *one* RV that underlies or "generates" any one acquired actual outcome. Now we shall consider a more complex case, a situation that will necessitate various extensions of familiar concepts.

Ordered Pairs and the Outcome Plane

Superficially, the situation we shall introduce may not seem particularly different from our familiar framework. Basically, it arises when an actual outcome comprises *two* numbers instead of *one*. A simple example would be an "experiment" where, after a subject had been subjected to some level of treatment or treatments, two kinds of performances are measured separately. For example, one might measure academic performance by one suitable test, and athletic performance by another, for each subject in some "treated" group. Let us assume this to be the case. We shall administer an academic test that yields a score that is an integer from 1 to 10 and a test of athletic ability that yields an integer score from -2 to $+3$. Thus, in that kind of an experimental situation, two scores are acquired from each subject.

The previous RV framework can be extended to deal with these kinds of experimental yields. The first formal step from a statistical point of view is to extend the concepts of potential and actual outcome to accommodate the new formal characteristics of the experimental yield. We simply specify that an actual outcome from these kinds of experimental situations is a *pair* of numbers. For example, if subject A scored 7 and -1 on the academic and athletic test, respectively, then we would represent the "sample value" acquired from that subject by the pair $(7, -1)$.

Let us note carefully that in this case, the *order* of the two quantities makes a difference. For example, the dyad $(6, 3)$ is *not* the same as the oppositely ordered dyad $(3, 6)$. As a matter of fact, the reverse order of some kinds of pairs produces an outcome that is inadmissible in our hypothetical study: while the score pair $(7, -1)$ *is* a possible pair of scores, its reverse or inverse, the pair $(-1, 7)$, is *not* admissible. The latter pair is inadmissible for two reasons: the range of the first, academic, test does not include negative values, and the range of the second, athletic, test does not include values greater than 3. The pair $(-1, 7)$ cannot occur in our experiment.

These considerations lead to the concept of an *ordered pair*. That concept and term merely formalize the matters we have just considered informally. In an ordered pair of numbers, the order of the two numbers is part of the information contained in that dyad. That is, if we are dealing with a pair that is *not* ordered, then we may consider the pair (x, y) to be equivalent to the pair (y, x); for example, the not-ordered pair $(7, -1)$ would be equivalent to $(-1, 7)$. For an ordered pair, however, (x, y) and (y, x) usually are two different pairs (see problem 19.2); the pair $(1, 2)$ is not the same as $(2, 1)$.

The extension of the concept of actual outcome to include ordered pairs implies a corresponding extension in the potential outcome and its geometrical representation. Previously, as we know, a potential outcome set could be represented in one dimension, that is, along a single axis. Since we now have actual outcomes that are pairs of numbers, we correspondingly need a pair of axes to represent that kind of an actual outcome. The familiar outcome axis therefore now must become an *outcome plane*. Figure 19.1 illustrates that concept for our hypothetical study. We see that scores from the academic test are represented along one outcome axis, and scores from the athletic test on a second axis. By this method of representation, any ordered pair of scores can be represented by a corresponding coordinate location or point in the outcome plane that is defined by the two outcome axes. In figure 19.1, the location in the outcome plane that corresponds to the score (7, −1) has been identified. One usually labels the first axis x and the second y, although sometimes some alternative labeling methods are used instead. We shall follow the usual practice; the first number in an ordered pair will be represented geometrically as an x coordinate, and the second number, as a y coordinate, in the outcome plane. We see that all ordered pairs that have the same *first* number lie along the one line parallel to the y axis that has the same x value; for example, all pairs of the form $(7, y)$, where y can be any number in the second dimension of the potential outcome, lie along the line $x = 7$ indicated in figure 19.1. All ordered pairs having the same *second* number would, of course, lie along some one line (y = constant) perpendicular to the kind of line we have just considered.

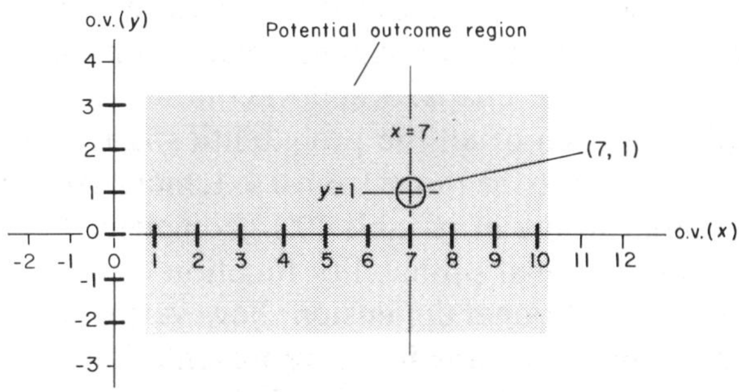

FIGURE 19.1 The outcome plane and a potential outcome region

The "Big" Probability Function

We have been considering a methodology that can be used to formalize outcomes obtained from two separate discrete measures. We know in general from chapter 4 that if we have a discrete potential outcome set, then in order to construct a probability function we need only to assign *probability values* to the *actual outcome values* in the potential outcome. That had been the procedure introduced and implemented in chapter 4 for the single-valued outcome case. We follow a substantially identical procedure to construct a pf when the actual outcomes are ordered pairs. We merely assign *one probability value* to *each ordered pair* that is in the potential outcome. Thus, the principal difference between the pf we are considering now and those considered in previous chapters lies in the difference between two types of potential outcomes. Our old familiar pf assigned probability values to outcomes located along a single outcome axis, actual outcomes that were single numbers; now we are considering a pf that assigns probability values to ordered pairs. As we shall see in the remaining chapters, most of the other characteristics of a pf remain substantially unaltered.

In terms of our hypothetical experiment, a pf would assign one probability value to each one of the 10×6 or 60 ordered pairs that can arise from our measurement procedure. We can therefore specify that pf by means of a table that lists for every one of those 60 possible outcome pairs a corresponding assigned probability value. Table 19.1 shows a hypothetical pf. We see that one probability value has been assigned to each one of the ordered pairs. We also see that the usual requirements placed on such a set of probability values (see chaps. 3 and 4) continue to be satisfied. For example, the sum of all the probabilities is 1, exactly; each probability value lies in the range from 0 to 1, inclusive, and so on.

We can represent the pf in table 19.1 geometrically, just as we could a one-dimensional probability function (see figs. 4.1-4.5). We now need an additional dimension, however; since the potential outcome requires a plane for its representation, the assigned probability values must be represented along yet another dimension. In other words, the representation of a pf whose potential outcome comprises ordered pairs requires a *three-dimensional* graph. That pf is a three-dimensional entity. A page in a book offers only two dimensions, of course; therefore, to represent a three-dimensional pf, we must resort to a sketch. Figure 19.2

Table 19.1

A bivariate probability function

o.v.	p	o.v.	p	o.v.	p
(1, −2)	0.005	(1, 0)	.01	(1, 2)	.0075
(2, −2)	.005	(2, 0)	.01	(2, 2)	.0075
(3, −2)	.01	(3, 0)	.02	(3, 2)	.015
(4, −2)	.01	(4, 0)	.02	(4, 2)	.015
(5, −2)	.025	(5, 0)	.05	(5, 2)	.0375
(6, −2)	.015	(6, 0)	.03	(6, 2)	.0225
(7, −2)	.01	(7, 0)	.02	(7, 2)	.015
(8, −2)	.01	(8, 0)	.02	(8, 2)	.015
(9, −2)	.005	(9, 0)	.01	(9, 2)	.0075
(10, −2)	.005	(10, 0)	.01	(10, 2)	.0075
(1, −1)	.0075	(1, 1)	.015	(1, 3)	.005
(2, −1)	.0075	(2, 1)	.015	(2, 3)	.005
(3, −1)	.015	(3, 1)	.03	(3, 3)	.01
(4, −1)	.015	(4, 1)	.03	(4, 3)	.01
(5, −1)	.0375	(5, 1)	.075	(5, 3)	.025
(6, −1)	.0225	(6, 1)	.045	(6, 3)	.015
(7, −1)	.015	(7, 1)	.03	(7, 3)	.01
(8, −1)	.015	(8, 1)	.03	(8, 3)	.01
(9, −1)	.0075	(9, 1)	.015	(9, 3)	.005
(10, −1)	.0075	(10, 1)	.015	(10, 3)	.005

presents a sketch of the graph of the pf shown in table 19.1. The probability value attached to a given ordered pair is indicated by the height of a vertical line placed at the appropriate coordinate location in the outcome plane. Figure 19.1 illustrates only a few of the 60 assigned probability values so that the illustration will not become cluttered.

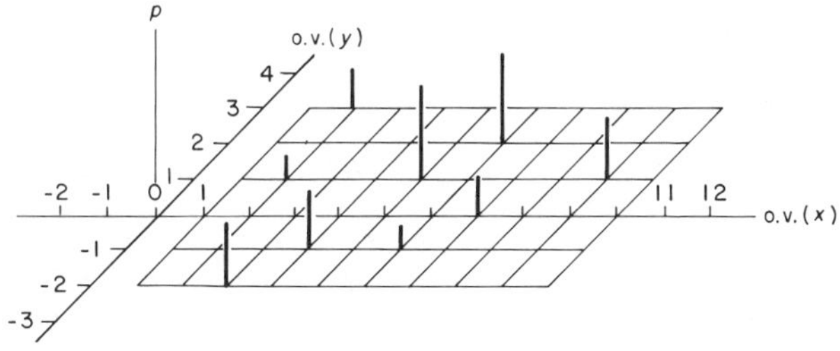

FIGURE 19.2 Graph of a bivariate pf

This kind of a graph suggests an alternative approach to tabulating a pf whose potential outcome comprises ordered pairs. The familiar format used in table 19.1 has been particularly well suited for representing a pf whose potential outcome contains single numbers. It is appropriate that basically tables of these kinds of pfs should be columnar; a single column of outcome values and associated probability values suggests and reflects the one-dimensional characteristic of the potential outcome. Now we have a two-dimensional potential outcome; therefore, a two-dimensional tabular format seems appropriate. Accordingly, data such as those presented in table 19.1 often are converted into the format presented in table 19.2. We see the two-dimensional aspect of the potential outcome reflected in a table that is a two-dimensional matrix rather than a one-dimensional column. The arrangement suggests that the horizontal direction corresponds to the dimension represented by one outcome axis (say, the x axis) and the vertical direction to the other dimension. There is a direct formal analogy between the matrix of the table and the two dimensions of the outcome plane; in table 19.2, the ten columns correspond to the ten outcome values in the first, x dimension, while the six rows correspond to the six outcome values in the second, y dimension. Thus, a cell at the intersection of a column and a row

Table 19.2

A matrix format for a bivariate probability function

y outcome values	x outcome values									
	1	2	3	4	5	6	7	8	9	10
−2	0.005	.005	.01	.01	.025	.015	.01	.01	.005	.005
−1	.0075	.0075	.015	.015	.0375	.0225	.015	.015	.0075	.0075
0	.01	.01	.02	.02	.05	.03	.02	.02	.01	.01
1	.015	.015	.03	.03	.075	.045	.03	.03	.015	.015
2	.0075	.0075	.015	.015	.0375	.0225	.015	.015	.0075	.0075
3	.005	.005	.01	.01	.025	.015	.01	.01	.005	.005

corresponds to a particular point in the outcome plane. For example, the intersection of the third column (representing $x = 3$, the third outcome value in the x dimension) with the second row (representing $y = -1$, the second outcome value in the y dimension) is a cell that corresponds to the ordered pair (3, −1); that ordered pair also is identified with a particular point in the outcome plane—the point $x = 3$, $y = -1$. The value entered into that cell of table 19.2 is, of course, the probability value assigned to (3, −1) by the pf defined in table 19.1.

We shall frequently use the matrix format to specify RV situations whose potential outcome comprises ordered pairs. We need to remember, however, that although tables 19.1 and 19.2 differ in format, they contain the same information. It is merely a matter of rearranging a columnar pf format into a two-dimensional matrix to reflect the corresponding change in the formal characteristics of potential outcomes.

In the remaining chapters, a pf such as that represented in tables 19.1 and 19.2 will be viewed from two different but complementary perspectives. On the one hand, a discrete pf whose outcome values are ordered pairs can be thought of as a mathematical situation constructed from two "ordinary" discrete RVs. From that perspective, one can imagine that an ordered pair has been generated by one trial of each of two different RVs or pfs of the "old type." We can imagine that one trial of the first RV—let us call it RV_X or pf_X—has generated the first value in an ordered pair—let us call that value x—while one trial of the second RV or pf, RV_Y or pf_Y, has generated the second outcome value, y. This is just a very slight elaboration of a familiar situation. One RV underlies any one academic test score; the score is viewed as one sample value generated by RV_X (an RV_P). Another RV underlies an athletic test score; that score is viewed as one sample value generated by RV_Y (another RV_P).

On the other hand, we can conceptualize the generation of an ordered pair in a different way. Instead of considering each member of an ordered pair separately, we can imagine that we have obtained a single actual outcome value by one single trial of a "big" RV or pf. These "big" probability distributions are simply entities whose potential outcomes comprise ordered pairs and concomitantly entities that directly assign one probability value to each ordered pair in the potential outcome. This alternative method of conceptualizing the genesis of an ordered pair may not seem much different from the first conceptualization that we have discussed (the perspective that conceptualizes two RVs, RV_X and RV_Y). However, as we shall see, the two views imply considerable differences, and allow considerable extensions of our familiar mathematical framework. For the moment, we mainly need to understand clearly that one can conceptualize the acquisition of a pair of numbers from a single experimental subject either as two numbers generated separately by two different RVs of the old, familiar type, or else as one actual outcome, one ordered pair generated by a single trial of one "big" RV or pf. We shall need both perspectives.

We can illustrate these general considerations in terms of our hypothetical experiment and the pf tabulated in 19.2. Let us suppose that we had obtained the ordered pair (6, −2) by administering the two different tests to some one particular experimental subject. From the point of view of the "big" entities, we can say that we performed *one* trial of a big RV and obtained one actual outcome, (6, −2). We can also say that according to table 19.1 or 19.2, that big pf assigns a probability of 0.0125 to that actual "outcome value." Alternatively, we can say that we performed *two* separate trials, one trial of RV_X that yielded the actual outcome value $x = 6$ and one trial of RV_Y that yielded the outcome value $y = -2$. *Notice that we have said nothing as yet about the probabilities assigned by either of these two "small" RVs or pfs to their respective potential outcomes*. That is an issue we shall begin to address in the next chapter.

This, then, is the basic conceptual framework on which we shall build in the remainder of part V. Let us agree on a terminology. To distinguish the "small," one-dimensional RV case from the "big" or two-dimensional RV case, let us call the former the *univariate*; and the latter, the *bivariate* case. Furthermore, the bivariate case is one particular kind of *multivariate* case; "multivariate" simply refers to "more than one RV," and thus includes the bivariate (two RV) situation as a special case.

Joint Probability

We have discussed that from one perspective, the generation of an ordered pair can be viewed as the joint occurrence of two separate events. For example, if our "big" pf generates the pair (3, 1), we may equally well imagine that two events have occurred jointly: RV_X has generated 3, and RV_Y, 1. Therefore, one may conceptualize the occurrence of an ordered pair as the occurrence of a *joint* event: $x = 3$ *and* $y = 1$. Accordingly, to distinguish the probability assigned to an ordered pair from a probability assigned to a single outcome value, we call the former probability the *probability of a joint event*, or, colloquially, the *joint probability*. The probabilities in tables 19.1 and 19.2 are joint probabilities.

In most respects, joint probabilities are entities just like any other probability value and must conform to the usual requirements placed on those kinds of quantities. The main difference between a joint probability and an "ordinary" probability is that, at least in our applications, the former is assigned to ordered pairs, while the latter probability is assigned to actual outcomes that are single numbers. That is, the principal difference lies in the *potential outcomes*, *not* in the types of probabilities. (It might be well to remember an admonition from an early chapter: no matter how complicated things become, do not forget that probability distributions always comprise two different sets of numbers—probability or probability density values and outcome values.) Another way of stating these matters is to say that "big" bivariate RVs or pfs are entities that assign joint probabilities (to ordered pairs), while "small," univariate RVs or pfs are entities that assign "ordinary" probabilities (to single values).

The Continuous Case

In our introduction to bivariate RVs we have focused exclusively on discrete potential outcomes and probability distributions. Since much of the work in part IV had been conducted in terms of continuous univariate RVs, you might be wondering about the corresponding continuous bivariate situation.

The most fundamental difference between *discrete* univariate and bivariate RVs lies in differences in types of potential outcome, as we have seen. The same is true for the principal differences between univariate and bivariate *continuous* RVs. The potential outcome of a univariate pdf is of course a segment of an outcome axis; the corresponding potential outcome of a bivariate pdf is a region in the outcome plane. Consequently, bivariate pdfs basically are three-dimensional entities, just as are bivariate pfs; two dimensions are required to represent the outcome plane, while a third dimension is required for assigning (joint) probability density values to points in that plane. This increase in dimensionality is clearly visible if one considers graphs of bivariate pdfs. The lines that characterize graphs of univariate pdfs now will become surfaces set within a three-dimensional situation; segments of the outcome axis become areas in the outcome plane; areas that represent a probability assigned to an outcome axis segment become volumes assigned to regions in the outcome plane, etc. Obviously, matters become more complex mathematically and formally.

It is an extremely clumsy, unwieldy, and thankless task to attempt to develop the continuous case for bivariate RVs or pdfs without mathematical tools that are more advanced than those presently at our disposal. While it can be done, it would require a disproportionate amount of development. Therefore, we shall not address continuous multivariate RVs in this text, leaving that kind of presentation to a later course when more advanced mathematical tools will have become available. The loss is not as great as one might at first believe, however. The concepts that we shall develop in the context of the discrete bivariate case will apply with relatively little basic modification to the continuous bivariate case as well. The issues again involve the transition from probability to probability density, a move whose conceptual implications we explored in some detail in chapter 5. Therefore, with that background you ought to be able to imagine at least in a very general fashion how the parallel transition would be accomplished in the bivariate case (see Freeman, chap. 6).

PROBLEMS

19.1 What is the formal difference between outcome values generated by the pfs considered in parts I through IV, and the outcome values generated by a "big" probability function?

19.2 In general, is the ordered pair (a, b) the same as (b, a)? What is the only case where these two are identical?

19.3 For the bivariate case, what entity replaces the outcome axis?

19.4 For ordered pairs of the form (x, y), what line in the outcome plane contains the three pairs (2, 7), (4, 7), and (−12, 7)? Sketch the locations and the line.

19.5 Why does a graphical representation of a bivariate pf require three dimensions? What are they?

19.6 What are the kinds of probabilities called that are assigned by a "big" pf? To what kinds of entities are these probabilities assigned?

19.7 Discuss the two alternative formats that can be used to tabulate a bivariate pf.

19.8 Describe the two ways in which the RV origin of an ordered pair can be conceptualized.

19.9 One dimension of a bivariate pf has 15 outcome values in its potential outcome, and the other dimension has 4 values.

(a) How many outcome values (ordered pairs) are there in the potential outcome of that bivariate pf?

(b) Let us say that there are N such pairs. The bivariate pf assigns one probability to each of these. What is the sum of all the probabilities? Why?

19.10 For a bivariate pdf, what replaces the univariate concept "area under the curve"?

CHAPTER 20

Statistical Dependence and Independence

We have begun to learn about bivariate random variables, and have encountered a different kind of actual outcome, the ordered pair, that has a new type of formal structure. This new feature allows us to develop several other conceptual extensions of the univariate RV framework. One set of these elaborations pertains to the kind of statistical ties that exist between the two univariate dimensions of a bivariate RV. It is in this context that the concepts of statistical dependence and independence arise.

We shall develop these and related concepts in the present chapter. Before we launch into a more formal development, let us survey the subject matter briefly to indicate in a general way the kinds of issues that we shall be addressing. Roughly, the ideas of dependence and independence concern the kind and amount of information that knowledge about outcomes in one dimension of a bivariate RV furnishes about outcomes of the other dimension. For example, if we have performed a bivariate RV trial and obtained some particular ordered pair (x_0, y_0) as the actual outcome (the two symbols merely represent specific values of the general variables symbolized by x and y), and if we have examined or "looked at" only one of these, say, x_0, does the fact that we now know one of the two numbers obtained in the bivariate trial give us any new statistical information about the value of the second number in the ordered pair, or does it not? Does the fact that we know the value of x improve a guess concerning y? If knowing x provides additional statistical information about y, we say that the two dimensions or variables *x* and *y* are dependent. Otherwise, if knowing *x* leaves us in no better position concerning a knowledge of *y*, we say that these quantities are independent.

The question of whether or not two kinds of quantities are statistically independent is of considerable theoretical as well as practical importance in statistics. Some of the theoretical issues arise in conjunction with statistics we had developed in part IV. The *t* statistic specified as the ratio (16.2) illustrates this kind of relevance. We asserted that its underlying RV_D is a member of the *t* pdf family (provided RV_P is a normal pdf). One step in the formal mathematical demonstration of that claim requires one to show that the two quantities principally involved in that *t* ratio (the sample mean and the sample variance) are statistically independent. A similar demonstration also is required during a proof that pertains to ANOVA. As we recall, an *F* ratio involved two quantities, *A* and *B*; one was constructed from a between-groups sample variance; and the other, from a set of within-group sample variances. To prove that the pdf underlying that *F* ratio is an *F* probability distribution, one must show, among other things, that *A* and *B* are statistically independent. There are many other theoretical proofs and similar formal mathematical procedures where the concepts of dependence and independence are relevant. We shall mention some of these in chapter 21.

As an example of a practical application of these concepts, consider the following common experimental situation. Suppose we use an experimental procedure that yields several measurements from each member of a group of experimental subjects. For instance, suppose we were to administer the two different types of tests discussed in the previous chapter (see fig. 19.2) to a group of students. As we shall discuss in the next section, the data obtained from that and similar kinds of experiments could be put into the form of a bivariate frequency matrix. Each cell would show how frequently a particular combination of the two test scores had occurred among the experimental subjects. In order to then establish whether or not a mathematically meaningful relationship exists between the two types of test scores, we should have to evaluate the frequency data matrix to see whether the frequencies suggested statistical dependence or independence among the two test dimensions. That evaluation could be performed by one of several available statistical tests of inference.

In order to develop the concepts of dependence and independence, we shall need to introduce three kinds of probability. Each of these, as we shall see, differs from our familiar kind of probability first introduced in chapter 3 primarily only in terms of its conceptual origin; each of the new kinds of probability basically is still the same kind of an entity that has become familiar from our previous work.

Joint Probability

We already have briefly met joint probabilities in chapter 19. We learned that these are probabilities assigned to a "joint event" (x, y) by a bivariate ("big") pf. Because it assigns joint probabilities, we shall refer to this kind of a bivariate RV as a *joint RV* or *joint probability distribution*, to distinguish it from a univariate entity.

We shall now explore the ties between empirical data and joint probabilities in more detail. We shall continue to use the illustrative bivariate potential outcome set introduced in chapter 19 (see table 19.2) that was composed of 60 possible ordered pairs. Let us assume that we had performed a set of repeated observations. Specifically, let us assume that we had performed 2,000 repeated trials (i.e., administered two tests to each of 2,000 subjects), and obtained the results summarized in the frequency data matrix presented in table 20.1. That kind of matrix is very similar to table 19.2. The main difference is that in table 20.1, the numbers entered into the 60 cells are frequencies of joint events—*joint frequencies*—while the corresponding numbers in table 19.2 had been joint probabilities.

Here we have a situation that shares the basic formal characteristics of familiar situations encountered in many earlier discussions. We have a set of actual outcome values that constitute a potential outcome set (in this case, a set of 60 ordered pairs); we perform repeated trials or observations; the actual outcome of each trial is one of the values (an ordered pair) in the potential outcome set; and, in a series of repeated trials, each of the possible kinds of outcome values will occur with some particular fre-

Table 20.1

A bivariate frequency data matrix

y outcome values	x outcome values 1	2	3	4	5	6	7	8	9	10	Marginal frequencies for y
−2	10	10	20	20	50	30	20	20	10	10	200
−1	15	15	30	30	75	45	30	30	15	15	300
0	20	20	40	40	100	60	40	40	20	20	400
1	30	30	60	60	150	90	60	60	30	30	600
2	15	15	30	30	75	45	30	30	15	15	300
3	10	10	20	20	50	30	20	20	10	10	200
Marginal frequencies for x:	100	100	200	200	500	300	200	200	100	100	Total: 2,000 trials

quency. We therefore may treat this situation in our standard fashion. We can convert observed frequencies to relative frequencies, and invoke the principle of equivalence to equate these relative frequencies to corresponding probability values. The procedures, approaches, and concepts introduced in chapters 3 and 4 and applied in subsequent chapters continue to apply virtually without modification.

In terms of our specific illustrative example, the hypothetical frequency data matrix of table 20.1 represents the frequency with which each of the 60 possible outcome values in our potential outcome set had been observed in a series of 2,000 repeated observations of a "big," bivariate joint RV. Let us consider one particular outcome value—say, the pair (3, −1). We see that its frequency is 30. Therefore, its relative frequency is 30/2,000 or 0.015; by the principle of equivalence, that is also the probability. In our new terminology, we would say that the joint probability of (3, −1) is 0.015. If you compare that value to the corresponding joint probability listed in table 19.2, you will see that the two probability values are the same. That is not accidental; the hypothetical frequencies selected for table 20.1 are such that they will yield the same relative frequencies and/or probability values as those listed in the matrix 19.2. (If the discussion concerning potential outcome sets, frequencies, relative frequencies, and probabilities is not quite clear, you will need to review chaps. 2, 3, and 4.)

Marginal Probability

The genesis of the second kind of probability that we shall consider can be conceptualized in the following manner. Let us ask ourselves: how frequently in our 2,000 repeated observations did we obtain some one particular value of *one* of the two bivariate dimensions—for example, how often did we obtain the value $y = 2$? We obtained that value every time a trial of the bivariate joint pf generated an ordered pair that had the form $(x, 2)$; in other words, we obtained $y = 2$ every time we obtained any one of these 10 types of ordered pairs as an actual outcome of a trial: (1, 2), (2, 2), . . . , or (10, 2). The ten corresponding joint frequencies are found in the fifth row of table 20.1; they appear in that row because the value $y = 2$ is the fifth value in the potential outcome set of y. In order to find how frequently we did obtain the value $y = 2$ in 2,000 trials, we simply add the ten frequencies in that row; we find that we obtained the value $y = 2$ 300 times in that series of trials.

That kind of a frequency is usually called a *marginal frequency*, because traditionally it is entered into the margin of a table such as table 20.1. We have followed that practice, and you will find the marginal frequency of $y = 2$ at the right-hand side of the fifth row.

Notice that a marginal frequency contains information only about *one* of the two dimensions or variables. The information concerning x has been completely lost—all that the marginal frequency of $y = 2$ tells us is that y occurred 300 times out of 2,000 trials; x, the second dimension, has been removed from the picture.

If the marginal frequency of $y = 2$ is 300, then, obviously, its relative frequency in 2,000 trials is 300/2,000, or 0.15. That, by the principle of equivalence, is also the probability of that outcome value. Since that probability has been calculated from a marginal frequency (and relative frequency), it is called a *marginal probability*. It also is called an *unconditional probability*, for reasons that will soon become apparent.

Basically, a marginal probability is a probability just like any other. The main distinction between a marginal or unconditional probability and any other kind of probability value is the ancestry of the former; the qualifier "marginal" or "unconditional" merely serves to remind us that we are dealing with a probability that has arisen in the context of a bivariate situation. Otherwise, these entities are probabilities very much like those that had been assigned to various events in chapter 3, to roulette wheel numbers in chapter 4, and so on. The usual empirical interpretations continue to apply.

We had calculated a marginal frequency and probability for $y = 2$, but the approach and procedures apply equally also to the other five outcome values in the potential outcome of this dimension. Table 20.2 repeats the list of six marginal frequencies shown in the vertical margin of table 20.1 for $y = -2, -1, \ldots, 3$, while table 20.3 lists the corresponding six marginal or unconditional probabilities (or, equivalently, marginal relative frequencies).

Let us examine table 20.3 more closely. What kind of a table is it? It should be readily apparent that since table 20.3 lists a set of

Table 20.2

Marginal frequencies for y
(from table 20.1)

y	Marginal frequency
−2	200
−1	300
0	400
1	600
2	300
3	200
Marginal frequency total:	2,000

Table 20.3

Marginal probabilities for y

y	Marginal probability
−2	0.10
−1	.15
0	.20
1	.30
2	.15
3	.10
Total marginal probability:	1.00

outcome values of a discrete potential outcome set (−2, −1, 0, 1, 2, and 3) and a probability corresponding to each of these, table 20.3 is in effect just a *probability function for y*. It is an ordinary, univariate probability distribution RV_Y. Since the other dimension, x, has essentially been removed from the picture, RV_Y is just like any of the pfs we had encountered previously, beginning with the work of chapter 4. The only real difference is that now the probabilities happen to have originated in a bivariate situation. They happen to be marginal or unconditional probabilities; therefore, the univariate probability function RV_Y is called a *marginal* or *unconditional probability function* for y; the qualifiers "marginal" or "unconditional" primarily serve to remind us of the conditional probability distribution's bivariate ancestry.

The concepts and terms we have just introduced have been developed with respect to the dimension y of a joint RV, but that choice was arbitrary. The material could just as well have been developed in terms of the other dimension, x. Only the details—the potential outcome set, frequency values, etc.—would have been different. Tables 20.4 and 20.5 present the data for x that parallel the data for y presented in tables 20.2 and 20.3. It should be obvious that table 20.4 is the table of marginal frequencies for x, while table 20.5 is the corresponding tabulation for RV_X. That marginal or unconditional probability distribution is also just an

Table 20.4

Marginal frequencies for x
(from table 20.1)

x	Marginal frequency
1	100
2	100
3	200
4	200
5	500
6	300
7	200
8	200
9	100
10	100
Marginal frequency total:	2,000

ordinary univariate pf; now it is y that has been completely removed from consideration.

Table 20.5

Marginal probabilities for x

x	Marginal probability
1	0.05
2	.05
3	.10
4	.10
5	.25
6	.15
7	.10
8	.10
9	.05
10	.05
Total marginal probability:	1.00

Conditional Probability

Let us next perform the following simple operation with the data in table 20.1. Let us "lift out" one of the columns or rows of data, and view the extracted information in isolation. For example, let us lift out the third column for closer scrutiny. Table 20.6 lists the six frequencies in that column. What kind of information does this listing contain? It is simply a record of how frequently we obtained each of the six ordered pairs whose *first* outcome value is 3—the pairs (3, −2), (3, −1), . . ., (3, 2). The table thus contains only a very partial record of all the events recorded in table 20.1; all empirical information about the other 54 pairs has been ignored. We now have a record that pertains to only 200 of the 2,000 trials; as far as the data of table 20.6 are concerned, it is as though the other trials never occurred.

Table 20.6

A column of data extracted from table 20.1

y	Frequency (conditional on $x = 3$)
−2	20
−1	30
0	40
1	60
2	30
3	20
Total conditional frequency (equals marginal frequency for $x = 3$):	200

What table 20.6 therefore represents is a frequency table for y, but a specialized frequency table: it is the table of frequencies associated with the six outcome values of y that are recorded whenever the other outcome value, x, is equal to 3, and only then. We say that it is a frequency table for y *under the condition* that $x = 3$, or a table of *conditional frequencies* for y "with x equal to 3."

Once again, except for its ancestry in a bivariate situation, table 20.6 is essentially just a univariate frequency table for y. It records how the outcomes of 200 trials were distributed among six types of outcomes. We can treat this in exactly the same ways as we treated tables such as 20.3 and 20.5, and obtain corresponding relative frequencies, probabilities, and a probability function. The results are listed in table 20.7. It lists six probabilities corresponding to six outcome values of y. From a formal point of view, therefore, table 20.7 is just a table of one particular univariate probability distribution for y.

Table 20.7

A conditional pf for y (from table 20.6)

y	Conditional probability (condition: $x = 3$)
−2	20/200 = 0.10
−1	.15
0	.20
1	.30
2	.15
3	.10
Total conditional probability:	1.00

The probabilities derived in the preceding manner are called *conditional* probabilities, because they are derived from and conceptualized in terms of conditional frequencies and conditional relative frequencies. They are the probabilities assigned to y *under the imposed condition* that $x = 3$, as we know.[1] Accordingly,

[1] We can now state a fact to which we could only allude in part IV, particularly in chapter 13 (see n. 6); α and β are conditional probabilities. (See problem 20.14.)

an RV such as that tabulated in table 20.7 is called a *conditional probability distribution*. It is a univariate probability function just like any other, except that it describes the probabilistic behavior for y *under the restriction* that the other outcome value, x, had been 3.

We have derived a conditional probability distribution for y under the restriction that $x = 3$, but that value of x had been selected arbitrarily to illustrate the new concepts. We could have equally well developed a conditional RV for y under any one of nine other restrictive conditions. That is, we can develop one conditional pf for y in conjunction with any one of the 10 values of x (the values $x = 1; 2, \ldots, 10$ in the potential outcome set of the joint, "big" bivariate RV). We have 10 columns in table 20.1, and could have extracted any of these to construct a table such as 20.7. Furthermore, although we developed a conditional RV for y, we could just as well have developed a conditional RV for x. How many such pfs could we have constructed from the data in table 20.1? We could have constructed six conditional probability distributions for x, one from each of the six rows. Therefore, if in the general case we have M outcome values in *one* dimension of a joint RV and N values in the *other*, we can construct $(M + N)$ conditional probability distributions from that kind of a situation. From a mathematical point of view, each of these is just a univariate RV.

We have been considering three different kinds of probability and, concomitantly, three different kinds of probability distributions: (1) joint probabilities and joint "big" bivariate pfs; (2) marginal or unconditional probabilities and marginal or unconditional pfs; and (3) conditional probabilities and conditional pfs. In our example, we had *one* joint RV (table 19.2 or 20.1), *two* marginal pfs (one for x and one for y), and *16* conditional pfs (six for x, and ten for y). The development of most of the material in the remainder of part V will be based on these kinds of probabilities and RVs. It is therefore essential that you have mastered the preceding material adequately if you plan to understand the discussions that follow. None of these new entities should pose serious difficulties for you because they are really not so different; they are straightforward extensions of univariate concepts that should by now be very familiar. The mastery of new material may take time, however.

Accordingly, you should review the preceding discussions until the material has become familiar and simple to you.

The Conditions for Dependence and Independence

We are ready to address the subject of statistical dependence and independence. Let us return to the performance of a single trial of a bivariate RV such as the joint pf specified in table 19.2. What do we know, statistically, about any one of the outcome values in one of the two dimensions of an ordered pair—say, y—*before* the trial is performed? If we consider that question, we see that all we can know about the statistical characteristics of the outcome value y is the information contained in an RV that pertains to y *only*. Which RV is that? What probability function describes the statistical behavior of y only, and ignores x? It is, of course, the marginal or unconditional probability function RV_Y. That is exactly the RV that describes y alone. In its construction, we removed x from the picture, as it were, and considered the frequencies of y only in 2,000 trials.

Now let us suppose instead that on some particular trial of the bivariate pf we had obtained an ordered pair that contained the value 3 for x. What do we know *now* about the statistical properties of y? What RV describes y now? It is, of course, the conditional pf for y with the restriction $x = 3$, the conditional pf for y shown in table 20.7. That is exactly the probability distribution that describes the statistical properties we would expect y to exhibit if we know that the value of x, the first term of an ordered outcome pair, had been 3.

Thus, *before* each trial of the bivariate RV, all we know statistically about y is the information provided by the *marginal* or *unconditional* probability function RV_Y. *After* a trial, however, after we know what value of x had been obtained but before we "look at" the obtained value for y, *the correct statistical description for* y *is provided by the conditional probability distribution corresponding to the obtained value of* x. If we had obtained the ordered pair $(3, y)$ (with y as yet unknown), then the pf that would define the statistical behavior of y under these conditions would be the conditional probability distribution for y with the condition

$x = 3$; for any of the nine other possible outcome values of x, there would be one corresponding conditional probability function that would define the statistical behavior of y. If we had obtained the pair $(1, y)$ on a trial, the statistical properties of y would be defined by the conditional pf for y under the restriction $x = 1$, etc.

The next step is obvious. If we want to know whether obtaining $x = 3$ on a trial will provide any additional statistical information about y, we only need to compare the *marginal or unconditional* pf for y with the *conditional* pf for y under the condition $x = 3$. If these two pfs are the same, then knowing that $x = 3$ will provide no new statistical information about y. We could similarly compare the marginal pf with each one of the remaining nine conditional pfs for y. If in *each* of these comparisons the pair of probability distributions for y would be exactly the same, then we could conclude that in general, knowing x does not provide additional statistical information about y. Thus, we finally arrive at a definition of the statistical independence of y from x: if *every* conditional probability distribution for y is the same as the (one) unconditional or marginal probability distribution for y, then y is *independent* of x. Otherwise, if *any* of the conditional pfs differ from the marginal pf, then y is *dependent* on x (but see problem 20.11).

We have been considering the dependence of y on x, but that choice had been arbitrary. We could have followed the same steps and considered the dependence of x on y. We would have reached the same basic conclusions, of course. We would have concluded that x is independent of y if, and only if, each of the six conditional pfs for x were exactly the same as the unconditional, marginal pf for x.

Furthermore, it is true that one needs to demonstrate dependence (or independence) for only *one* of the two dimensions. Dependence, as well as independence, is a reciprocal, bilateral, symmetrical relationship; if we can show that x is independent of y, then y necessarily must be independent of x; if we can show that x is dependent on y, then y must necessarily be dependent on x. Thus, we do not need to say "x is independent of (or dependent on) y"; it is sufficient to say "x and y are independent (or dependent)."

How do we know that these two relationships are reciprocal? So far, nothing has been said or demonstrated that would suggest that in a given statistical situation one would not need to examine both dimensions to evaluate dependence. The missing link is provided by a mathematical equation that establishes a formal relationship between the three kinds of probabilities that we have been discussing. It mathematically connects joint, marginal or unconditional, and conditional probabilities. The relationship is always true, whether or not x and y are independent; it is presented in Appendix C.

Furthermore, the equation has another very important consequence that has been ignored so far. We have developed the concepts of marginal and conditional probabilities, and thus of marginal and conditional probability functions, almost entirely in the context of *empirical data*. The development has been based on joint *frequencies* of ordered pairs, such as those presented in the data matrix (20.1). However—and this is a very important point—we can also define marginal and conditional *probabilities* (and thus marginal and conditional RVs) *solely* from the specification of a "big" bivariate joint RV. We do not need a data matrix such as (20.1); we could have defined the two marginal RVs and the sixteen conditional RVs from the joint probability data in figure 19.2 *alone*—in other words, from a joint RV, *without reference to frequency data*.[2] The demonstration of this very important principle requires mathematical manipulations that might distract us from our main line of conceptual development. Therefore, the demonstration of the principle is presented in Appendix C. Even though it has been relegated to an appendix, it should be studied carefully. We shall need to understand the principles involved in the demonstration, particularly for the discussion of the Bayesian methods presented in chapter 22.

I have asserted without explanation that we can construct marginal and conditional RVs from a given joint RV. What about the

[2]The importance of defining "descriptors"—quantities we now know are parameters—in terms of RVs rather than in terms of averages computed from data—quantities we now know are sample values—was already stressed in part II, especially chapter 7. That distinction eventually enabled us to speak on the one hand about statistics and sample values, and on the other hand about underlying RVs specified by parameters.

reverse? Can we construct a joint, "big" bivariate RV from two given univariate marginal or from a set of univariate conditional RVs? It turns out that in general we cannot. The joint RV is basic; the two types of univariate RVs can be derived from it. The reverse procedure will not work in general unless a certain special condition is met, or certain special assumptions are made. We shall briefly discuss the special condition next, since it pertains to the issue of dependence and independence. As to the special assumptions, we shall see later that these are the basic ingredients of the Bayesian methods.

It can be shown that *if* x and y are independent, then certain special relationships must hold between marginal and joint probabilities.[3] Specifically, if x and y, two dimensions of a bivariate joint RV, are independent, then, and only then, will the following set of simple relationships exist between marginal and joint probabilities: for *every* ordered pair, the joint probability will be equal to the product of the two corresponding marginal probabilities. For example, if in a bivariate RV such as that tabulated in figure 19.2 the two dimensions x and y are independent, then the *joint* probability of a pair such as (3, −1) will be equal to the *product* of the *marginal* probability of $x = 3$ and the *marginal* probability of $y = -1$. Thus, *if* we know that x and y are independent, then we can obtain the joint probability of (3, −1) from the values of marginal probabilities in tables 20.5 and 20.3; it would be 0.10×0.15, or 0.015.

We see that if we do know that x and y are independent, and if we have only the two marginal pfs RV_X and RV_Y, then in this one particular case we can construct a "big" joint multivariate RV from these two univariate pfs. We can obtain the joint probability of any and all of the 60 ordered pairs, and thus the "big" RV, by multiplying for each of these pairs the two appropriate marginal probability values. In other words, if we know that the two dimensions of a bivariate RV are independent, then, and only then, can we reconstruct or recover that bivariate "parent" RV from two

[3]Alternatively, as we shall mention below, the "certain special relationships" we are about to consider can be viewed as definitions of dependence and/or independence, rather than as consequences.

given univariate marginal RVs. Otherwise, if we cannot assume that x and y are independent, then there is no available method that will allow us to reconstruct the originating bivariate joint RV from its marginal RVs. To summarize: we can *always* construct two *marginal* univariate RVs from a *bivariate* joint RV, but we can invert that process legitimately only if we know the two dimensions to be independent.

These product relationships that hold when two dimensions are independent suggest an alternative definition for dependence and independence: two dimensions of a joint bivariate RV are independent if, and only if, each of the joint probabilities is the product of the two applicable marginal probabilities.[4] Previously we had defined independence and dependence in terms of comparisons between marginal and conditional probability distributions. Now the product relationship we have been considering suggests that independence and dependence could also be defined in terms of relationships between marginal and joint probabilities. The two approaches to definition are logically equivalent in the sense that if we define independence and dependence by one of these approaches, then the other definitions follow as a corollary. One definition logically entails the other (see Appendix C).

Weak and Strong Dependence

So far, we have only considered frequency data from a joint RV whose two dimensions were independent. We shall conclude this introduction to the concepts of dependence and independence by presenting two bivariate frequency data matrices acquired from two hypothetical bivariate RVs each of whose dimensions are *not* independent. The two frequency data matrices are shown in tables 20.8 and 20.9. In each case, the potential outcome set is the same as that presented in table 20.1. Furthermore, in each case the two sets of marginal frequencies are also the same as the correspond-

[4]Actually, if two dimensions are independent, we do not need to calculate *all* sixty joint probabilities to verify independence. If the two dimensions are independent, it is impossible for just *one* joint probability value in a bivariate matrix not to be equal to the product of the corresponding two marginal probabilities (see problem 20.11).

ing two sets in table 20.1. Therefore, we know immediately that the three pairs of marginal univariate probability distributions are equal to one another (why?).

Table 20.8

Weak dependence

y	x 1	2	3	4	5	6	7	8	9	10	Marginal frequency for y
−2	15	15	25	30	50	30	15	10	5	5	200
−1	20	20	35	40	75	45	25	20	10	10	300
0	20	20	40	40	100	60	40	40	20	20	400
1	30	30	60	60	150	90	60	60	30	30	600
2	10	10	25	20	75	45	35	40	20	20	300
3	5	5	15	10	50	30	25	30	15	15	200
Marginal frequency for x:	100	100	200	200	500	300	200	200	100	100	Total no. of trials: 2,000

Table 20.9

Strong dependence

y	x 1	2	3	4	5	6	7	8	9	10	Marginal frequency for y
−2	30	20	40	40	70	—	—	—	—	—	200
−1	40	40	50	50	120	—	—	—	—	—	300
0	30	30	100	100	140	—	—	—	—	—	400
1	—	10	10	10	170	200	100	80	20	—	600
2	—	—	—	—	—	100	100	80	20	—	300
3	—	—	—	—	—	—	—	40	60	100	200
Marginal frequency for x:	100	100	200	200	500	300	200	200	100	100	Total no. of trials: 2,000

The differences between the bivariate joint frequency data matrices 20.1, 20.8, and 20.9 thus lie in differences between corresponding joint frequencies only. Specifically, the joint frequencies in tables 20.8 and 20.9 have been altered so that in both cases the two dimensions x and y are dependent. However, table 20.8 represents a rather mild modification of the frequency data in table 20.1, while table 20.9 presents a much more drastic modification, as the following considerations will demonstrate.

How do we know whether a frequency data matrix differs little or a great deal from a matrix such as 20.1 that represents a situation where x and y are *independent*? One approach to evaluating a matrix would be to compare conditional and marginal RVs. Specifically, if the data from a given bivariate joint frequency matrix lead to a set of *conditional* RVs in one of the dimensions that are very different from the corresponding *marginal* RV of that dimension, then x and y are highly dependent. That situation would imply that if we knew one value of an ordered pair, we should have gained considerable statistical information about the other member. We would say that x and y are *strongly* dependent. Alternatively, if the conditional pfs for one of the two dimensions are not very different from the corresponding marginal pf, we say that the two dimensions are *weakly* dependent. In that case, information about one value in an ordered pair will furnish relatively little additional information about the other member of that actual outcome.

The data in table 20.8 suggest that for their underlying joint RV, x and y are but weakly dependent. We may see this by comparing conditional and unconditional RVs. Let us compare the conditional probability distribution for y under the condition that $x = 3$ with the unconditional probability distribution for y. Figure 20.1 shows these two pfs. We see that although there are some differences, they are relatively minor. As a matter of fact, if we were to compare each of the ten conditional RVs for y with the unconditional RV Y, we would see that some of these conditional pfs are exactly the same as the unconditional pf (see problem 20.11).

The situation is very different for the "big" (joint) RV that underies the data in table 20.9. Let us again compare the conditional pf for y under the restriction that $x = 3$ with the uncondi-

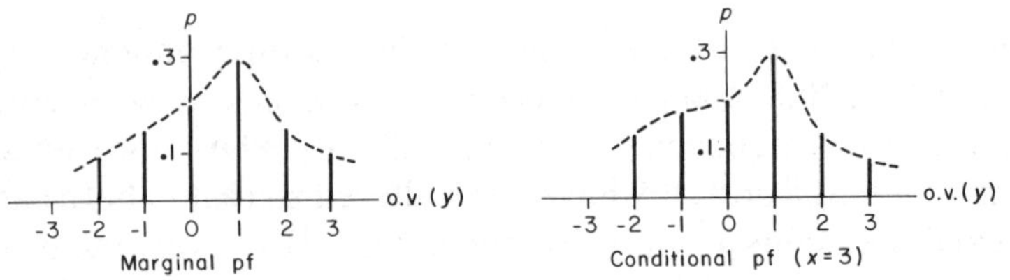

FIGURE 20.1 Comparison of marginal and conditional pfs for y: weak dependence

tional pf for y. These two probability functions are presented in figure 20.2. We see major differences; the two potential outcome sets are not even the same (why?). Therefore, now if we know that the first member of an ordered pair obtained as the result of one trial of this big RV had been 3, we would have thereby gained considerable statistical information about y. For example, before we know the value of x that had been obtained on a trial, we would know that we can obtain *any* integral value of y between -2 and 3, inclusive, from any one trial; however, if after a trial we knew that the outcome had been of the form (3, y), for example—in other words, if we knew that the result included the value $x = 3$—then we know immediately that we cannot obtain certain values of y that previously were possible. That is quantitatively and qualitatively highly significant statistical information; x and y are strongly dependent.

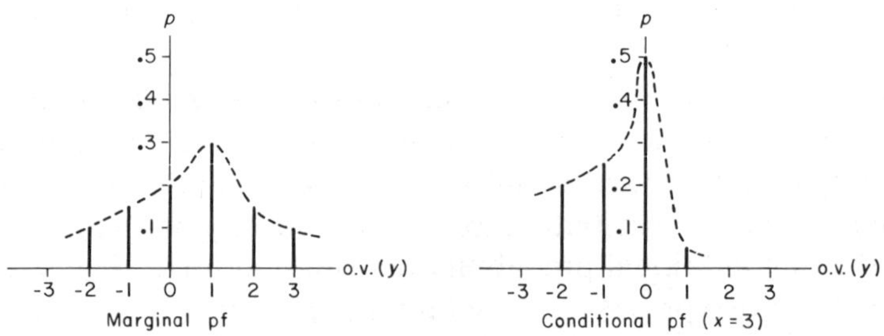

FIGURE 20.2 Comparison of marginal and conditional pfs for y: strong dependence

These considerations suggest that dependence and independence might be relevant to the process of prediction. That is, whether x and y are dependent at all, as well as the strength and kind of dependence, should have some bearing on the amount and kind of statistical information one member of an ordered pair of outcomes furnishes about outcome values of the other member. This is the topic we shall examine next.

PROBLEMS

20.1 In a bivariate situation, how are

(a) marginal frequencies and marginal probabilities related?

(b) joint frequencies and joint probabilities related?

20.2 Given an "ordinary," i.e., univariate, pf, can one tell by examining it carefully whether it is

(a) a marginal pf?

(b) a conditional pf?

Explain your answers.

20.3 How was table 19.2 constructed from table 20.1?

20.4 A bivariate pf has R outcome values along one of its dimensions, x, and S outcome values along the other dimension, y.

(a) How many unconditional pfs can you construct?

(b) How many conditional pfs can you construct?

(c) How would you establish whether x and y are independent?

20.5 For table 20.8, construct

(a) the marginal pf for x

(b) the conditional pf for x, with $y = 2$.

20.6 You are told for a table of frequencies for y (such as table 20.6) that these frequencies are really conditional frequencies, with $x = 4$. Do you need any other information before you can construct the conditional probability function for y with $x = 4$? If so, what would that information be?

20.7 If you are given a joint frequency data matrix such as table 20.1, how do you use the data to construct

(a) the unconditional pfs?

(b) the conditional pfs?

20.8 When one constructs relative frequencies (and thus, probabilities) from a set of frequencies observed in repeated trials of an experiment, one needs to know the total number of repeated observations (see chap. 3). For constructing a conditional pf, what kind of a quantity is used as "the total number of observations"?

20.9 If the dimensions x and y of a joint RV are independent, must each conditional pf for x have the same potential outcome as the marginal pf for x? Explain. Does your conclusion apply equally to the other dimension?

20.10 In a joint pf with the dimensions x and y, suppose that the potential outcome of each conditional pf for x is the same as the potential outcome of the marginal pf for x, and similarly for the other dimension y. Are the two dimensions necessarily independent? [Hint: examine table 20.8.]

20.11 Consider a joint frequency data matrix for a discrete bivariate RV where the two dimensions are independent. Suppose you must change one or more of these joint frequencies, but only under the restriction that all the marginal frequencies are to remain unchanged.

(a) What is the *smallest* number of changes you can make? Explain.

(b) Accordingly, what is the *least* number of conditional pfs that must be different from the original conditional pfs?

20.12 If one looks at table 20.9, why is it possible to see immediately, without further analysis, that the two dimensions must be dependent?

20.13 Suppose we know that the joint probability for the ordered pair (3, 1) is 0.0005, and that the unconditional probabilities for $x = 3$ and $y = 1$ are 0.05 and 0.01, respectively.

May we legitimately conclude that therefore x and y are independent? Why, or why not?

20.14 We know that in tests of significance, the probability of committing an error of the first kind is α; we also know that we can commit that kind of error only when the null hypothesis is in fact true.

(a) What kind of a probability is α? Explain and discuss your answer.

(b) What is the parallel situation for β? I.e., what kind of a probability is that quantity?

20.15 Is the distinction between weak and strong dependence made on a qualitative or on a quantitative basis? Discuss.

20.16 What are the two alternative approaches to defining statistical independence?

20.17 If x is independent of y, is y necessarily independent of x? Does the same conclusion apply to statistical dependence?

CHAPTER 21

Regression and Correlation

Let us review certain general characteristics of statistical prediction that apply to the univariate case. Suppose we have some probability function, and wish to use it to predict the outcome of a trial. What value should we guess? We discussed that question briefly in part II, and discovered that the answer would depend on the criterion used; different criteria lead to different values that would be "best" guesses.

The criterion we shall use in this chapter is one that leads to the *mean* as the "best predictor." It is one of the most frequently used criteria, because it is scientifically meaningful as well as mathematically tractable. The criterion is called the *least-squares* criterion (Freeman, p. 58), and is defined in the following way. Suppose we perform a series of N repeated RV trials, predicting the outcome of each trial to be some number that we represent by a_0. In the usual trial, we shall not be correct in our prediction. Each trial will therefore generate an *error*, the quantity [(actual outcome) − (a_0)]. (If on a particular trial our guess happens to be correct, we simply consider the error to be 0, and treat that quantity mathematically like any other error value.) Next, we *square* each of these N error terms, and *average* the resulting N squared numbers. Then, as we allow N to become increasingly large, that is, as we perform more and more trials, the "long-term average" of these squared error terms will tend toward some particular numerical value, say, b_0. In general, that quantity will depend on our choice of a_0, our predicted outcome. Different predictor values a will lead to different long-term averages b. The value of a_0 that will *minimize* the long-term average b_0 of squared error terms is the *mean* of the RV that generated our observations. In fact, if we set $a_0 = \mu$, then b_0 will be 0. We say that for a given RV, μ is the best predictor "according to the least-squares criterion" or "in the least-squares sense."

If we use the mean of an RV as our predicted value, we know that although it is the best predictor in the least-squares sense, it is unlikely that we will obtain precisely that value as an outcome of a trial. Therefore, we are interested not only in what the best number for us to guess would be but also in knowing something about the kind of error we should expect to obtain in a given situation. If we perform a series of repeated RV trials, guessing the mean each time, how closely will the actual results cluster about our predicted value, the mean? In general, it is the magnitude of σ^2, the variance (or, equivalently, the magnitude of σ, the square root of the variance, the standard deviation) that provides a quantitative index of the degree of clustering of outcomes about the mean. We discussed this meaning of the variance and of the standard deviation previously in the context of normal pdfs, but the meaning is true in general; the magnitude of either or both of these quantities provides information about the degree of clustering of outcomes about the mean.[1] Thus, the size of the standard deviation and/or variance provides a measure of how far one would expect the outcome of a usual, average, typical trial to lie from the mean. We are now ready to apply these considerations to the bivariate case.

Regression

We have seen that according to the least-squares criterion, the best value to predict for an actual outcome before performing a trial is the mean of the probability distribution. It is not difficult to apply this principle within a bivariate framework. Indeed, we have already considered the issue of prediction while we were developing the concepts of statistical dependence and independence. We learned that *prior* to performing a trial of a joint, bivariate ("big")

[1]There is a very general equation (the Bienaymé-Chebychev Theorem; see Freeman, pp. 30-31) that specifies relationships between the standard deviation of any RV and certain outcome regions away from the mean of that RV.

RV, the probability function that describes the statistical behavior of one of the two dimensions is the unconditional or marginal probability function for that dimension. In terms of the dimension y, for example, it is the unconditional probability distribution for y that defines the statistical behavior of that variable when we have no information about the value of the other variable x. After a trial, however, after we know that the value we had obtained for x is, say, 3, the probability function that now best describes the statistical behavior of y is the probability function for y *conditional* on that obtained value of x. In the light of our preceding discussion, it is obvious what our bivariate prediction procedure should be according to the least-squares criterion: to predict y *before* a trial of a joint RV, guess the value of the mean of the unconditional pf; *after* the trial, after we know what value had been obtained for x, but before we had actually observed the value obtained for y, we should guess the mean of the probability function for y that is conditional on the obtained outcome value for x. Furthermore, we also have the tools for evaluating whether a knowledge of x will result in a "tighter" prediction for y. We know in general that the quantitative index that measures this degree of cluster about the mean is the standard deviation (or, alternatively, the variance). Therefore, to evaluate whether knowing x provides information that will reduce the average error of our guess, we also need to consider and compare the standard deviation of the unconditional probability distribution for y with the standard deviations of all the conditional probability distributions for y.

In summary, for some bivariate RVs, knowing the outcome value x generated by a trial will allow us to improve the prediction of the outcome y obtained on that trial, while for other bivariate RVs that will not be the case. To discern which of these two cases we have in a given instance, we derive the marginal and the set of conditional probability distributions for y from the bivariate probability distribution, and compare corresponding parameters. If *all* the means of conditional RVs are the same, then knowing x will not help us to improve on the *value* of our guess for y; in some of those instances, however, knowing x may enable us to make a "tighter" guess for y, even though all the means of the conditional RVs for y are the same. These are but preliminary, general statements of matters we shall explore in considerable detail in the remainder of this chapter.

The preceding discussion has been conducted in terms of predicting y from x, but we could equally well have chosen to discuss these matters in terms of predicting x from y. The two situations are always parallel and conceptually equivalent; therefore, it would be redundant to discuss each issue pertaining to prediction twice—once in terms of predicting y from x, and once in terms of predicting x from y. We shall arbitrarily conduct discussions in terms of one or the other procedure, with the understanding that the choice is arbitrary, and that the discussion could just as well have been conducted in terms of the reverse case.

We shall illustrate some of the general properties of the prediction process by two examples. We can dispose of our first example quickly. It is the joint RV specified in tables 19.2 and 20.1. In this example, a knowledge of x will not help in predicting y; the knowledge will neither lead us to change the value of our prediction, nor will it enable us to make a "tighter" guess. We draw these conclusions by comparing the unconditional with the conditional probability distributions for y. Specifically, we base the conclusion that a knowledge of x will not alter our predicted guess for y on the fact that *all* the *conditional* RVs for y have the *same mean* as the *marginal* RV for y; we base the conclusion that our guess after knowing x is not likely to cluster more closely about the mean on the fact that *all* the *standard deviations* of the *conditional* RVs for y are the *same* as the *standard deviation* of the *marginal or unconditional* RV for y. We should have expected these conclusions in this example. We know from our work in chapter 20 that for the RV in table 19.2, x and y are independent. Therefore, a knowledge of x cannot help us in our prediction of y; that conclusion follows from the definition of independence. We could repeat an identical argument to show that a knowledge of y will not help us in predicting x in the present situation.

Let us next examine a situation where x and y are strongly dependent, namely, the case of the bivariate joint frequency data matrix of table 20.9. Let us see whether a knowledge of x will in this case help to predict y more accurately. To evaluate the situation, we must compare the unconditional or marginal RV for y

with the conditional probability distributions for that dimension. We can obtain the needed probability distributions directly from the joint frequency data in table 20.9. Table 21.1 shows the results. It tabulates all 10 conditional probability distributions for y, one for each of the 10 outcome values in the potential outcome for x, as well as an 11th RV—the unconditional or marginal RV for y. Each column shows the list of probabilities assigned by one RV to the six outcome values in the potential set of y. In addition, table 21.1 also presents for each of the 11 RVs the mean, variance, and standard deviation. These are obtained for a given probability function by the techniques introduced in chapter 7.

Table 21.1

The unconditional and 10 conditional pfs for y

	Probabilities for y, conditional on:										
y	$x = 1$	$x = 2$	$x = 3$	$x = 4$	$x = 5$	$x = 6$	$x = 7$	$x = 8$	$x = 9$	$x = 10$	Unconditional probability
−2	0.30	.20	.20	.20	.14	0	0	0	0	0	.10
−1	.40	.40	.25	.25	.24	0	0	0	0	0	.15
0	.30	.30	.50	.50	.28	0	0	0	0	0	.20
1	0	.10	.05	.05	.34	.67	.50	.40	.20	0	.30
2	0	0	0	0	0	.33	.50	.40	.20	0	.15
3	0	0	0	0	0	0	0	.20	.60	1.00	.10
μ	−1.0	−0.7	−0.6	−0.6	−0.18	1.33	1.50	1.80	2.40	3.0	0.55
σ^2	0.60	0.81	0.74	0.74	1.11	0.22	0.25	0.56	0.64	0	2.048
σ	0.78	0.90	0.86	0.86	1.05	0.47	0.50	0.75	0.80	0	1.43

It should be readily apparent that in this situation a knowledge of x will influence our guess for y. Prior to a trial, our best guess for y in the least-squares sense would be the outcome value 0.55, the mean of the unconditional RV for y. After a trial, the best guess for y will depend on the value obtained for x. That best guess will of course be the mean of the probability distribution for y conditional on the obtained value of x: we can find that conditional mean from table 21.1. Figure 21.1 illustrates the situation graphically. It indicates for each of the ten possible outcome values of x a corresponding best guess for y.

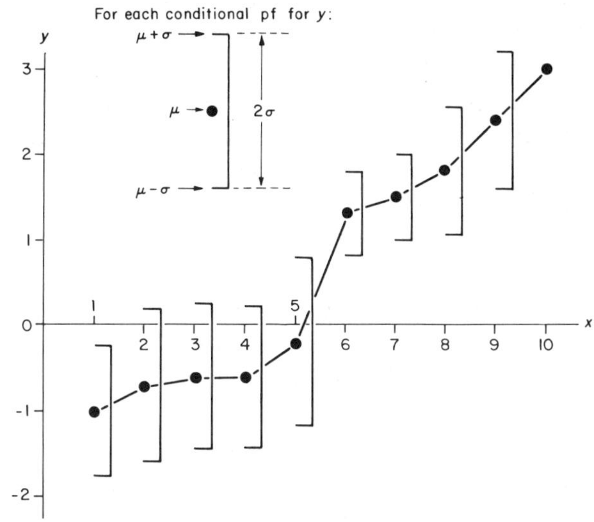

FIGURE 21.1 Predicting y from x

In the present example, a knowledge of x not only causes us to alter our predicted value for y; it also makes possible "tighter" predictions. This observation is based on a comparison of standard deviations. We see from table 21.1 that the magnitude of the standard deviation of the unconditional RV for y is 1.43, while the standard deviations for the ten conditional RVs range from 0 to approximately 1.1. The magnitudes of these standard deviations are indicated in figure 21.1 by square brackets; these show the span $\pm\sigma$ on either side of μ. Since smaller standard deviations imply outcomes that cluster more closely about the mean, we would expect to obtain smaller errors if we knew x before we guess y.

This kind of an effect will *always* be present, for reasons that will become apparent later in this chapter: *if the means of all the conditional RVs for* y *are not equal to one another, then, "on average," the standard deviations of these conditional probability distributions must be smaller than the standard deviation of the unconditional or marginal probability distribution for* y. The same is true for the other variable, x, of course.

We have one rather extreme illustration in the present case, since the probability distribution for y conditional on $x = 10$ has only one possible outcome value, 3. Its standard deviation is *zero*, whereas that of the unconditional pf for y is 1.43. Therefore, each time we obtain the outcome value $x = 10$ on a trial, not only do we modify our "best guess" from $y = 0.55$ to $y = 3$, but we should also expect a drastic reduction of the magnitude of the error. If we obtain the outcome value $x = 10$, we know that our prediction for y will necessarily be correct; the error will be zero, every time. Less extreme examples of improvement in the precision of our guess are provided by the standard deviations associated with the conditional RVs in table 21.1 for $x = 6$ and $x = 7$.

We could equally well have developed these ideas by discussing how one would predict x from a knowledge of y. The data in table 20.9 can also be used to construct the six conditional probability distribution functions for x, as well as the unconditional RV for x. The results are indicated in figure 21.2. We see six data points, each representing the best guess for x conditional on a particular value of y.

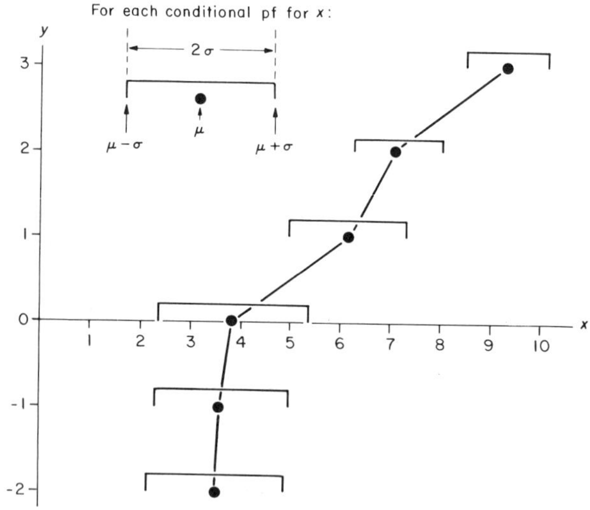

FIGURE 21.2 Predicting x from y

If we connect the means of the conditional probability distributions in either figure 21.1 or 21.2 by a line, we obtain an example of a graph called a *regression line*. (The origin and meaning of that term relates to certain issues that we shall not address here; see Hays, p. 616.) A regression line is simply a geometrical representation of the rule that governs our best guess for y, given x. A regression line that tells us what value of y to predict *from* an obtained value of x is a regression line *of* y *on* x (fig. 21.1); in the reverse case, where one predicts x from y, one has a regression line *of* x *on* y (fig. 21.2). It is a graph that is particularly useful for prediction in the case of continuous RVs. Its direct application is very simple, even for the case where x and y are continuous variables; to predict y for any specified value of x, one simply "reads off" the value of y that corresponds to that x value on the regression line of y on x.

In our particular example, the regression line is the "best" line in the sense that it actually contains or passes through all the values that according to the least-squares criterion are best predictors for y. The regression line is quite jagged, however, and this can be inconvenient in some ways. For example, the mathematical description of a jagged line tends to be clumsy and therefore difficult to manipulate in other mathematical operations. To avoid these and similar complications one frequently replaces this "ideal" regression line by a smoother line which, while it may not pass through all (or even any) of the "best" predictor values, is easier to manipulate mathematically. One sacrifices goodness of prediction to some extent in return for greater mathematical convenience.

The smoother regression lines are usually defined by a relatively simple algebraic equation. The most common procedure is to use a regression line that can be represented by a polynomial, an equation of the form $y = ax^n + bx^{n-1} + \ldots + q$. The degree n of the polynomial that is used in a particular instance usually is a compromise between convenience and accuracy. On the one hand, higher degree polynomials are more complex and difficult to manipulate, while, on the other hand, the higher the degree of the equation, the more closely is one able to fit a curve to data points such as those in figures 21.1 and 21.2.[2] After one selects a suitable value of n, the values of the coefficients that produce the "best fitting" curve for a particular joint RV can be obtained from that probability distribution by suitable mathematical techniques. Smooth regression lines are called *curvilinear*; figure 21.3 shows several regression lines that could serve to approximate the "best" (but jagged) line shown in figure 21.1.

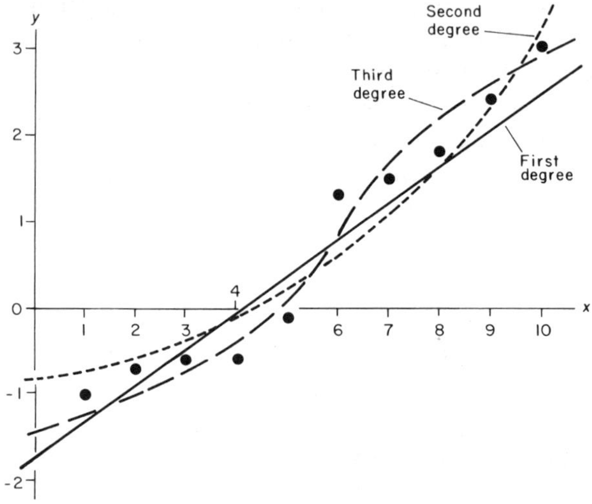

FIGURE 21.3 Various degrees of the regression line of y on x

The simplest of all the nth degree regression lines is the graph represented by a first degree polynomial, the straight line whose equation has the form $y = ax + b$. Prediction that is based on this kind of an equation and curve is called *linear prediction*, or prediction based on *linear regression*. While linear regression is frequently used in the behavioral disciplines because of its mathematical simplicity, it is likely to provide considerably less than ideal prediction unless, in a given case, the "best" predictor values (that is, the means of the conditional probability functions) happen to fall into a more or less straight line pattern. This

[2]In general, if we have N points in a plane, an algebraic equation of degree $(N-1)$ is required to define a graph that passes exactly through all N points. For example, if $N = 2$, we need a first degree equation—a straight line—to pass through these two points; for three points, we shall need a second degree equation, and so on.

consideration raises the question of goodness of prediction: in a given bivariate RV, how good a prediction of one dimension from the other is provided by a linear regression? This apparently innocuous question leads to a number of issues that fall under the general heading of "correlation." We shall next discuss that major subject.

The Correlation Coefficient

Let us reconsider a "big" joint bivariate RV, a pf that assigns joint probabilities to a set of ordered pairs. We shall approach our study of correlation by introducing a new parameter of this type of RV. First of all, as we have seen in the previous chapters, we can derive two marginal probability distributions RV_X and RV_Y directly from any given joint pf. (We do *not* need to use sample value data, i.e., the joint frequencies of ordered pairs generated by repeated trials of the given bivariate RV.) These unconditional pfs will be two ordinary univariate RVs. We therefore can compute the usual set of univariate parameters for each pf by the methods explained in chapter 7. Let us represent the means, variances, and standard deviations of RV_X and RV_Y by μ_x and μ_y, $\sigma^2{}_x$ and $\sigma^2{}_y$, and σ_x and σ_y, respectively.

We next perform N repeated trials of the joint bivariate RV, obtaining N ordered pairs of the form (x, y). Let us represent this set in terms of a simple subscript notation, thus:

$$(x_1, y_1); (x_2, y_2); \ldots; (x_N, y_N). \tag{21.1}$$

We now have acquired N values of x, and N values of y. From these two sets of outcome values and the two means μ_x and μ_y we can form *two* sets of N deviations from a mean, one for x and one for y, thus:

$$\begin{aligned}&\text{one: } (x_1 - \mu_x), (x_2 - \mu_x), \ldots, (x_N - \mu_x), \text{ and}\\&\text{two: } (y_1 - \mu_y), (y_2 - \mu_y), \ldots, (y_N - \mu_y).\end{aligned} \tag{21.2}$$

We shall next construct an average from these sets of deviations that will lead to our new parameter. We shall multiply corresponding pairs of deviations and average these products, thus:

$$\frac{[(x_1 - \mu_x) \times (y_1 - \mu_y)] + [(x_2 - \mu_x) \times (y_2 - \mu_y)] + \ldots + [(x_N - \mu_x) \times (y_N - \mu_y)]}{N}. \qquad (21.3)$$

We have thus reduced a set of N sample values (ordered pairs) to a single number, an average—in other words, we have computed a statistic. If we now perform still more trials, acquiring more and more actual outcomes and allowing N to become larger and larger, the value of our statistic would tend toward, or "converge to," some particular value. This numerical value, obtained as an extension of the arithmetical averaging procedure shown in (21.3) (allowing N to become increasingly large, without limit), is the bivariate RV parameter called the *covariance*.[3]

We note that we have defined an RV parameter by using one of the two basic approaches introduced in chapter 7, namely, the approach that relied on developing a *long-term average* of a statistic. (See also the parallel discussions in chaps. 13 and 15 that consider the parameters μ and σ^2 as long-term averages of the statistics M and S^2, respectively.) We learned earlier that alternatively, an RV parameter could also be defined *solely* in terms of a probability distribution, without reference to data (see chaps. 7 and 8)—at least for the univariate case. This alternative approach remains viable and valid for the bivariate case. We shall not pursue the matter, but for a given bivariate RV, its parameters, including the covariance, can be defined entirely in terms of that joint probability distribution; any parameter in the family of moments can be calculated directly from the joint RV, without reference to empirical data. Specifically, the covariance can be also defined solely in terms of the information contained in a joint probability function. Furthermore, this second, alternative approach yields numerical values that are the same as those obtained from long-term averages. The two approaches remain

[3]This parameter is called a "mixed" moment. It is a moment because it involves an average of deviations from the mean, and mixed because in the present case it involves a mixture of two variables or dimensions, x and y.

equivalent, in the sense that they produce the same quantitative results.

Let us remind ourselves that we are still seeking to obtain a method that for a given joint RV will quantify the goodness of prediction furnished by linear regression. In the course of obtaining that measure, we have defined a parameter of a joint bivariate pf, the covariance. While the covariance will be the basis of the index we are seeking, it cannot by itself serve as that index, for the following reasons. The covariance fails to provide the desired measure of goodness of prediction because it contains information that for our present purposes confuses the issue. The problem is, in a given instance, the covariance is sensitive to the *scale* of the joint RV, while the measure or index we are seeking should be insensitive to scale factors. What that means is the following. Suppose we have a joint RV such as that defined in the joint probability data matrix in table 19.2. That hypothetical bivariate pf specifies the joint probabilities of ordered outcome pairs that represent two sets of test scores. Now, let us suppose for the moment that we had changed our method of scoring each test; let us suppose that we had simply taken each one of the two scores obtained from a given subject, and multiplied it by some arbitrary number, say, 10. We are assuming that everything else in the situation had remained the same—we had simply regraded each test score according to our simple arithmetical procedure. The only thing that would have changed in our bivariate joint frequency matrix would be the sets of outcome values. Instead of the ten values (1, 2, . . ., 10) in the x dimension and the 6 values (-2, -1, . . ., $+3$) in the y dimension, we would have the two corresponding potential outcomes (10, 20, . . ., 100) and (-20, -10, . . ., $+30$). Only the outcome labels would have been changed in table 19.2; the joint probabilities would remain the same.

We say that this restructuring of the situation has introduced a "scale factor," a magnification, that in a sense does not change the basic configuration of the RV. All the parameters of the joint RV will have been affected by this change in various very simple ways. For example, the means of RV_X and RV_Y, the marginal pfs, will each have been multiplied by 10; the variances of these two univariate RVs will each have been multiplied by 100, etc. The covariance of the joint RV will also have been multiplied by 100, as can be easily demonstrated. However—and this is the crux of the matter—in an important sense, the goodness of prediction afforded by linear regression methods will *not* have been changed by introducing a scale factor, as we shall eventually come to recognize. Certain salient features of linear regression are unaffected by a change in scale; they are "insensitive" to that kind of a change. Accordingly, the measure of goodness of linear prediction that we are attempting to develop should likewise be insensitive to the effects of scale factors.

The measure we are seeking, while based on the covariance should have the "scale factor effect" removed from it to render the measure insensitive to phenomena that are irrelevant for our present purpose. The desired change is accomplished by the same sort of simple mathematical procedure that was used to change an "ordinary" RV outcome value x into a corresponding "standardized" (sometimes called a "normalized") outcome value z: one *divides* the nonstandard quantity by a *standard deviation* to transform it into an entity that is insensitive to scale factors; see (11.2). In the present case, there are two scale factors that prevent the covariance from being a meaningful measure of the goodness of linear prediction; these are σ_x and σ_y, the standard deviations of the unconditional RVs of the two dimensions of the bivariate RV. We shall therefore need to take one more step to finally obtain the index we have been seeking. We shall remove scale factor effects from the covariance by dividing it by $(\sigma_x) \times (\sigma_y)$. The resulting quantity is our index. It is the "standardized covariance," the important quantity called the *correlation coefficient* of a probability distribution. It is usually symbolized by the Greek letter ρ (rho). In more formal terms,

$$\rho_{xy} = \frac{\text{covariance}_{xy}}{(\sigma_x) \times (\sigma_y)} . \tag{21.4}$$

We should note carefully that this quantity, the correlation coefficient ρ, is no longer a parameter of an RV. While for any given bivariate RV, the correlation coefficient is closely related to one of the RV parameters (the covariance), ρ has had certain scale factors specific to that RV (the standard deviations σ_x and σ_y) removed. We might say that ρ is a "parameterlike" quantity. It is *not* a statistic, because it may be obtained directly from an RV rather than from data, but it is not exactly a parameter, either.

We shall consider the correlation coefficient in considerable detail in the material that follows. In order to give some rough first idea of its meaning, we shall mention a few of its major characteristics and implications before delving into more complex matters. First, it can be mathematically demonstrated that ρ has a specific, delimited range. The value of the correlation coefficient must lie between -1 and $+1$, inclusive. Between these two extremes it can assume any value. Second, certain values of ρ have special significance; these are the values ± 1, and 0. If for a given bivariate RV, ρ has either the value of $+1$ or -1, that means that perfect prediction of one dimension from the other can be obtained by using a straight regression line. (We shall presently explore what "perfect prediction from linear regression" means.) If for a given bivariate RV the two dimensions are *independent*, then the value of ρ for that RV will necessarily be 0, exactly. Linear prediction (or any other kind of prediction, as we have already seen in chap. 20) is of no help in that case. The converse, however, does *not* hold; if in a given instance ρ is equal to 0, then in general we *cannot* conclude that the two dimensions of that bivariate RV are independent. They may be, or they may not; one cannot tell just from the value $\rho = 0$.

In general, the meaning of any intermediate value of ρ is quite complex. For example, it is not at all obvious—nor, in a sense, fully specified—what it means to say that $\rho = +0.35$, for example. It is this issue that we shall consider next; it will illuminate the meaning of "the measure of goodness of linear prediction."

Linear Regression and the Correlation Coefficient

We shall begin to examine the implications of saying that for some particular bivariate RV, ρ has a certain value. From a narrowly mathematical point of view, saying that for a given RV, $\rho = +0.35$, for example, means that this is the particular value one obtains for the standardized covariance of that probability distribution, of course. However, the correlation coefficient has considerably more meaning than that, as we shall see. In this section we shall explore the meaning of ρ in a more or less intuitive fashion, reserving a more specific analysis of these issues for the subsequent section.

We are seeking to understand what it means to speak about the goodness of prediction provided by linear regression, and how the correlation coefficient provides a measure of that goodness. Let us ask: how can linear regression provide good prediction, and how can it provide poor prediction? That is, what factors determine the effectiveness of predicting, for a given bivariate RV, y from x, using a straight regression line such as that shown in figure 21.3? Basically, there are two different (although, as we shall later see, not entirely unrelated) factors that determine the goodness of prediction provided by a straight regression line. *First*, there is the matter of where the *means* of the *conditional* RVs lie. If they fall close to or even exactly into a straight line pattern, then a straight line prediction method may be quite good. We see in the examples illustrated in figures 21.1 and 21.2 that the means of the conditional RVs do *not* fall close to a straight line; accordingly, that kind of a regression line would not be a particularly good predictor in those cases. *Second*, there is the matter of the *standard deviations* of the conditional RVs. Even if the means of these pfs were to lie on a straight line, the goodness of linear prediction will to some extent still depend on the dispersion within each of the conditional RVs.

To facilitate an intuitive grasp of the issues that are involved here, we shall present and briefly discuss a series of illustrative examples. Each of these will be presented in terms of a sketch of the x-y outcome plane that describes certain features of one hypothetical bivariate RV. In each figure, we shall indicate the *means* of a number of conditional RVs for y, as well as the *mean* of the *unconditional* RV for y; we shall also indicate by *square brackets* the magnitude of the *standard deviation* of each of the various RVs. Furthermore, we shall show the straight regression line that is "best" according to some (unstated) mathematical criterion.

The first of this series of figures (fig. 21.4) shows the means of various conditional RVs for y that might have been developed from a bivariate RV whose two dimensions were independent. At any rate, we see immediately that knowing x will not help in predicting y—all the conditional RVs for y have the same means. The "best" regression line, while it fits these means perfectly, is *horizontal*, and that implies that it is a regression line that will yield the *same* predicted value for y for each and every value of x. A horizontal regression line thus *always* indicates the presence of a bivariate situation where *linear* prediction is, in general, ineffective. (Other curvilinear predictions, however, may be good and even perfect, as we shall see.) Furthermore, knowing x will not improve the *precision* of our guess; the scatter of any one RV for y is the same (why?). In this example, the correlation coefficient has the value 0. We shall not discuss the basis for that conclusion until a later section of this chapter, but merely note that the value 0 for ρ indicates that linear prediction is as poor as it can be in a given case.

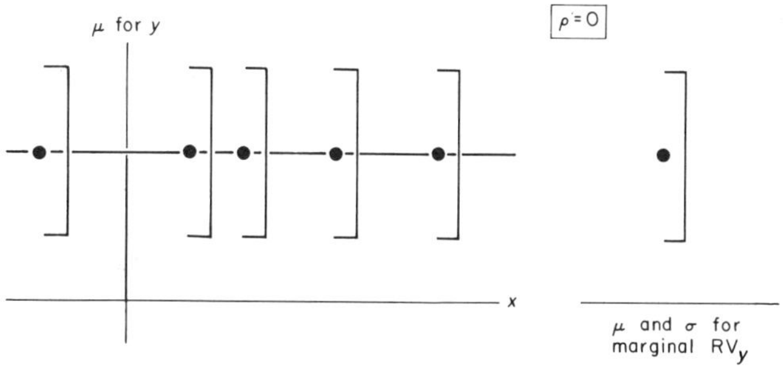

FIGURE 21.4 No linear prediction is possible (x and y independent)

Figure 21.5 illustrates a situation very much like that shown in figure 21.4, except that certain conditional RVs for y have a standard deviation that is different from that of the unconditional RV for y. We see that by examining the brackets. In this case, while knowing x will in some instances enable us to improve the *precision* of our guess, knowing x still will not induce us to *change the value* of our predicted guess for y. The regression line is still horizontal, and the value of the correlation coefficient is still 0. Linear prediction is completely ineffective.

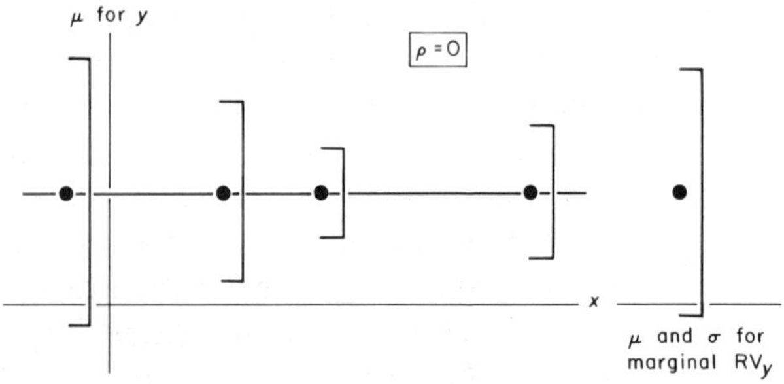

FIGURE 21.5 No linear prediction is possible

Figure 21.6 shows a situation where the means of the conditional RVs for y follow a straight-line pattern exactly. In this example, knowing x *will* induce us to change our unconditional guess for y. This is indicated on the graph by a regression line that is not horizontal. It has a *slope*; therefore, different values of x imply different "best guesses" for y according to our linear regression procedure. Prediction is not yet perfect, however, even though the means of the conditional RVs do fall along a straight line exactly. The reason is that for any one conditional RV for y, y still displays some scatter about the mean of its probability distribution. That is indicated in figure 21.6 by the presence of brackets in each of the conditional RVs. Thus, even if we knew the value of x that had been obtained on a given bivariate trial, there still would be some remaining uncertainty about the value of y on

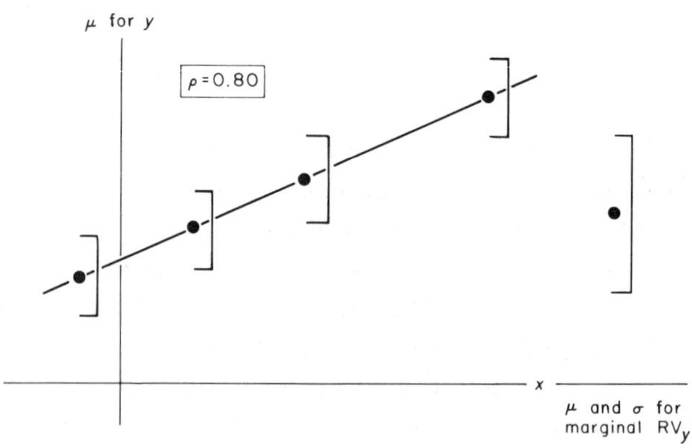

FIGURE 21.6 Good linear prediction

that trial, and that would detract from the goodness of linear prediction. Linear prediction now is moderately good; ρ may have a value of about 0.8.

Figure 21.7 represents the ideal case for using linear regression methods. Linear prediction will be perfect, because (1) all the conditional RV means lie on a straight line, exactly; and (2) each of the conditional RVs has zero variability or scatter—the absence of brackets indicates that for each conditional RV, $\sigma = 0$. In this example, if we know the value of x obtained on a given trial, linear regression will enable us to predict y exactly. Linear prediction is perfect, and the correlation coefficient is exactly +1.0. The *sign* of ρ only indicates the direction of the *slope* of the correlation line. A correlation coefficient of −1.0 also indicates perfect linear prediction; a minus sign merely indicates that one has a bivariate situation where the regression line slants from the upper left to the lower right, rather than, as in figure 21.7, from the lower left to the upper right.

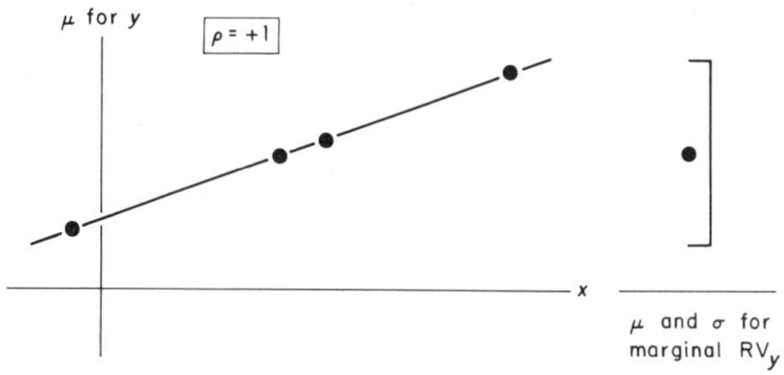

FIGURE 21.7 Perfect linear prediction

Figure 21.8 represents a situation where *perfect prediction* of y from x is still possible, because the standard deviation of each conditional RV for y is still 0. Therefore, if we know what value had been obtained for x, we are able to predict y with utter certainty. However, linear prediction is now very poor, because the means of these conditional RVs absolutely fail to fall along a straight nonhorizontal line. The regression line is once again horizontal, indicating that a change in x will *not* induce us to change our "best guess" for y *if we use linear regression*. The correlation coefficient in this example is 0. Even though we can predict y *perfectly* from x (were we to use the appropriate "non-linear" regression curve), if we attempt this prediction by using a *straight* regression line, we shall perform very poorly.

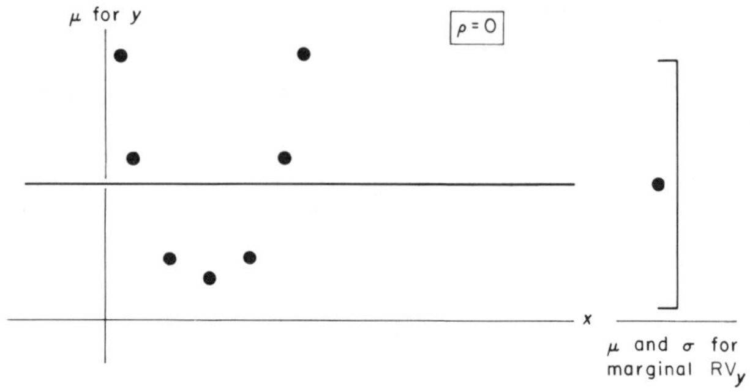

FIGURE 21.8 No linear prediction is possible (perfect curvilinear prediction)

Figure 21.9 illustrates another instance of a situation in which linear prediction is very poor. In this case, it is poor for an additional reason. We see that the means of the conditional RVs depart drastically from a straight-line pattern; *in addition*, there is a great deal of variability for y at any given value of x—the standard deviations of the conditional RVs are quite large. The "best" straight regression line is once more horizontal. The correlation coefficient in this case would also be 0.

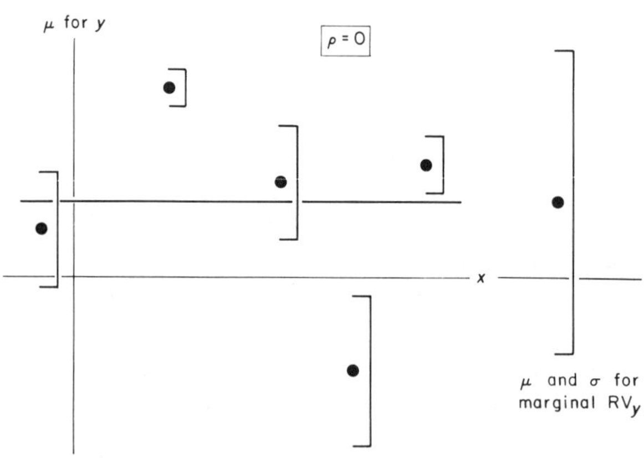

FIGURE 21.9 No linear prediction is possible

The last example (fig. 21.10) represents a situation that is quite typical. Prediction by linear regression is quite good, but it is less

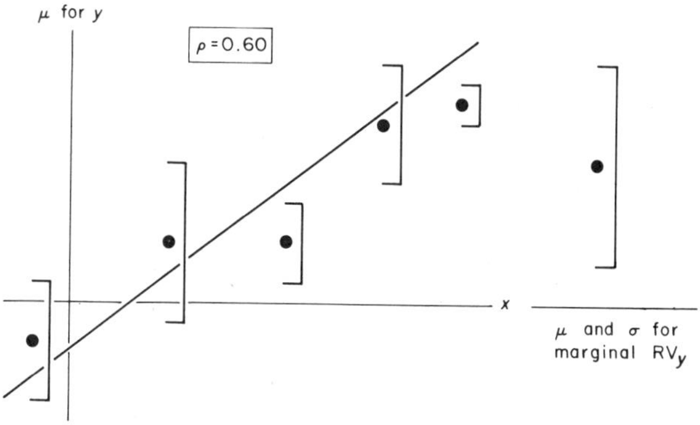

FIGURE 21.10 Moderately good linear prediction is possible

than perfect, for two reasons. First, while the means of the conditional RVs do fall reasonably close to a sloping straight line, they do not form an exact straight-line pattern. Second, y exhibits some dispersion within each conditional RV; these RVs have nonzero σ's. In this case, the value of ρ might be approximately $+0.6$. We should note once again the meaning of the *algebraic sign* of ρ: it only concerns the *slope* of the regression line and says nothing about the goodness of prediction. That is indicated solely by the absolute value of ρ (ignoring the sign of ρ). That is, $+0.60$ and -0.60 would indicate the same goodness of linear prediction. More generally, if a is a positive number between 0 and $+1$, and if two bivariate situations have correlation coefficients of $+a$ and $-a$, respectively, then that means that for these two RVs, prediction by linear regression will be equally effective (or equally ineffective). The closer a is to the value 1 (the closer the absolute value of ρ is to 1), the more effective is prediction by linear regression.

The preceding considerations demonstrate that the interpretation of the magnitude of a correlation coefficient is not a straightforward matter. If ρ is $+1$ or -1, the case is clear: the means of all the conditional RVs lie on a straight, sloping (nonhorizontal) line exactly, *and* each conditional RV has a zero standard deviation (and variance). Perfect prediction is then possible by using a straight regression line of y on x. If, however, ρ is not ± 1.0, then the meaning of that kind of intermediate value is not clear. The correlation coefficient may differ from ± 1 for one or both of two different reasons: (1) the means of the conditional RVs may fail to fall into a perfect, nonhorizontal straight-line pattern (figs. 21.4, 21.5, 21.8-21.10); and/or (2) the conditional RVs exhibit scatter—i.e., they have nonzero variances or standard deviations (figs. 21.4-21.6, 21.9, 21.10). In a given instance, one cannot tell from the value of ρ alone which of these factors, or what mixture of these, exists. In that sense, the meaning of a specific value of ρ is ambiguous (except for the two extreme values, ± 1).

We should mention one matter that has been skirted so far, namely, the matter of the "best" regression line. We had conducted the previous discussions with reference to that kind of line, tacitly assuming that it had somehow been available. We shall now consider what we mean by a "best" regression line, and how it is specified.

It should come as no surprise that "best" implies a criterion and a choice; different criteria may lead to different "best" regression lines. We shall continue to apply the least-squares criterion introduced earlier in this chapter. We shall now apply it with reference to the error in linear prediction, in the following way. Let us assume that we have a bivariate RV, and wish to predict y from x on each trial by means of linear regression. We specify a regression line that has the general form $y = ax + b$, where a and b are two constants whose values we are free to select; a given selection specifies a particular regression line. We now use that line: after each trial of the "big" RV, we look at the value of x obtained on that trial, and predict the value of y from the regression line. We then look at the actual value of y obtained on that trial, and observe the error committed on that trial—the difference between the predicted and observed value of y. Next, we square that error. Finally, in a series of repeated trials, we average these squares of the errors. There will be *one* particular pair of values for the constants a and b that will define the one line that will minimize that average of squared errors in the long run: that is the "best" line according to the least-squares criterion.

Mathematical techniques allow one to translate this approach into quantitative specifications. For a given bivariate RV, the regression line that is best according to the mean-squares error criterion is the line whose coefficients can be determined from certain parameters of that RV—specifically, from the means and variances of the two marginal RVs—and by its correlation coefficient, the standardized covariance (Freeman, p. 58; Hays, p. 638). Thus, the correlation coefficient is an ingredient in the specification of the regression line that is best in the least-squares sense. For a given RV, ρ will enter into the specification of either one of the two "best" regression lines—the regression line of y on x, or that of x on y. (These are usually different—compare figs. 21.1 and 21.2, for example.)

We have become familiar with some of the qualitative ideas pertaining to the correlation coefficient and linear regression. We shall next deepen our understanding of these topics by considering bivariate RVs from a somewhat different perspective.

The Partitioning of the Variance

The central issue will be the origins of the variability of one or the other dimension of a bivariate RV. It would be best to present the discussion in mathematical terms (see Freeman, pp. 54-57, 61), but unfortunately that approach is beyond our scope. We shall have to rely on a more intuitive, qualitative development.

Let us consider one dimension of a bivariate RV, say, y. (As usual, we could just as well have elected to conduct the discussion in terms of the other dimension x; the choice is arbitrary.) Let us first consider y by itself. That is, let us for the moment attend only to the value of y obtained on a trial of a bivariate RV, ignoring x, the other value in the ordered pair. In a typical RV, y will display some dispersion; its value will not be the same on every trial. That dispersion can be quantified by a variance, of course. Specifically, it is $\sigma^2{}_y$, *the variance of the marginal or unconditional RV for* y, that measures and indicates the amount of dispersion of y about the mean of its univariate pf, RV_Y. All this ought to be quite familiar from many previous discussions.

When we introduce x into the picture, other factors come into play and can be analyzed. We know that if on some trial we obtain a specific value of x, then there is a corresponding specific pf that describes the statistical behavior of y under these circumstances;

that pf is, of course, the RV for y that is conditional on the specific value obtained for x. Unless the variance of that conditional RV happens to be 0, y will display some dispersion about the mean of that conditional pf. That is, on the single trial we have been discussing, it will in general not be possible to predict y with complete certainty when we have looked at x only. Furthermore, and this is one of the important points, the dispersion of y may in that situation be *relatively* large or small—"relatively" meaning, in this instance, in comparison with the dispersion of the *marginal* or *unconditional* pf for y, in comparison with *the total dispersion* of y. For example, if we examine our previous figures, we see that in some cases (figs. 21.4 and 21.5), most if not all of the variances of the *conditional* RVs for y are about as large as the variance of the *unconditional* variance; in other cases, the variances may be considerably smaller (figs. 21.6, 21.9, and 21.10), or even 0 in some cases (figs. 21.7 and 21.8).

Thus, y may exhibit dispersion about its mean when we know a specific value of x (figs. 21.4-21.6, 21.9, 21.10), or it may not (figs. 21.7 and 21.8). If y does exhibit that kind of dispersion, if in a given bivariate RV at least some of the variances of the conditional RVs are nonzero, y can be viewed as having a dispersion that occurs "regardless of x"; it occurs *within* a conditional pf, when x is constant. In that sense, one could say that this is the kind of dispersion or variation in y THAT IS NOT ACCOUNTED FOR by changes in x—the portion of the variance of y that "is unexplained by x."

What about the remaining portion of σ^2_y, the total variance of y? The other, second kind of contribution arises from a source that is quite different conceptually from the first kind: it is contributed by differences (if any) that exist *between* the *means* of the conditional RVs for y.[4] Let us introduce that idea by an example. For each of the hypothetical RVs shown in figures 21.7 and 21.8, the variances of *all* the conditional RVs for y are 0 (no square brackets are indicated). For a given value of x, y exhibits no variation

[4]If the terminology reminds you of ANOVA, it should; these relationships and the notion of partitioning of variances are the core of ANOVA procedures. A detailed consideration of the relationships between the topics we are considering now and ANOVA would take us too far afield.

whatsoever; there is no dispersion "within" these conditional RVs. Hence, if y *does* vary from trial to trial of the bivariate RV, that must be because different values of x are being obtained. The typical bivariate case would not be quite as extreme, but figures 21.7 and 21.8 are useful examples because they illustrate the "pure" case—a bivariate RV where *all* the variation in y occurs only in conjunction with variations in x.

The previous examples illustrate the second source of the variation in y: the dispersion that IS ACCOUNTED FOR or "explained by" variations in x. Thus, in those bivariate RVs where the expected value or mean of y *does* depend on x (in the previous figures, all cases except figs. 21.4 and 21.5), that difference between the means of the conditional RVs for y will "explain" at least some portion of the total variation in y.

We conclude that if the total variance of y has the magnitude σ^2_y, then some percentage of that quantity, say $A\%$, will be "accounted for" by the dispersion of y *within* one or more of its conditional probability distributions, while the remaining percentage, say, $B\%$, will be "accounted for" by variations *between* the means of those conditional RVs.

For any one given bivariate RV, A and B will have specific values; these can range from 0 to 100%, inclusive, with only the restriction that $(A + B) = 100\%$, naturally. Thus, in a given instance, the variation in y may be completely accounted for by one or the other kind of variation, or by some mixture of the two kinds. One says that the variance of y (or x) can be *partitioned* or divided into two distinct, different parts. Let us note explicitly that this partition is a very general concept and not restricted to the topic of linear regression.

The correlation coefficient and linear regression enter into this already complex picture as additional complicating factors. We shall explain their role informally and only quasi-quantitatively. We must consider one more partition of σ^2_y. It is a further partitioning of B, the contribution to σ^2_y that arises when all the means of the conditional RVs for y are not equal to one another. If B is nonzero, it may be subdivided into (1) a portion related to the *straight-line* pattern of the means of the conditional RVs, and (2) a portion related to the *curvilinear* (or "nonlinear") pattern of those means. Let us represent the two percentages resulting from this new partition as B_1 and B_2. Both are part of B and thus are measures of variations in y that originate in variations between the means of the conditional RVs for y. As we shall see from a number of examples, B may be composed of B_1 only, B_2 only, or some mixture; in any event, $(B_1 + B_2)$ must add to $B\%$. We now finally can relate the size of the correlation coefficient to our previous discussion: the magnitude of B_1 (expressed as a decimal) is equal to the magnitude $(\rho)^2$, the *square* of the correlation coefficient. The correlation coefficient tells us how much of the total variation in y, what proportion of $\sigma^2{}_y$, is associated with LINEAR *variations between the means* of the conditional RVs. It tells us the magnitude of B_1, but—and this is an important point—it does *not* tell us how the remaining percentage of $\sigma^2{}_y$ is apportioned between A and B_2! That is, if we only know B_1 (and thus, ρ), then all we are able to conclude is that the remaining percentage of $\sigma^2{}_y$, or $(1 - B_1)\%$, is somehow distributed between A and B_2, the variations within and the "nonlinear" variations between. That, basically, is the reason for a certain ambiguity in the information furnished by ρ. Let us examine these matters with reference to our previous illustrative RVs shown in figures 21.4 through 21.10.

In figures 21.4 and 21.5, there are no variations "between." All the means of the conditional RVs have the same value. Therefore, A is 100%, and B is 0; of course, since B_1 and B_2 are the two components of a 0 quantity, they are 0 as well (percentages cannot be negative). Furthermore, since as we have explained $\rho^2 = B_1$, ρ in this case must be 0 also.

In figure 21.6, we see both kinds of dispersions of y. Let us assume that 35% of $\sigma^2{}_y$ is accounted for by "variations within"—A is 35%. B then must be 65%. How much of that amount of $\sigma^2{}_y$ is due to *straight-line* variations in the means of the conditional RVs of y? All the means lie on a straight, nonhorizontal line; therefore, all of B is B_1. If B_1 is 65%, then $\rho^2 = 0.65$, and $\rho = 0.8$, approximately. (If $\rho^2 = B_1$, then from an algebraic standpoint, ρ could be either positive or negative. For a given RV, we identify whether $\rho = +\sqrt{B_1}$ or $-\sqrt{B_1}$ by noting the slope of the pattern of the means of the conditional RVs. Alternatively, if we calculate ρ

directly from a given RV—a procedure we shall not discuss—we automatically obtain the correct sign for ρ.)

In figure 21.7, there is no variation "within." A is 0, and B is 100%. Furthermore, since *all* the means of the conditional RVs lie exactly on a straight line, *all* of B is accounted for by B_1; B_1 is 100% or 1.00. Thus, $\rho^2 = 1.0$, and $\rho = +1$. (If the line containing the means were to slope in the other direction, then ρ would be -1.)

In figure 21.8, there still is no dispersion "within." A remains 0, and B is 100%. Now, however, the means of the conditional RVs do not follow a straight-line pattern at all. Therefore, all of B is accounted for by B_2. B_1 is 0, and so is ρ.

Figure 21.9 shows a mixture of A and B. We see that there is dispersion within at least some (in this example, within all) of the conditional RVs for y. Let us say that these account for approximately 40% of $\sigma^2{}_y$; A is 40%. B is 60%. As in the previous case, the means fail to exhibit any semblance of a straight-line pattern. Therefore, all of B is B_2; B_2 is 60% or 0.60, and B_1 and ρ each are 0.

In figure 21.10, A is approximately 30%. (We are deriving these numbers from a rough visual estimate.) The means lie fairly close to a straight line. Let us assume that half of B can be attributed to straight-line variations in the means of the conditional RVs for y; and the remainder, to nonlinear variations in these means. B_1 and B_2 each are one half of B, or 35%. Therefore, $\rho^2 = 0.35$, and $\rho = 0.6$, approximately.

We may use this last example as a reminder that we *cannot* work backward from ρ and/or B_1 to specific values of A and B_2. If we only know the value of ρ—in this case, 0.6—and thus know that the value of ρ^2 or B_1 is approximately 0.35, can we specify the remaining partitions of $\sigma^2{}_y$? We cannot; all that we can say is that the other two components of $\sigma^2{}_y$, A and B_2, must add to 65%. There are two extreme cases possible. At one extreme, A may be 65% and B_2 may be 0; there is variation within, but all the means lie exactly on a straight nonhorizontal line. At the other extreme A may be 0 and B_2 may be 65%; there is no variation within, but the means depart significantly from a straight-line pattern. In either of these cases, ρ would be 0.6. We see that the case illustrated in figure 21.10 falls somewhere between the two extremes. Thus, there are an infinite number of possible cases that each would give rise to a ρ of 0.6. We have identified the two limiting, extreme cases, and an intermediate case. The ambiguity of ρ should now be more understandable.

This completes our exposition of the correlation coefficient of an RV. The final portions of this chapter will present a brief discussion of a statistic that is closely related to ρ, and some concluding comments concerning the differences between regression and correlation methods.

The Sample Correlation Coefficient

We had learned earlier (chaps. 7 and 8) that although RV parameters can be defined solely in terms of probability distributions, parameters can also be defined in terms of a long-term average. A long-term average is a mathematical idealization, a useful fiction based on an extension of an actual, "short-term" average of a set of N terms; see, for example, (21.3). In a number of instances, these short-term averages not only lead to a long-term average, but also in themselves define a *statistic*. We have had several examples of this kind of situation. The mean μ and the variance σ^2 each can be defined as long-term averages that are extensions of short-term averages that define the sample mean M and the sample variance S^2, respectively. Thus, there is a natural affinity between certain statistics and corresponding parameters. Typically, this pairing also implies that the statistic in such an allied pair can serve as an estimator of the corresponding parameter. We have seen that this is true for M and μ, and for S^2 and σ^2 (although S^2 is a biased estimator; see chap. 15).

This pairing is relevant to the correlation coefficient, even though ρ is not quite a parameter. There is a "paired" statistic that corresponds to ρ. It is called the *sample correlation coefficient*, and usually is represented by the letter r. Like M for μ, and S^2 for σ^2, r provides an *estimator* for ρ, the "quasi-parameter" of an RV.

The sample correlation coefficient is a statistic that is defined and calculated by means of the following procedure. We start with a set of N sample values generated by some RV_P, as usual. In this case, however, the RV is a "big," i.e., bivariate, RV, and the set of sample values is a set of N ordered pairs. We thus begin with a situation that has already been proposed when we developed the concept of the covariance. We start, then, with a set of N ordered pairs of the form $(x_1, y_1), (x_2, y_2), \ldots, (x_N, y_N)$. Next, we "split" each ordered pair into its two component numbers, and gather two sets of N terms: $(x_1, x_2, \ldots, x_N)$, and $(y_1, y_2, \ldots, y_N)$. We now in effect have two sets of ordinary, univariate sample values (except that each number in one set has an identified, corresponding counterpart in the other set). From these two sets of N outcome values we can form the two sample means M_x and M_y, and the two sample variances $S^2{}_x$ and $S^2{}_y$, in the usual fashion. We can also construct a new kind of statistic; we can compute the two *sample standard deviations* S_x and S_y. We have not previously met these, but they are defined in the obvious way: the sample standard deviation of a set of N sample values is simply the square root of the sample variance S^2. Thus, $S_x = \sqrt{S^2{}_x}$, and $S_y = \sqrt{S^2{}_y}$. As we might have expected, these sample standard deviations are "paired with" the corresponding RV standard deviations (parameters).

We now have N sample values of x, N sample values of y, and the statistics M_x and M_y, $S^2{}_x$ and $S^2{}_y$, and S_x and S_y. The next step in computing the sample correlation coefficient r is to form an average that is almost identical to the average in (21.3), the equation that had provided the point of departure for constructing the covariance and the correlation coefficient. We form the average

$$\frac{\begin{array}{c}(x_1 - M_x) \times (y_1 - M_y) + (x_2 - M_x) \times (y_2 - M_y) \\ + \ldots + (x_N - M_x) \times (y_N - M_y)\end{array}}{N} \quad . \tag{21.5}$$

The only difference between this average and the corresponding expression in (21.3) is that we now are using the sample means M_x and M_y instead of the RV parameters μ_x and μ_y. In other words, we are using estimators (or statistics) rather than actual parameter values in the numerator.

The last step parallels the step we had taken to "standardize" the covariance (21.4). We "standardize" (21.5) by dividing that average by the product of two standard deviations. In this case, however, these are the statistics S_x and S_y, rather than, as previously, the parameters σ_x and σ_y. Just as we had used estimators for μ_x and μ_y in (21.5), we shall now use estimators for σ_x and σ_y in the calculation that parallels (21.4). We "pseudostandardize" the average in (21.5) by dividing by statistics instead of by parameters, and obtain the statistic r, the sample correlation coefficient:

$$r = \frac{\begin{array}{c}(x_1 - M_x) \times (y_1 - M_y) + (x_2 - M_x) \times (y_2 - M_y) \\ + \ldots + (x_N - M_x) \times (y_N - M_y)\end{array}}{(N) \times (S_x) \times (S_y)} . \tag{21.6}$$

There is much more that could be said about this important statistic, but we shall limit ourselves to a brief observation about the conceptualization of r as the outcome value obtained from an RV trial. We can invoke our familiar logical structure and assert that if a bivariate RV_P has generated a set of N ordered pairs as sample values, and if we view the procedure in (21.6) as one that reduces that set of sample values to a single number, the statistic r, then there must be some RV_D that underlies that statistic. That underlying probability distribution must be jointly determined by the specific characteristics of the joint, bivariate RV_P and the procedure (21.6) that reduces a set of data to a single value. RV_D for r is, of course, a univariate RV_D, in principle just like any other RV_D that underlies a statistic.

In general, the relationship between the specific form of RV_P and the corresponding form of RV_D for r is quite involved. As a matter of fact, the analysis of this relationship has been accomplished only for a few specific kinds of bivariate RV_P profiles (see Walker, 1940, p. 262; Hays, pp. 661-667).

Differences Between Regression and Correlation Methods

The preceding discussion provides the basic conceptual ingredients of prediction procedures. There is, however, an important extramathematical distinction that is made in the behavioral disciplines, namely, the distinction between regression and correlation methodologies (Hays, pp. 618-620). Both are rooted in the same mathematical techniques, but the point of view differs. It is a matter of *interpretation*—a concept we shall explore further in the next chapter. Regression usually implies a certain kind of asymmetry between the two dimensions of a bivariate RV. Typically, if we speak about the regression of y on x, for example, we are implying an extramathematical dependence of y on x. That is, we usually treat one dimension as the independent variable; and the other, as the dependent variable.[5] We conceptualize these as the kinds of situations in which one dimension, say, x can be manipulated experimentally, and the results of these manipulations are observed. For example, if we were studying the relationships between food intake and body weight, we would consider food as the variable that is manipulated and body weight as the dependent variable that reflects the results of those manipulations. If we represent intake by x and weight by y, then to study the mathematical relationships between the independent and dependent variable, we would construct a regression line *of y on x*. We would conceptualize body weight as being affected by food intake—in other words, causality, an extramathematical concept, has entered the scene.

Correlation methods, in contrast, imply that two variables are treated symmetrically. Linear (or curvilinear) regression in that case does *not* carry any causal implications. For example, one might find that the amount of annual rainfall and certain economic indicators are linearly related. That finding would presumably carry no direct implications about causal relationships between these two entities. The presence of a nonzero ρ merely would indicate that it is possible to describe the relationships between these two kinds of quantities mathematically by a linear specifica-

[5]The terms "dependent" and "independent" are now being used in the same sense as in chapter 13. They pertain to distinctions between types of variables in an algebraic equation. This is an entirely different usage of these terms from that in chapter 20. This dual usage is unfortunate, but the sense in which these terms are being used in a given instance is usually quite apparent from the subject matter. Discussions that use the terms in the sense of chapter 13 usually concern algebra, equations, and the like; frequently, a dependent variable is contrasted with one or more independent variables (see chapter 13, and the discussion pertaining to equation 13.1). When the terms are used as they had been in chapter 20, the discussion is typically statistical in nature. Furthermore, in that kind of usage, two variables may both be dependent, or they may both be independent. As we learned in chapter 20, statistical dependence is a mutual, reciprocal, bilateral relationship.

tion. That specification could be used indifferently in either direction, without causal implications.

Correlation, regression, and the entities involved in these methodologies cover a great deal of material. We have been able to introduce only the most basic, general features that characterize this subject matter. Many details remain to be filled in; the voluminous literature on these subjects attests to that.

PROBLEMS

21.1 If you apply the least-squares criterion, what is the best outcome value to guess before a trial of a univariate RV?

21.2 About which RV parameter do outcome values tend to cluster? Which parameter provides an index of the degree of that clustering?

21.3 In a given bivariate RV, x and y are independent. Why does knowing the value of x obtained in a given trial fail to provide information about the expected value of y?

21.4 For the joint frequency data matrix in table 20.9, what would be the best value to guess for x, in general? What would it be if you knew that the result of a bivariate trial had been the ordered pair $(x, 3)$ (x unknown)?

21.5 What is a regression line? How is it used?

21.6 A regression line of y on x is horizontal. What does that tell you about predicting y from x?

21.7 A regression line of y on x is almost horizontal. On the basis of that information alone, can you evaluate how good a prediction of y can be obtained from x? [Hint: what do you know about the total range of x?]

21.8 Is the covariance a parameter? Is the correlation coefficient? Explain and discuss your answers.

21.9 In a bivariate pf, what are the two principal characteristics of the conditional pfs that affect the magnitude of ρ?

21.10 In general, what is the difference between a pf for which $\rho = -0.40$ and one for which $\rho = +0.40$?

21.11 What values can (a) the covariance, and (b) the correlation coefficient ρ, assume?

21.12 In what sense is the information that $\rho = 0.48$ ambiguous?

21.13 Describe a bivariate RV for which $\rho = -1.00$.

21.14 For bivariate RVs, what are the two extreme cases that each lead to a value of $\rho = 0$? [Hint: if B_1 is 0, what are the extreme values that A and B_2 may assume?] Sketch the two cases, using our usual method.

21.15 For a joint pf, what does "partitioning the variance of one of its dimensions" mean?

21.16 For one dimension of a bivariate RV, what two different kinds of variance constitute the components of the unconditional variance?

21.17 One particular conditional pf for x has a variance of 15. Does that quantity represent a variation in x that is "accounted for" by a variation in y, or does it not? Explain your answer.

21.18 In a given joint pf, 30% of $\sigma^2{}_x$ is accounted for by the dispersion within the conditional pfs.

(a) What accounts for the remaining percentage of $\sigma^2{}_x$?

(b) What is the largest value that ρ could have in this case?

(c) What is the smallest value that ρ could have in this case?

21.19 Describe and discuss the three components of the variance that have been called A, B_1, and B_2 in this chapter. Which of these indicates the magnitude of ρ?

21.20 What is the principal conceptual difference between ρ and r?

21.21 Is the concept of causality relevant to correlation? To regression? Discuss your answer.

CHAPTER 22

Bayesian Approaches

The Bayesian approaches that we shall explore in this chapter are important to contemporary statistics and therefore of interest in their own right. In addition, a consideration of these methods can serve to illuminate the distinction between intra- and extra-mathematical concerns, and enrich and solidify our grasp of the bivariate probabilistic framework in general.

General Issues

The mathematical basis of Bayesian approaches is Bayes's Theorem or Bayes's Rule (after the Reverend Thomas Bayes, 1702-61), a mathematical relationship that is "a simple and fundamental fact about probability" (Edwards et al., 1963, p. 193), "a true and trivial fact, or constellation of facts" (Savage, 1962, p. 162), a relationship that is "mathematically incontrovertible" (Freeman, 1963, p. 223). Nevertheless, one finds the Bayesian approach referred to as a "pioneering and controversial system of estimation" (*ibid.*, p. 221); the system *is* controversial. How can a system be based on a trivially true mathematical fact, yet engender continuing controversy? The answer is that the controversial issues are extramathematical rather than intramathematical in nature. Intramathematical issues pertain primarily or even exclusively to matters that can be addressed and resolved within a logical system of mathematics. They might, for example, concern the legitimacy of certain mathematical operations.[1] Extramathe-

[1]One example would be the use of the so-called *delta function* in operational calculus. At one time, this kind of a function was considered controversial; and

matical concerns, on the other hand, pertain to the relationship between mathematical procedures and their real-world referents. These are issues one might call issues of *interpretation;* they pertain to problematic aspects of the relationships between mathematical formalisms that are beyond dispute and the empirical events that the mathematics purports to represent.

We have briefly met several extramathematical issues in passing. For example, in the course of introducing tests of significance (chap. 13), I mentioned that there were extramathematical controversies concerning the use of directional against nondirectional tests of significance. The internal, narrowly mathematical issues pertaining to these tests are beyond question; one sets a level of α, chooses between a one- or a two-tailed test of significance, specifies critical values for a given RV_D, and so on. The controversial issues go beyond these mathematical procedures. For example, some statisticians claim that whether or not a directional test is appropriate in a given instance depends on the kinds of results obtained in previous, earlier experimental studies (Kirk, p. 279). Another example of an extramathematical issue is the treatment of numbers obtained by empirical measurements. Some statisticians tend to be more liberal, and act on the premise that most experimentally generated numbers may be treated as ordinary numbers. That is, persons with this orientation maintain that it is legitimate to perform the usual mathematical operations (addition, subtraction, multiplication, division, raising to a power, taking square roots, etc.) with just about any kind of experimentally acquired numbers. More conservative investigators would be inclined to limit the application of such operations, restricting them to empirical data that demonstrably conform to certain mathematical requirements or critieria (Kirk, pp. 47-80).

The controversial aspects of the Bayesian procedures seem to be primarily extramathematical. The controversies concern the legitimacy of making certain assumptions, and not the legitimacy of the mathematical procedures themselves. An example would

its use, possibly illegitimate. By now, delta functions are widely used and have been placed on a firm theoretical base. For that matter, the use of calculus itself was initially highly controversial.

be the question of whether it is legitimate to treat a parameter as an outcome value of an RV. In the more classical, conservative view, a parameter has some particular, "true" value, and no other; according to that view, it therefore is senseless or worse to speak about probability assigned to a "constant." The opposing view contends that if it is convenient to treat a parameter as a quantity that has an underlying probability distribution, then, why not do so? This latter view is a typical example of the philosophy espoused by practitioners of Bayesian approaches. Mathematical procedures are viewed in a somewhat casual light. The emphasis is on the practical consequences of the mathematical formalism, rather than on the rigor of the logical foundations. A good example of the differences between the Bayesian and more "classical" approaches is the difference in their conception of probability. The classical approach seeks to define probability in a rigorous fashion. The definition is based either on an abstract system of axioms, or on some procedures that are clearly related to objectively obtained empirical data (see Freeman, chap. 1). In contrast, the Bayesian view of probability includes a subjective or "personal" component. As we shall presently see, a characteristic step in Bayesian procedures involves the assignment of probabilties on the basis of subjective opinion. To Bayesians, if other information is unavailable, it is legitimate to assign probability values on the basis of subjective conviction. Probability then reflects what one would be willing to risk or bet in a given situation; it is clearly allied to decision-making, taking action when there is less than complete statistical information. Bayesians sometimes argue that it is better to go ahead with a less-than-ideal mathematical foundation than not to act at all. "Probability is orderly opinion, and . . . inference from data is nothing other than the revision of such opinion in the light of relevant new information" (Edwards et al., p. 194).

The point of this discussion has not been to advocate one or the other position, but rather to illustrate the way in which extra-mathematical issues become relevant to statistical methods. Let us next look at a simple example of a Bayesian procedure to see how subjective opinion combines with a "mathematically incontrovertible" rule.

Bayes's Rule and Its Application

We shall discuss one kind of Bayesian approach in terms of a contrived bivariate RV situation. While it may be possible to follow the general line of argument without additional preparation, a clear understanding of the matters to be presented would be greatly facilitated by mastery of the material presented in Appendix C. The mathematical results that are developed there will not be repeated here.

Let us continue to use a hypothetical experimental situation in which there are two different types of academic or similar tests available. We shall assume that the first test can yield one of five scores: 10, 20, 30, 40, or 50; we shall assign this score to the first dimension, x, of a bivariate RV. The second test can yield one of three scores: 2, 4, or 6; it will be assigned to the second dimension, y, of that RV. Thus, if we administer the pair of tests to any one subject, we shall obtain the ordered pair (x, y) as the result of that one "trial of the experiment." There are several other assumptions we need to make. We shall assume that the first test is considerably easier to administer than the second. Although in the present example that may seem contrived, it does represent a situation that is frequently encountered in practice. The second "score" may not even be an actual test score, but some other, formally similar measure that is difficult to obtain empirically.

Next, we shall assume that through some legitimate, unquestionably valid methods, we had been able to obtain all three *conditional* probability functions for x, one for each value of y. These are shown in table 22.1. Let us remember that each of these three conditional probability functions is an ordinary univariate RV for x, the only difference being that a conditional probability function points to a bivariate ancestry. Thus, each of the three conditional pfs in table 22.1 are *bona fide* discrete probability distributions. Their graphs are shown in figure 22.1, and we see their ordinary univariate character displayed. We are assuming that the statistical information they contain is entirely legitimate and valid. So far, the situation is beyond controversy.

The next step, however, does introduce controversial issues. What we should like to do is the following. We should like to

Table 22.1

Three conditional pfs for x

Conditional on:	x = 10	20	30	40	50
$y = 2$	0.3	.3	.2	.1	.1
$y = 4$	.1	.1	.4	.1	.1
$y = 6$	.1	.1	.1	.5	.2

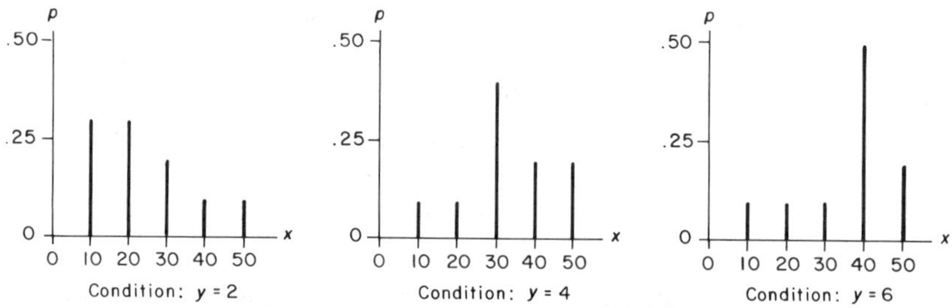

FIGURE 22.1 Three conditional pfs for x

invert the information in table 22.1, and convert it into a set of conditional RVs for y. The motivation for this step arises from the presumed ease of administering test x and difficulty of administering test y. Because of that difference in ease of administration, we should like to have a set of conditional RVs for y, one for each value of x. The reason should be apparent from the discussions in chapter 21; unless x and y happen to be independent, knowing an x value will in general enhance our statistical knowledge about y. If we do *not* have these conditional pfs for y, then, if we measure x for a given subject (easy), we shall thereby fail to take advantage of any new statistical information about the corresponding measure of y (difficult). If, however, we *do* have a set of conditional pfs for y, measuring x will provide a basis for improving the estimate of the corresponding value for y.

All we need to do, then, is to convert the three conditional RVs for x in table 22.1 to five conditional RVs for y, one for each of the five possible values of x in the potential outcome of that first bivariate RV dimension. Can we invert these conditional probabilities in the desired fashion? The crux of the matter is that we cannot do so without ambiguity or uncertainty, as a simple illustration will demonstrate.

Let us consider the two different joint bivariate RVs specified in table 22.2, noting carefully that these are totally different kinds of mathematical entities from the kind of entities presented in table 22.1. The probabilities in table 22.2 are joint probabilities, and each of the two tabulations is a pf, the fundamental specification of *one bivariate RV* (see table 19.2); table 22.1, on the other hand, is a table of *three* different univariate RVs for x, *conditional* on three values of y.

Table 22.2

Two joint (bivariate) RVs

A

y \ x	10	20	30	40	50
2	0.06	.06	.04	.02	.02
4	.07	.07	.28	.14	.14
6	.01	.01	.01	.05	.02

B

y \ x	10	20	30	40	50
2	0.03	.03	.02	.01	.01
4	.01	.01	.04	.03	.02
6	.08	.08	.08	.40	.16

We see that the two bivariate pfs specified in table 22.2 are quite different from one another. There are obvious differences between corresponding joint probabilities assigned to any one of the 15 possible sets of ordered pairs. For example, table 22.2A assigns a joint probability of .01 to (20, 6), while table 22.2B assigns a joint probability of .08 to that same ordered pair (outcome value). If we apply the methods developed in Appendix C, however, we shall find that although these two bivariate RVs are drastically different from one another, they each give rise to *exactly* the same set of conditional RVs for x—specifically, the three RVs specified in table 22.1. This illustrates the point made in the preceding chapters. A joint pf is the basic, unambiguous specification of a bivariate RV; we can always derive a pair of marginal and a set of conditional RVs from the basic joint bivariate pf, and these univariate RVs are fully and unambiguously specified by that antecedent bivariate RV. The reverse is not at all true, however. From a set of conditional RVs alone, we *cannot* reason backward to obtain one uniquely specified joint bivariate RV, as is demonstrated in table 22.2. Any number of different bivariate joint RVs could have been the ancestors of the three marginal univariate RVs for x shown in table 22.1. Furthermore, again applying the methods developed in Appendix C, we should find that the set of five conditional RVs for y obtained from the joint RV in table 22.2A is significantly different from the corresponding set obtained from the bivariate probability distribution in table 22.2B.

Thus, from the specification of the three conditional probability distributions for x in table 22.1, we cannot uniquely recover the five conditional RVs for y that we are seeking to obtain.

If we do wish to obtain the conditional RVs for y, some further assumptions must be made, and this is where the controversial step occurs. What we must do is to assume some values for the *marginal* distribution for y. If we specify the unconditional RV for y, if we specify the probability values for each of the three outcome values (2, 4, 6) in the potential outcome of that second dimension, we can proceed by applying Bayes's Rule (or, equivalently, by applying the basic definition of conditional, joint, and marginal probabilities). We shall now be able to reconstruct a *unique* joint RV, and thus unique conditional RVs for y, from the three conditional RVs for x in table 22.1 and the *assumed* marginal RV for y. The controversy is over the specification of that marginal RV for y. According to the Bayesian approaches, an informed experimenter usually has a defensible subjective opinion about the unspecified marginal probability value. For example, an experimenter might be willing to risk certain odds in betting on the values of y, and these odds can be translated into marginal probabilities for y. That is the experimenter's prior, *a priori* information about y.

Let us look at the results of two different sets of personal opinions concerning the probability of y. We shall assume that investigator A believes that the three unconditional probabilities for $y = 2$, 4, and 6 are, respectively, 0.2, 0.7, and 0.1. Another investigator, B, assumes a different set of unconditional probabilities for these three outcome values, namely, 0.1, 0.1, and 0.8. (These were the two sets of assumptions from which the two sets of joint probability data in table 22.2 were obtained. You may verify the computations by applying the mathematical relationships developed in Appendix C to table 22.1.)

These two different sets of *a priori* assumptions about y will lead to two entirely different sets of five conditional RVs for y. Those two sets of pfs are compared in figure 22.2, and listed in table 22.3. (They are obtained by applying the results of Appendix

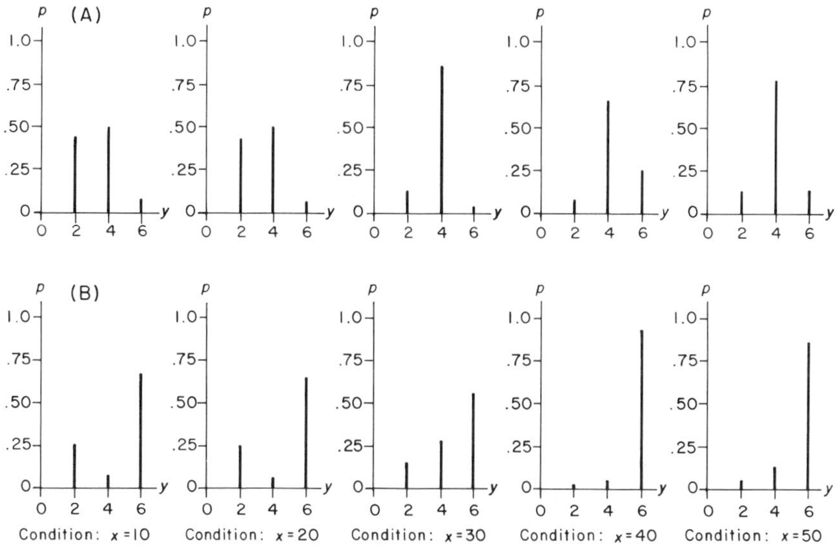

FIGURE 22.2 Two sets of five conditional pfs for y

C to table 22.2.) The two investigators, starting with the same three conditional RVs in table 22.1 and their own opinion about the marginal RV for y, will be led to different conclusions about y. For instance, if a subject obtains a test score of $x = 30$, investigator A will conclude that the most likely value of y for that

Table 22.3

Two sets of 5 conditional pfs for y

A

	Conditional on:				
y	$x = 10$	$x = 20$	$x = 30$	$x = 40$	$x = 50$
2	0.43	.43	.12	.09	.11
4	.50	.50	.85	.67	.78
6	.07	.07	.03	.24	.11

B

	Conditional on:				
y	$x = 10$	$x = 20$	$x = 30$	$x = 40$	$x = 50$
2	0.25	.25	.14	.02	.05
4	.08	.08	.29	.05	.11
6	.67	.67	.57	.93	.84

subject will be 4 (with a probability of 0.85) and the least likely value will be 6 (with a probability of 0.03), while investigator B will conclude that $y = 6$ is the most probable value (with a probability of 0.57) and that $y = 2$ is the least probable value (with a probability of 0.14). Their "posterior," *a posteriori* conclusions about y (after they know the x outcome value) will be different.

A Final Comment

This concludes our first tour through the RV framework. We have seen how several fundamentals—discrete and continuous probability distributions, mathematical data-reducing operations that convert a set of sample values to a statistic, the fact that an RV_D is jointly induced by an RV_P and a given data-reducing operation, and the extensions to the bivariate framework—can serve as a unifying and integrating conceptual framework or substructure for many apparently different topics and procedures.

A continued study of statistics based on an RV framework would comprise two major components. First, there are the many empirical ramifications that become relevant for "practical" applications of statistics. These have been only alluded to in the present work. Examples would be the subject matter classified under Issues in Experimental Design, or the kinds of issues we have called extramathematical, or a detailed study of the many kinds of inferential procedures that are elaborations of the basic approaches that we have investigated. The second component of the advanced study of statistics would be mathematics. Ideally, a knowledge of various advanced tools of mathematical analysis such as calculus, differential equations, and matrix methods becomes necessary if further competence in statistics is to be acquired.

If you pursue these two tracks of advanced study, you will find yourself returning to much of the material that has been introduced in this book. Although you will be passing through familiar territory, you will reconsider previously presented material in increasingly specific, detailed, and more deeply analytical ways. Familiar excerpts, methods, and issues should continually assume greater clarity and significance.

PROBLEMS

22.1 Why might one wish to invert a situation and obtain a set of pfs for y conditional on x, rather than use a set of available pfs for x conditional on y?

22.2 If one has a set of conditional pfs for x, why is it not possible to accomplish the inversion considered in problem 22.1

without making additional assumptions? What assumptions are needed?

22.3 If one has a joint pf available, does one need to make further assumptions before one can construct a set of conditional pfs for one or the other dimension? Discuss your answer.

22.4 In terms of the bivariate framework, what constitutes *a priori* information about one of the two dimensions? What constitutes *a posteriori* information about that dimension?

COLLATERAL READING IN MATHEMATICS

Elementary

Ayres, F., Jr. (1958), *First Year College Mathematics*. (Schaum's Outline Series.) New York: McGraw-Hill.

——— (1967), *Matrices*. (Schaum's Outline Series.) New York: McGraw-Hill.

Baggaley, A. R. (1969), *Mathematics for Introductory Statistics: A Programmed Review*. New York: Wiley.

Hays, W. L. (1973), Appendix A: Rules of Summation. In: *Statistics for the Social Sciences*, 2nd ed. New York: Holt, Rinehart & Winston, pp. 861-70.

——— Appendix B: The Algebra of Expectation. In: *Statistics for the Social Sciences*, 2nd ed. New York: Holt, Rinehart & Winston, pp. 871-77.

Kershner, R. B. & Wilcox, L. R. (1950), *The Anatomy of Mathematics*. New York: Ronald Press.

Walker, H. M. (1951), *Mathematics Essential for Elementary Statistics*, rev. ed. New York: Holt, Rinehart & Winston.

Intermediate

Drake, A. W. (1967), *Fundamentals of Applied Probability Theory*. New York: McGraw-Hill.

Lewis, D. (1960), *Quantitative Methods in Psychology*. New York: McGraw-Hill.

Lindgren, B. W. (1968), *Statistical Theory*. New York: Macmillan.

Morgan, B. W. (1968), *An Introduction to Bayesian Statistical Decision Processes*. New York: Prentice-Hall.

Tatsuoka, M. M. (1971), *Multivariate Analysis*. New York: Wiley.

van de Geer, J. P. (1971), *Introduction to Multivariate Analysis for the Social Sciences*. San Francisco: Freeman.

Winer, B. J. (1971), *Statistical Principles in Experimental Design*, 2nd ed. New York: McGraw-Hill.

APPENDIX A

Construction and Tabulation of the Standard Normal Probability Distribution

Construction

We shall generate a table of the standard normal probability distribution that will specify the probability density function as well as the cumulative distribution function of that RV. We shall tabulate these two closely related functions for a selected number of standard outcome values z by providing for each one of these values in the selected set a corresponding probability density value and a corresponding cumulative probability value.

In chapter 11, we learned that the algebraic equation that defines the standard normal pdf is the equation

$$y = \frac{1}{\sqrt{2\pi}} \times e^{-\frac{1}{2} z^2} . \tag{A.1}$$

This relationship is obtained from the more general specification (11.1) by inserting the particular parameters $\mu = 0$ and $\sigma = 1$.

In (A.1), y is the probability density value that corresponds to a given outcome value z. Thus, to tabulate the first of our two functions, the pdf, for a selected set of outcome values, all that we need to do is to "plug in" each of those values into (A.1) to obtain the corresponding value of y. (We use some computational aid such as a small electronic hand-held calculator for the required computation.) For example, if we wish to know the value of the standard normal pdf at $z = 0.25$, we compute the expression

$$\frac{1}{\sqrt{2\pi}} \times e^{-\frac{1}{2}(0.25)^2}.$$

We find that the corresponding probability density value is $y = 0.3866683$, to the nearest ten-millionth. The values of the pdf, rounded off to the nearest one-thousandths, are listed in the second column of table A for a set of outcome values ranging from "minus infinity" to "plus infinity." (These two bounding values are in quotation marks to remind us that they are mathematical fictions and not actual numbers.)

We now have obtained the tabulation of the pdf for selected values of z, and in effect have computed a set of selected points on the graph of the standard normal pdf shown in figure 11.4. What about the other function, the cumulative distribution function? Unfortunately, there is no simple algebraic formula such as (A.1) that relates outcome values and corresponding cumulative probabilities directly. We shall have to construct the cdf in some other way. Let us recall that for any given outcome value of an RV, the corresponding value of the cdf is *defined* as the probability assigned by that RV to the entire outcome region to the left of that given outcome value. That probability is numerically equal to the corresponding area under the curve of the pdf, as we know, and that fact will provide us with a method of constructing the cdf.

Consider a portion of the graph of the standard normal pdf such as the segment shown in figure A.1. Suppose that in some way we already knew the value of the cdf at some particular outcome value $z = a$; that is, suppose we know that the total area under the curve to the left of a in figure A.1 is some particular probability value. How could we use that information to obtain the value of the cdf at some other outcome value $z = b$ that lay near a? If we could compute the area under the curve in the strip from a to b, and thus the probability assigned to that narrow outcome axis region, we could then add that probability increment to the known cumulative probability at a and thus obtain the cumulative probability—the value of the cdf—at b. We could now repeat that procedure again and again, successively obtaining the value of the cdf at c, d, etc. (Alternatively, we could, by subtracting the area of thin strips, move in the other direction, to the left, along the outcome axis.)

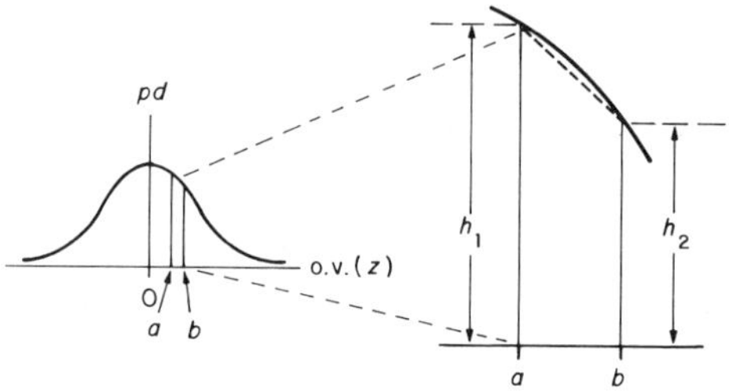

FIGURE A.1

Can we calculate the area of a strip such as that shown in figure A.1 precisely? We cannot; the upper boundary of that strip is defined by (A.1), and, as we have said, there is no simple algebraic formula analogous to (A.1) that would allow us to compute these kinds of areas exactly. We can, however, obtain an approximation to the strip area by replacing the curved upper boundary by a straight line. That replacement is shown as a dotted line in the magnified view of the narrow strip in figure A.1. The area of the thin trapezoidal strip now *can* be calculated in a very simple fashion according to a formula familiar from elementary geometry (or obtainable by simple logic). It is the formula

$$w \times \frac{(h_1 + h_2)}{2}, \tag{A.2}$$

where w is the width of the strip, and h_1 and h_2 are the vertical sides. In the present case, w is the known outcome axis distance from a to b, and h_1 and h_2 are the values of the pdf at a and b, respectively. These vertical distances can be obtained from (A.1) for given values of a and b. Thus, finally, if we know the value of the cdf at $z = a$, we can obtain an approximation to the cdf value at a nearby outcome value $z = b$ by computing the area of a thin trapezoidal strip and adding that incremental probability value to the previous, known probability value at a.

Let us illustrate this general procedure with a specific numerical example. Suppose we know that at $z = 0.37$, the value of the cdf is 0.6443088. Let us find the approximate value of the cdf at $z = 0.38$. From (A.1) we find that the values of h_1 and h_2 are 0.3725481 and 0.3711583, respectively. The width w is $(0.38 - 0.37)$ or 0.01. By using (A.2), we find that the area of the trapezoidal strip is 0.003718509. We add that quantity to the previous value of the cdf, and find that the value of the cdf at $z = 0.38$ is 0.6480273, approximately.

It should be intuitively obvious, and is in fact true, that the accuracy of the approximation will depend on the width of the trapezoidal strip. The narrower the strip, the closer will the straight line lie to the actual curved strip boundary, and the better the approximation. For the greater portion of our table of the cdf we shall use a spacing of 0.01 between neighboring z outcome values. The error that arises from this incremental value is about one part in 100 million.

We now know in principle how to obtain an approximation for the cdf of a standard normal RV *if* we are given *one* value of that function that can be used as a starting point for our procedure. In the preceding example, that information was furnished as if by magic. Do we have some starting point that is available in a less obscure manner? We do. We know from chapter 11 that $z = 0$ is the mean, median, and mode of the standard normal RV. Therefore, the value of the cdf at $z = 0$ must be 1/2, exactly. That provides our starting point. We use the procedure that we have just developed to construct the third column of table A. These cdf values were calculated to an accuracy of one part in ten million, and rounded off, for the sake of legibility, to the nearest ten-thousandths for the tabulation.

That completes the explanation of the tabulation procedure, except for two relatively minor points. First, you may have noticed that for those z values that lie relatively far from $z = 0$ (the values greater than $z = 2$), a wider spacing than the usual 0.01 increment has been used. The reason is that in these more remote regions, the two functions change quite slowly; the probability density remains very close to 0, and, consequently, the cdf also changes but little as one traverses those more distant outcome axis regions. When a function remains almost constant in value, there is little point in tabulating that function at frequent intervals.

Second, there is the matter of negative outcome values. We could calculate and tabulate pdf and cdf values in the negative outcome axis range by continuing to use the previous procedure and format. That, however, would be tedious and unnecessary. If we know pdf and cdf values for a set of positive z values, we can use the symmetry properties of the normal RV to easily obtain corresponding data for negative z values. (See fig. 11.7, the related discussion, and problems 11.7 and 11.8) Accordingly, table A lists pdf and cdf values for only a few illustrative outcome values in the negative outcome axis region.

We have presented a rationale that was used to find the pdf and cdf values for a *normal* RV. The procedures can be used more generally, however. They can be applied to *any* (nonnormal) kind of an RV, provided only that we have (1) an algebraic equation such as (A.1) that defines pdf values for given outcome axis values, and (2) *one known* cumulative probability value (in our case, the value 0.5000 . . . at $z = 0$) that can serve as the starting point for our step-by-step (or, in more esoteric terms, our "iterative" or "recursive") procedure.

Table A

The standard normal probability distribution

z	*pd*	*cp*
$-\infty$	-0-	-0-
−3.00	0.0044	0.0013
−2.00	0.0540	0.0228
−1.00	0.2420	0.1587
−0.50	0.3521	0.3085
−0.25	0.3867	0.4013
0.00	0.3989	0.5000
.01	.3989	.5040
.02	.3989	.5080
.03	.3988	.5120
.04	.3986	.5159
0.05	0.3984	0.5199
.06	.3982	.5239
.07	.3980	.5279
.08	.3977	.5319
.09	.3973	.5359
0.10	0.3970	0.5398
.11	.3965	.5438
.12	.3961	.5478
.13	.3956	.5517
.14	.3951	.5557
0.15	0.3945	0.5596
.16	.3939	.5636
.17	.3932	.5675
.18	.3925	.5714
.19	.3918	.5753
0.20	0.3910	0.5793
.21	.3902	.5832
.22	.3894	.5871
.23	.3885	.5910
.24	.3876	.5948

z	*pd*	*cp*
0.25	0.3867	0.5987
.26	.3857	.6026
.27	.3847	.6064
.28	.3836	.6103
.29	.3825	.6141
0.30	0.3814	0.6179
.31	.3802	.6217
.32	.3790	.6255
.33	.3778	.6293
.34	.3766	.6331
0.35	0.3752	0.6368
.36	.3739	.6406
.37	.3725	.6443
.38	.3712	.6480
.39	.3697	.6517
0.40	0.3682	0.6554
.41	.3668	.6591
.42	.3652	.6628
.43	.3637	.6664
.44	.3621	.6700
0.45	0.3605	0.6736
.46	.3589	.6772
.47	.3572	.6808
.48	.3555	.6844
.49	.3538	.6879
0.50	0.3521	0.6915
.51	.3503	.6950
.52	.3485	.6985
.53	.3467	.7019
.54	.3448	.7054
0.55	0.3429	0.7088
.56	.3410	.7123
.57	.3391	.7157
.58	.3372	.7190
.59	.3352	.7224

Table continues on next page

Table A (*continued*)

z	pd	cp	z	pd	cp
0.60	0.3332	0.7257	1.00	0.2420	0.8413
.61	.3312	.7291	.01	.2396	.8438
.62	.3292	.7324	.02	.2371	.8461
.63	.3271	.7357	.03	.2347	.8485
.64	.3251	.7389	.04	.2323	.8508
0.65	0.3230	0.7422	1.05	0.2299	0.8531
.66	.3209	.7454	.06	.2275	.8554
.67	.3187	.7486	.07	.2251	.8577
.68	.3166	.7517	.08	.2227	.8599
.69	.3144	.7549	.09	.2203	.8621
0.70	0.3123	0.7580	1.10	0.2179	0.8643
.71	.3101	.7611	.11	.2155	.8665
.72	.3079	.7642	.12	.2131	.8686
.73	.3056	.7673	.13	.2107	.8708
.74	.3034	.7704	.14	.2083	.8729
0.75	0.3011	0.7734	1.15	0.2059	0.8749
.76	.2989	.7764	.16	.2036	.8770
.77	.2966	.7794	.17	.2012	.8790
.78	.2943	.7823	.18	.1989	.8810
.79	.2920	.7852	.19	.1965	.8830
0.80	0.2897	0.7881	1.20	0.1942	0.8849
.81	.2874	.7910	.21	.1919	.8869
.82	.2850	.7939	.22	.1895	.8888
.83	.2827	.7967	.23	.1872	.8907
.84	.2803	.7995	.24	.1849	.8925
0.85	0.2780	0.8023	1.25	0.1826	0.8944
.86	.2756	.8051	.26	.1804	.8962
.87	.2732	.8078	.27	.1781	.8980
.88	.2709	.8106	.28	.1758	.8997
.89	.2685	.8133	.29	.1736	.9015
0.90	0.2661	0.8159	1.30	0.1714	0.9032
.91	.2637	.8186	.31	.1691	.9049
.92	.2613	.8212	.32	.1669	.9066
.93	.2589	.8238	.33	.1647	.9082
.94	.2565	.8264	.34	.1626	.9099
0.95	0.2541	0.8289	1.35	0.1604	0.9115
.96	.2516	.8315	.36	.1582	.9131
.97	.2492	.8340	.37	.1561	.9147
.98	.2468	.8365	.38	.1539	.9162
.99	.2444	.8389	.39	.1518	.9177

Table continues on next page

Table A (*continued*)

z	*pd*	*cp*	*z*	*pd*	*cp*
1.40	0.1497	0.9192	1.80	0.0790	0.9641
.41	.1496	.9207	.81	.0775	.9649
.42	.1456	.9222	.82	.0761	.9656
.43	.1435	.9236	.83	.0748	.9664
.44	.1415	.9251	.84	.0734	.9671
1.45	0.1394	0.9265	1.85	0.0721	0.9678
.46	.1374	.9279	.86	.0707	.9686
.47	.1354	.9292	.87	.0694	.9693
.48	.1334	.9306	.88	.0681	.9699
.49	.1315	.9319	.89	.0669	.9706
1.50	0.1295	0.9332	1.90	0.0656	0.9713
.51	.1276	.9345	.91	.0644	.9719
.52	.1257	.9357	.92	.0632	.9726
.53	.1238	.9370	.93	.0620	.9732
.54	.1219	.9382	.94	.0608	.9738
1.55	0.1200	0.9394	1.95	0.0596	0.9744
.56	.1182	.9406	.96	.0584	.9750
.57	.1163	.9418	.97	.0573	.9756
.58	.1145	.9429	.98	.0562	.9761
.59	.1127	.9441	.99	.0551	.9767
1.60	0.1109	0.9452	2.00	0.0540	0.9772
.61	.1092	.9463	.02	.0519	.9783
.62	.1074	.9474	.04	.0498	.9793
.63	.1057	.9484	.06	.0478	.9803
.64	.1040	.9495	.08	.0459	.9812
1.65	0.1023	0.9505	2.10	0.0440	0.9821
.66	.1006	.9515	.12	.0422	.9830
.67	.0989	.9525	.14	.0404	.9838
.68	.0973	.9535	.16	.0387	.9846
.69	.0957	.9545	.18	.0371	.9854
1.70	0.0940	0.9554	2.20	0.0355	0.9861
.71	.0925	.9564	.22	.0339	.9868
.72	.0909	.9573	.24	.0325	.9875
.73	.0893	.9582	.26	.0310	.9881
.74	.0878	.9591	.28	.0297	.9887
1.75	0.0863	0.9599	2.30	0.0283	0.9893
.76	.0848	.9608	.32	.0270	.9898
.77	.0833	.9616	.34	.0258	.9904
.78	.0818	.9625	.36	.0246	.9909
.79	.0804	.9633	.38	.0235	.9913

Table continues on next page

Table A (*continued*)

z	pd	cp
2.40	0.0224	0.9918
.42	.0213	.9922
.44	.0203	.9927
.46	.0194	.9931
.48	.0184	.9934
2.50	0.0175	0.9938
.52	.0167	.9941
.54	.0158	.9945
.56	.0151	.9948
.58	.0143	.9951
2.60	0.0136	0.9953
.62	.0129	.9956
.64	.0122	.9959
.66	.0116	.9961
.68	.0110	.9963
2.70	0.0104	0.9965
.72	.0099	.9967
.74	.0093	.9969
.76	.0088	.9971
.78	.0084	.9973
2.80	0.0079	0.9974
.82	.0075	.9976
.84	.0071	.9977
.86	.0067	.9979
.88	.0063	.9980
2.90	0.0060	0.9981
.92	.0056	.9982
.94	.0053	.9984
.96	.0050	.9985
.98	.0047	.9986
3.00	0.0044	0.9987
3.25	0.0020	0.9994
3.50	0.0009	0.9998
3.75	0.0004	0.9999
4.00	0.0001	0.9999+
∞	-0-	1.000

APPENDIX B

A Demonstration Concerning a *t* Ratio Statistic

In most introductory and even some intermediate textbooks of statistics for students in the behavioral or social disciplines, the fact that a particular statistic is a particular outcome value—i.e., that it has a particular kind of underlying RV_D—is presented without explanation. In many cases, that omission is unavoidable. As I have discussed in chapter 12, the procedures which allow one to deduce that for a given RV_P and a given mathematical data-reducing operation a statistic will have a particular kind of underlying RV_D are based on advanced mathematical techniques and concepts. In certain cases, however, the underlying RV_D can be explicated without using advanced methods, provided that one has laid the necessary conceptual groundwork. Because it is typical of this latter class of cases, and also because it is important in its own right, we shall examine the statistic

$$\frac{M - \mu_P}{\sqrt{\dfrac{S^2}{(N-1)}}} \qquad (16.2)$$

to see why it is a *t* outcome value—i.e., why its underlying RV_D is a *t* pdf.

How does one demonstrate that a quantity is a *t* outcome value? One procedure would be to appeal to the fundamental definition developed in the first part of chapter 16 in conjunction with the ratio (16.1). According to that definition, if the numerator and denominator of a particular statistic each satisfies certain formal mathematical requirements, then the RV underlying that statistic is a *t* pdf. That is the method we shall use; we shall demonstrate that (16.2) is a quantity that has exactly the same formal properties as (16.1).

The demonstration will be accomplished in several steps. First, let us consider the statistic *M* computed from a set of *N* sample values generated by a normal RV_P, $\mu = \mu_P$ and $\sigma^2 = \sigma^2_P$. We know from chapter 13 what the underlying RV_D is in this case. It is a normal pdf whose mean μ_D is equal to μ_P, and whose variance σ^2_D is equal to σ^2_P/N. *M*, then, is an outcome value of a normal pdf. How do we convert that kind of value to a *standard* outcome value *z*? According to (11.2), we form the quantity

$$\frac{M - \mu_D}{\sigma_D}. \tag{B.1}$$

Using the relationships between the parameters of RV_P and RV_D, and using the definition of $\sigma_D = \sqrt{\sigma^2_D}$, we may rewrite (B.1) as

$$\frac{M - \mu_P}{\sqrt{\dfrac{\sigma^2_P}{N}}}. \tag{B.2}$$

That quantity, like (B.1), is a standard normal outcome value; that is, its underlying RV is a standard normal pdf. Therefore, (B.2) meets the criterion that was stipulated for the *numerator* of (16.1).

Next, consider the sample variance S^2 computed from our *N* sample values. We know from chapter 15 that the RV that underlies the quantity

$$\frac{N \times S^2}{\sigma^2_P} \tag{B.3}$$

is $\chi^2_{(N-1)}$, the member of the chi-square pdf family that has $(N - 1)$ degrees of freedom. Since (B.3) is a χ^2 outcome value, if we divide it by its number of degrees of freedom and take the square root of the resulting quotient, we have a quantity

$$\sqrt{\frac{\dfrac{N \times S^2}{\sigma^2_{\text{P}}}}{(N - 1)}} \tag{B.4}$$

that meets the requirements specified for the *denominator* of (16.1).

The next step should be obvious. Using (B.2) and (B.4), we form a quotient that has the formal properties of the statistic (16.1), for the reasons just explained. We obtain the ratio

$$\frac{\dfrac{M - \mu_{\text{P}}}{\sqrt{\dfrac{\sigma^2_{\text{P}}}{N}}}}{\sqrt{\dfrac{\dfrac{N \times S^2}{\sigma^2_{\text{P}}}}{(N - 1)}}} \, . \tag{B.5}$$

According to the discussion in chapter 16 that pertains to the generation of (16.1) and from the demonstrated properties of the numerator and denominator of (B.5), the RV that underlies (B.5) is the t probability distribution with $(N - 1)$ degrees of freedom.

All that remains to be done is to demonstrate that (16.2) and (B.5) are identical. That can be accomplished in a few simple algebraic steps, and is left as an exercise.

APPENDIX C

Relationships Among Probabilities in the Bivariate Situation

We shall develop various relationships that exist between the different kinds of probabilities in the bivariate situation and discuss some of the consequences of these relationships. First, in order to facilitate the discussions let us agree on a system of notation. We shall develop these notations in terms of one specific ordered pair from the bivariate situation defined in tables 19.2 and 20.1; let us arbitrarily conduct the discussions in terms of the pair $(3, -1)$. I am using one specific ordered pair because it simplifies the presentation. A general development that would follow the same steps and rationale as our specific demonstration could be presented, of course. For our purposes, however, it is sufficient to recognize that our notations, arguments, and conclusions would hold equally well for any other ordered pair, or any other discrete RV.

Notation

We shall need to symbolize two different kinds of frequencies. The first is the joint frequency, i.e., the observed frequency of an ordered pair in N trials of a "big" bivariate RV. Let us use the notation $f(3, -1)$ to represent the joint frequency of the ordered pair. From table 20.1 we see that $f(3, -1)$ is 30.

We shall also need to represent marginal or unconditional frequencies. Let us use the notation $f(x = 3)$ for the marginal frequency of $x = 3$, and $f(y = -1)$ for the marginal frequency of $y = -1$. We cannot use a simpler notation such as $f(3)$ because it would be ambiguous; in the general case, it would not tell us whether it referred to the marginal frequency of $x = 3$ or of $y = 3$. From table 20.1 we find that $f(x = 3)$ is 200 and $f(y = -1)$ is 300.

We shall also need to develop notations for three kinds of relative frequencies. The first of these is the joint relative frequency. Let us represent the joint relative frequency of $(3, -1)$ by $rf(3, -1)$. By definition,

$$rf(3, -1) = \frac{f(3, -1)}{N}. \tag{C.1}$$

For the bivariate trials in table 20.1, N is 2000. Hence, $rf(3, -1)$ is 30/2000 or 0.015.

The second kind of relative frequency is the unconditional or marginal relative frequency. We shall represent the relative frequency of $x = 3$ by $rf(x = 3)$. By definition,

$$rf(x = 3) = \frac{f(x = 3)}{N}. \tag{C.2}$$

From table 20.1, we find that $rf(x = 3)$ is 200/2000 or 0.10. The parallel procedure and notational convention leads to

$$rf(y = -1) = \frac{f(y = -1)}{N}. \tag{C.3}$$

That value is 300/2000, or 0.15.

The third kind of relative frequency is the conditional rf. We shall use a standard notation that separates the frequency variable from the conditional variable by a vertical bar. Thus, we shall represent the relative frequency of $x = 3$ under the condition that $y = -1$ by the symbol $rf(x = 3 | y = -1)$. By definition, $rf(x = 3 | y = -1)$ is equal to the number of times the value $x = 3$ occurred among those trials in which the value $y = -1$ occurred. Thus,

$$rf(x = 3 | y = -1) = \frac{f(3, -1)}{f(y = -1)}. \tag{C.4}$$

In our example, $rf(x = 3 | y = -1)$ is 30/300, or 0.10. The parallel expression for the relative frequency of $y = -1$ under the condition that $x = 3$ is

$$rf(y = -1 \mid x = 3) = \frac{f(3, -1)}{f(x = 3)} \cdot \tag{C.5}$$

In our example, the numerical value of $rf(y = -1 \mid x = 3)$ is 30/200 or 0.15.

The last set of symbols we shall need are those for the three kinds of probability. We use symbols for the joint, marginal, and conditional probabilities that parallel the symbolism used for relative frequencies in the obvious fashion. The joint probability of $(3, -1)$ is represented by $p(3, -1)$. The marginal probability of $x = 3$ is represented by $p(x = 3)$, and that of $y = -1$, by $p(y = -1)$. The conditional probability of $x = 3$ under the condition that $y = -1$ is represented by $p(x = 3 \mid y = -1)$, while the conditional probability of $y = -1$ under the condition that $x = 3$ is represented by $p(y = -1 \mid x = 3)$.

By invoking the principle of equivalence, we can immediately draw the following inferences:

$$p(3, -1) = rf(3, -1), \tag{C.6}$$

$$p(x = 3) = rf(x = 3), \tag{C.7}$$

$$p(y = -1) = rf(y = -1), \tag{C.8}$$

$$p(x = 3 \mid y = -1) = rf(x = 3 \mid y = -1), \tag{C.9}$$

$$p(y = -1 \mid x = 3) = rf(y = -1 \mid x = 3). \tag{C.10}$$

We now are ready to develop a number of important relationships pertaining to the bivariate situation.

The Necessary Relationships Between Joint, Conditional, and Marginal Probabilities

Consider the definition of $p(x = 3 \mid y = -1)$, the (conditional) probability of $x = 3$ under the condition $y = -1$. From (C.9) and (C.4) we have

$$p(x = 3 \mid y = -1) = \frac{f(3, -1)}{f(y = -1)} . \tag{C.11}$$

We can divide the numerator and denominator of the right-hand side by N without changing the value of the quotient. We obtain

$$p(x = 3 \mid y = -1) = \frac{\dfrac{f(3, -1)}{N}}{\dfrac{f(y = -1)}{N}} . \tag{C.12}$$

We observe that the numerator of the right-hand side is (C.1) and the denominator is (C.3). Therefore we can write (C.12) as

$$p(x = 3 \mid y = -1) = \frac{rf(3, -1)}{rf(y = -1)} , \tag{C.13}$$

which, by (C.6) and (C.8), leads to

$$p(x = 3 \mid y = -1) = \frac{p(3, -1)}{p(y = -1)} . \tag{C.14}$$

This very important equation specifies the fundamental relationship that must hold in all cases between a joint, conditional, and unconditional probability.

We can verify (C.14) for our particular case. We know from our previous discussions and calculations that $p(x = 3 \mid y = -1) = 0.10$, $p(3, -1) = 0.015$, and $p(y = -1) = 0.15$. We see that (C.14) is satisfied by these three numerical values.

The same kind of relationship is true for the parallel case concerning $p(y = -1 \mid x = 3)$, $p(3, -1)$, and $p(x = 3)$:

$$p(y = -1 \mid x = 3) = \frac{p(3, -1)}{p(x = 3)} . \tag{C.15}$$

You may wish to verify that our data satisfy that relationship as well.

Independence

In chapter 20 we formalized the idea of independence by defining "x is independent of y" in terms of certain equivalences between conditional and marginal probabilities for x. In our present example, according to that definition, if x is independent of y, then

$$p(x = 3 \mid y = -1) = p(x = 3). \tag{C.16}$$

We can rewrite (C.16) by using (C.14) (which is always true):

$$\frac{p(3, -1)}{p(y = -1)} = p(x = 3),$$

or

$$p(3, -1) = p(x = 3) \times p(y = -1). \tag{C.17}$$

In other words, *if* x is independent of y, then the joint probability $p(3, -1)$ is equal to the product of the two marginal or unconditional probabilities $p(x = 3)$ and $p(y = -1)$. (That relationship will hold for *all* ordered pairs in a discrete RV if x is independent of y.)

There is a further conclusion that follows from (C.17). By using (C.15), we can substitute $p(y = -1 \mid x = 3) \times p(x = 3)$ for $p(3, -1)$ in (C.17), obtaining

$$p(y = -1 \mid x = 3) \times p(x = 3) = p(x = 3) \times p(y = -1),$$

or

$$p(y = -1 \mid x = 3) = p(y = -1). \tag{C.18}$$

According to our definition of independence, (C.18) specifies that y is independent of x. Thus, we find that *if* x is independent of y, then it follows that y is independent of x! Strictly speaking, we should have to demonstrate (C.18) for *all* values of x and y in a bivariate RV. Our development demonstrates at least informally the claim made in chapter 20 that independence is a reciprocal relationship.

Yet another property of independence follows from the various relationships developed above, although we shall not pursue the matter in detail. We used a definition of independence based on the equivalence between conditional and unconditional probabilities, and found that this definition entailed the "product rule" (C.17) as a logical consequence. Alternatively, one could use the product rule as a *definition* of independence. One could then show, by using (C.14) and (C.15) in some simple algebraic manipulations, that the equivalence of unconditional and conditional probabilities would follow as a corollary. Thus, there are two alternative approaches to defining independence; each approach logically entails the other relationship as a corollary.

Marginal Probabilities

In our work in part V we obtained values for the marginal or unconditional probabilities from *frequency* data such as those in table 20.1. I claimed that these probabilities could also be obtained directly from *joint probability* data such as those in table 19.2. We shall now see how that would be accomplished.

We know that according to (C.2) we may obtain $rf(x = 3)$, and thus $p(x = 3)$, from $f(x = 3)$. We obtain $f(x = 3)$ by adding all the joint frequencies in the third column of table 20.1 (see chap. 20):

$$f(x = 3) = f(3, -2) + f(3, -1) + \ldots + f(3, 3). \qquad \text{(C.19)}$$

Therefore, according to (C.2),

$$rf(x = 3) = \frac{f(3, -2) + f(3, -1) + \ldots + f(3, 3)}{N}, \qquad \text{(C.20)}$$

or

$$rf(x = 3) = \frac{f(3, -2)}{N} + \frac{f(3, -1)}{N} + \ldots + \frac{f(3, 3)}{N} \cdot \qquad \text{(C.21)}$$

We now recognize that each term of the sum in the right-hand side of (C.21) is a relative frequency and thus, by the principle of equivalence, a probability. Specifically, each term is a joint relative frequency such as (C.1). Therefore, by using (C.6), we may rewrite (C.21) as

$$p(x = 3) = p(3, -2) + p(3, -1) + \ldots + p(3, 3). \qquad \text{(C.22)}$$

This informal development, actually based on a simple interchange in the order of addition and division, suggests that we can obtain unconditional probabilities by adding the appropriate set of joint probabilities. We do not need a set of frequency data, but can obtain marginal probabilities directly from a joint frequency table such as table 19.2—in other words, directly from the tabulation of a joint, bivariate RV.

The same procedure can be applied to y, the other variable, of course:

$$p(y = -1) = p(1, -1) + p(2, -1) + \ldots + p(10, -1). \qquad \text{(C.23)}$$

Let us now note a very important consequence of these considerations. If we are given a bivariate RV (i.e., a joint frequency-data matrix) such as table 19.2, we can obtain all the marginal probabilities by using relationships such as those illustrated by (C.22) and (C.23). Then, by using relationships such as those illustrated by (C.14) and (C.15), we can also obtain all conditional probabilities and thus all the conditional pfs. *The joint probability matrix is basic*. Given that mathematical specification, we can derive all other probability information.

The converse is not true, however. If we know only marginal probabilities, or know only conditional probabilities—in other words, if we only know either the unconditional pfs or the conditional pfs—then we cannot recover the "parent" bivariate RV without making some further assumptions. That should be apparent from a study of (C.14) and (C.15). As we saw in chapter 22, that issue is at the root of the Bayesian approaches; to implement these, one has to make some assumptions about the value of a set of marginal probabilities. That thought leads us to the final topic of this appendix.

Bayes's Rule

Bayes's Rule or Theorem is a simple algebraic formulation based on the basic relationships developed in the preceding sections. There are several roughly equivalent versions of this rule (Freeman, p. 223; Hays, pp. 147 and 383). We shall consider one representative form.

Let us say that for the reasons discussed in chapter 22, we wish to invert one set of conditional probabilities into the other. In other words, let us assume that we are given the set of conditional probabilities for one of the dimensions—say, x—of a bivariate RV, and wish to use these probabilities to obtain the set of conditional probabilities for the other dimension, y. As we have just seen, we cannot accomplish that goal without knowing (or assuming) what the unconditional probabilities are for y. If we do have these marginal probabilities, we are able to construct the joint RV, and then, from that basic probability distribution, we are also able to calculate the other set of conditional probabilities—in our example, those for y; we only need to use formulae such as (C.14), (C.15), (C.22), and (C.23). We can obtain the desired conditional probabilities without any new "rule" or "theorem."

We can, however, consolidate these kinds of computational steps within a single algebraic formula. We can express a conditional probability distribution such as $p(y = -1 | x = 3)$ solely in terms of known or presumed conditional probabilities for x and marginal probabilities for y. That consolidation adds nothing that is conceptually new; the algebraic condensation is merely a computational convenience. Let us see how this would be accomplished for one conditional probability, $p(y = -1 | x = 3)$. The identical procedure would, of course, be followed for any other similar conditional probability.

We know from (C.15) that

$$p(y = -1 | x = 3) = \frac{p(3, -1)}{p(x = 3)} .$$

We can now use (C.14) to change the numerator of the right-hand side of (C.15), and use (C.22) to change the denominator, thus:

$$p(y = -1 \mid x = 3) = \frac{p(x = 3 \mid y = -1) \times p(y = -1)}{p(3, -2) + p(3, -1) + \ldots + p(3, 3)}. \quad \text{(C.24)}$$

There actually are six terms in the denominator, and we can again use (C.14) to express each of these joint probabilities as the product of a conditional and a marginal probability:

$$p(y = -1 \mid x = 3) = \frac{p(x = 3 \mid y = -1) \times p(y = -1)}{\begin{array}{c} p(x = 3 \mid y = -2) \times p(y = -2) \\ + \, p(x = 3 \mid y = -1) \times p(y = -1) \\ + \ldots + p(x = 3 \mid y = 3) \times p(y = 3) \end{array}}. \quad \text{(C.25)}$$

We have accomplished our goal. We have obtained an expression for the conditional probability of one dimension, y, in terms of the marginal probabilities for that dimension and the conditional probabilities of the other dimension, x.

List of Abbreviations and Symbols

$a, b, c, \ldots$	constants
α	(alpha) level of significance; magnitude of a type I error
β	(beta) magnitude of a type II error
cdf	cumulative distribution function
χ^2	(chi-square) a class of probability distributions or one of its outcome values
cp	cumulative probability
D	subscript indicating a derived entity
e	a constant equal to 2.718281 . . .
f	frequency, observed frequency
F	a class of probability distributions or one of its outcome values (R.A. Fisher)
H_0	null hypothesis concerning sample values
H_0'	null hypothesis concerning a statistic
H_1	alternative hypothesis concerning sample values
H_1'	alternative hypothesis concerning a statistic
M	sample mean
μ	(mu) mean of a probability distribution
N	an integer; usually, the sample size
ν	(nu) number of degrees of freedom
o.v.	outcome value

p	probability
$p(\ \ )$	probability of the entity in parentheses
pd	probability density
pdf	probability density function
pf	probability function
P	subscript indicating a population entity
π	(pi) a constant equal to 3.1415926 . . .; the ratio of the circumference of a circle to its diameter
r	sample correlation coefficient
rf	relative frequency
RV	random variable
ρ	(rho) correlation coefficient
S	sample standard deviation
S^2	sample variance
σ	(sigma) standard deviation of a probability distribution
σ^2	(sigma, squared) variance of a probability distribution
t	a class of probability distributions or one of its outcome values ("Student")
x, y	variables
(x, y)	ordered pair
z	outcome value of the standard normal probability distribution
$\mid$	conditional probability indicator
$\mid\ \mid$	absolute value
$>; <$	greater than; less than
∞	infinity

References

Campbell, J. C. and Stanley, D. D. (1963), *Experimental and Quasi-Experimental Designs for Research*. Chicago: Rand McNally.

Carnap, R. (1953), What Is Probability? *Scientific American*, 188-189:128-138.

Coombs, C. H., Dawes, R. M., and Tversky, A. (1970), *Mathematical Psychology*, Englewood Cliffs, N.J.: Prentice-Hall.

Edwards, W., Lindman, H., and Savage, L. J. (1963), Bayesian Statistical Inference for Psychological Research. *Psychological Review*, 70:193-242.

Freeman, H. (1963), *Introduction to Statistical Inference*. Reading, Mass.: Addison-Wesley.

Gaito, J. (1960), Scale Classification and Statistics. *Psychological Review*, 67:277-278. Also in: Kirk (1972).

Hays, W. L. (1973), *Statistics for the Social Sciences*, 2nd ed. New York: Holt, Rinehart & Winston.

Kaplan, A. (1964), *The Conduct of Inquiry*. Scranton, Penn: Chandler.

Kirk, R. E., ed. (1972), *Statistical Issues*. Monterey, Cal.: Brooks/Cole.

Lewis, D. (1960), *Quantitative Methods in Psychology*. New York: McGraw-Hill.

Lindgren, B. W. (1968), *Statistical Theory*. New York: Macmillan.

MacLane, S. and Birkhoff, G. (1967), *Algebra*. New York: Macmillan.

Savage, L. J. (1962), Bayesian Statistics. In: *Decision and Information Processes*. New York: Macmillan, pp. 161-194.

Stevens, S. S. (1946), On the Theory of Scales of Measurement. *Science*, 103:667-680.

———, ed. (1951), *Handbook of Experimental Psychology*. New York: Wiley.

Suppes, P. and Zinnes, J. L. (1963), Basic Measurement Theory. In: *Handbook of Mathematical Psychology*, ed. R. D. Luce, R. R. Bush, and E. Galanter. New York: Wiley, vol. 1, pp. 1-76.

Walker, H. (1940), Degrees of Freedom. *Journal of Educational Psychology*, 31:253-269.

Wright, G. H. von (1973), Probability. In: *Encyclopedia Britannica*, ed. W. E. Preece. Chicago: William Benton, vol. 18, pp. 570-574.

Index
